NELSON STANDARD GRADE

PHYSICS

John Campbell Ken Dobson

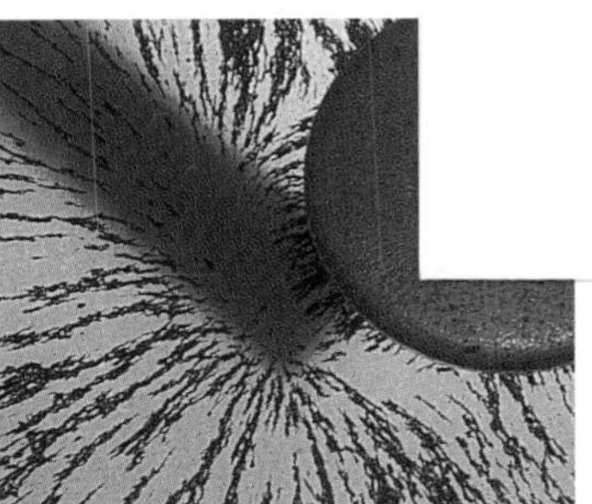
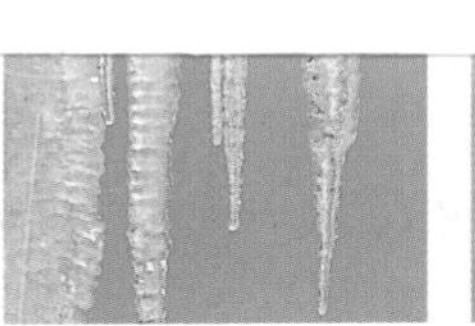
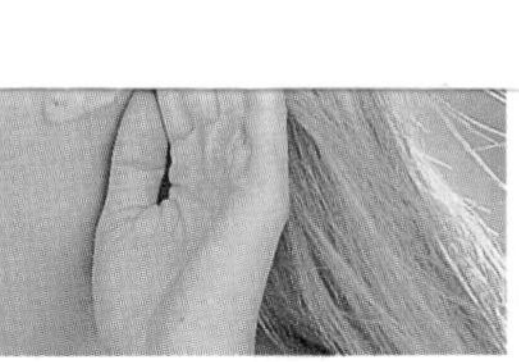
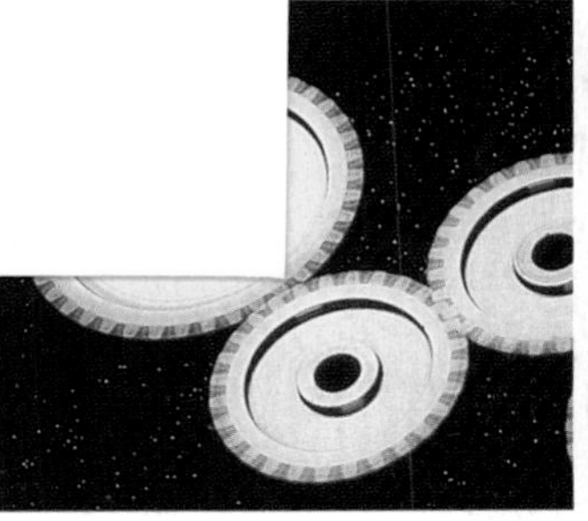

Nelson

Thomas Nelson and Sons Ltd
Nelson House
Mayfield Road
Walton-on-Thames
Surrey KT12 5PL
United Kingdom

I(T)P® Thomas Nelson is an International Thomson Company

I(T)P® is used under licence.

First Published by Thomas Nelson & Sons Ltd 1997
ISBN 0-17-438714-8
9 8 7 6 5 4 3 2
01 00 99

Typeset by Pentacor, High Wycombe
Printed in Croatia by Zrinski, Cakovec
Picture Research Image Select International Ltd

The publishers are grateful to the following for permission to reproduce photographs. While every effort has been made to trace copyright holders, if any acknowledgement has been inadvertently omitted, the publishers will be pleased to make the necessary arrangements at the first opportunity.

Allsport 124.1, 132.1; **Barnaby's Picture Library** 11.5, 125.5; **Stuart Boreham** 20.1; **Carrington Counter Associates** 46(all), 49.8; **J Allan Cash** 42.1, 141.5; **CEGB** 156.1; **J Urling Clark** 165.5; **East Anglian Daily Times** 88.1; **Ford** 138.14; **Getty Images** 7.5, 8.9, 116.1, 135.5; **Griffin & George** 44.8; **Hutchinson Library** 150.7; **Image Bank** 116.1; **Image Select International** 8.8, 181.8, 197.1, 204.9; **Imperial War Museum** 189.3; **NASA** 179.3, 180.5, 180.6; **Nelson** 196.1; **Redferns** 116.1; **Chris Ridgers** 27.5, 34.1, 35.5, 35.6, 36.7, 52.2, 125.3, 140.1, 171.3, 173.6, 201.1; **Ann Ronan** 16.1, 16.2, 16.3, 16.4, 20.2; **Science Photo Library** 15.8, 24.14, 30.3, 32.3, 47.4, 66.1, 69.3, 70.7, 80.2, 83.5, 84.7, 84.8, 85.12, 86.13, 86.14, 89.4, 92.1, 92.2, 94.5, 94.6,148.2, 153.3, 154.4, 179.2, 180.4, 182.9, 182.10, 182.11, 182.12, 184.1, 185.5, 186.7, 186.8, 190.4, 190.5, 192.2, 192.3, 192.4, 194.6, 196.2, 202.1, 202.2, 203.4, 204.6; **Martin Sookias** 49.9, 56.1, 106.1, 174.8, 174.9; **Wild Leitz** 188.2

Certain questions have been adapted from past Standard Grade Physics examination papers (© Scottish Examinations Board).

To the reader

This book is about physics. It deals with the forces that shape the world, from the smallest particle to the galaxies of stars that the universe is made of. It also deals with the way that forces and energy are used by all of us – in living and moving, in work and play, in sending messages, in storing information and using it to control so many things in the modern world.

The book is split up into the seven Standard Grade Physics topics. Each topic includes Questions (with a mauve background) – some of which are based on questions from the Standard Grade Physics examination. There are also case studies and extension exercises (with a green background) which take some of the ideas a bit further.

John Campbell and Ken Dobson

We are grateful to many people who helped to write this book, and we would particularly like to thank John Holman and Michael Roberts. The following people helped by reading and making very useful comments on some of the material in the book:

Mark Tweedle, Heckmondwike Grammar School

Michael Brimicombe, Cedars Upper School, Leighton Buzzard

Professor EK Walton, Department of Geography and Geology, University of St Andrews

David Fielding, Radley College, Abingdon, Oxon

Joe Jefferies, ASE Lab Safeguards Committee

Charles Tracy, Watford Grammar School

Contents

A1 Signals and codes

Human beings need to exchange information. This unit is about the different methods used.

électron	French
electrón	Spanish
Elektron	German
elettrone	Italian
ηλετρόνιο	Greek
eletron	Portugese
אֶלֶקְטְרוֹן	Hebrew
电(電)子	Chinese
elektron	Dutch
электрóн	Russian
elektrono	Esperanto
ėlĕćtrŏn	phonetic
ইলেকট্রন:	Bengali

Picture 2 Different codes for the same word.

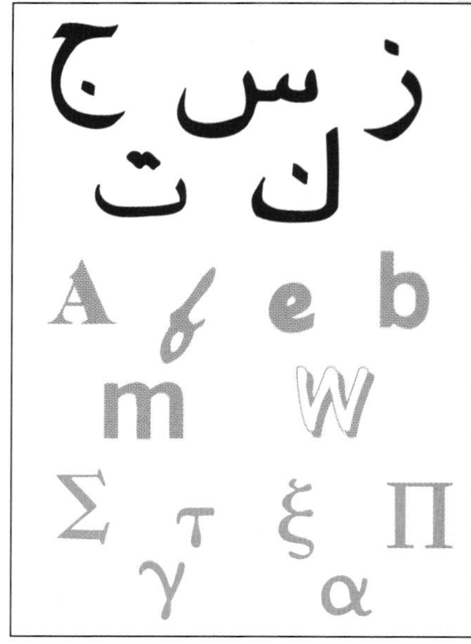

Picture 1 Codes for ideas.

One of the earliest methods of communication between living things was the use of sound. Animals give distress calls or warning growls. For long distances people have to rely on simple prearranged sound signals, such as the one o'clock gun fired from Edinburgh castle. Drums can carry sound messages a reasonable distance. The yodelling of Swiss mountaineers is a code that works well in mountain areas with many echoes. At short range, humans developed complicated patterns of sound, enabling us to carry much more information through the air – we invented *language*.

Codes

The language you speak is a code, and not everybody in the world understands it! Writing is a code. Picture 1 shows how different languages have tackled the problem of putting sounds into 'pictures'. The very oldest, like Ancient Egyptian, used drawings of what the sounds meant.

It is easier to break the words up into their different sound parts, and have a symbol for each of these. In English we can just about manage with 26 of these symbols – the letters of the alphabet. Picture 2 shows some of the codes used in the world today.

When we learn to read we are learning which sounds go with which symbols. In Western languages we 'scan' the letters from left to right. In Arabic, Hebrew and some other languages the symbols are scanned from right to left.

Carrying messages

Before writing was invented messengers needed very good memories.

Even after the invention of writing they also needed strong legs, like the messenger who carried the news of the battle of Marathon to Athens in 49 BC. He ran so hard that he died after delivering the news, and so never knew that he had just invented marathon running. But sending a messenger was a slow way of carrying information.

Light travels a lot more quickly – at 300 million metres a second. The ancient Romans used light to send messages very long distances. The Roman army built a network of signal stations criss-crossing Europe. Each station had large wooden 'flags' to send messages many kilometres across country (see picture 3).

Picture 3 The Romans sent messages using light, over 2000 years ago.

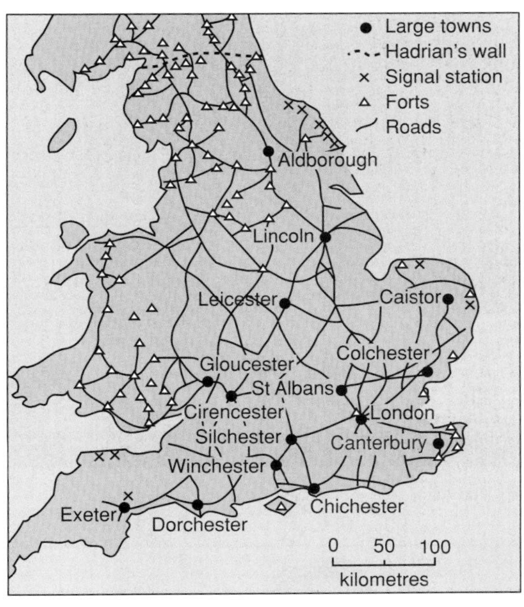

To make use of 'light messages' new codes had to be invented. To have a different flag movement for each letter of the alphabet would have been a very slow way of doing it. Standard messages, like HELP!, would be given one flag movement. But even so, messages had to be kept very simple. Long, chatty letters were still sent by messengers on ship or horseback.

Electric messages

Electric current was discovered at the beginning of the 19th century. It was soon used as a message carrier. In fact that was its first main use, in the form of the **electric telegraph**. A new code – the **Morse Code** – was invented for this kind of message carrier (see picture 4).

Then in 1876 a Scotsman, Alexander Graham Bell, invented the first artificial **transducers**, which allowed speech to be transmitted over long distances. He had invented the **telephone**.

A transducer is a device that transfers signals from one energy system to another. For example, our ears change sound waves into electric signals that the brain can understand. Bell had found another way of changing sound signals into electric signals – the **microphone**. He also had to invent the transducer at the other end to change the electric signals back into sound – a **receiver** or **loudspeaker**.

Even after the telephone was invented, light was still one of the main means of sending messages long distances. Armies and navies used flags, lamps and flashing mirrors (heliographs). They were cheap, quiet and didn't need a network of wires to carry the message.

Then a young Italian called Guglielmo Marconi (picture 5) took up an idea that university physicists had already been experimenting with, and made it practical. He invented a message carrying system that didn't need wires – a '**wireless' telegraph**. To carry messages, this system used what we now call radio waves. These are an invisible part of the **electromagnetic spectrum**, the family of waves which also includes light.

Picture 5 Guglielmo Marconi.

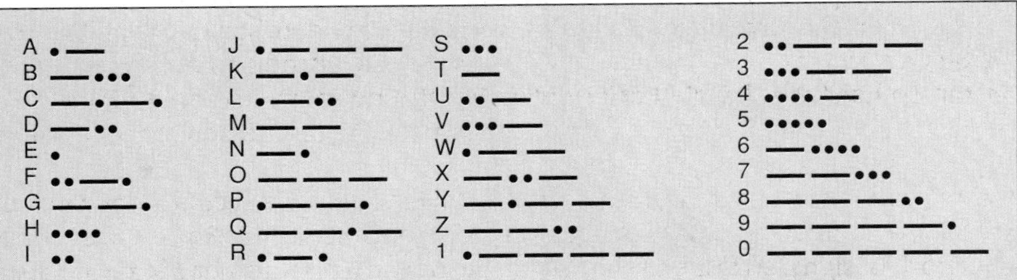

Picture 4 The earliest electric message carrier and the code it used.

Picture 6

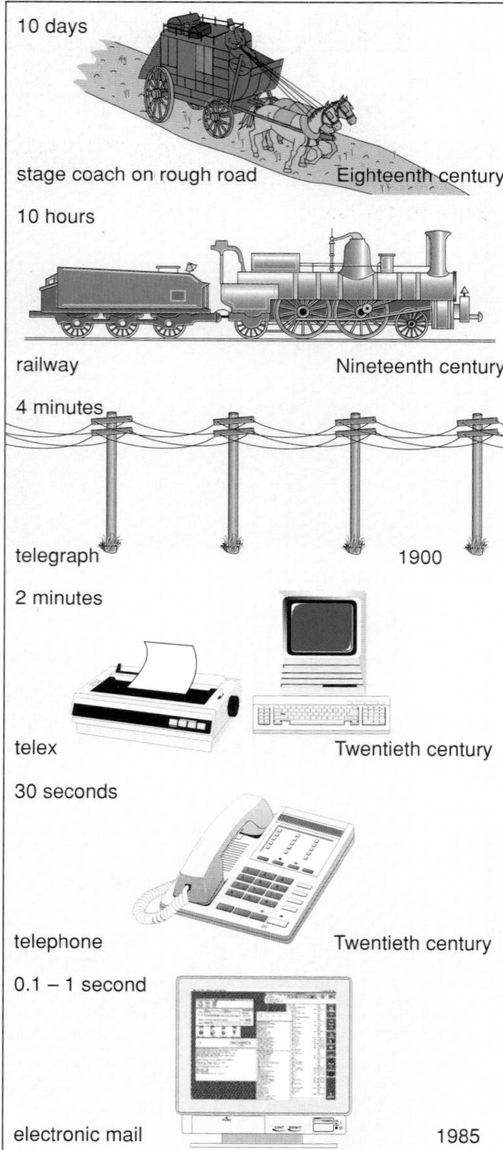

Picture 7 The time needed to send a short message from Glasgow to London has fallen sharply since the 18th century.

A world without distances

The telegraph and then the telephone provided instant communication from person to person.

The age of radio also meant that the spoken word could be transmitted and received instantly, but by *many* people at the same time. One person could now talk to *millions*. As radio developed, for the first time huge numbers of people could hear events *as they happened*, regardless of the distances involved.

The moving image was soon to follow. In the 1930s a young Scotsman, John Logie Baird, began to experiment with ways of transmitting pictures. His system used a mechanical method of 'capturing' the picture, which was rather large and clumsy. Despite Baird being first to produce television pictures, it was a rival electronic system that was finally adopted by the BBC. When television allowed people to *view* a scene, growing numbers could watch live sporting events and entertainment. Television had its biggest impact however, when people were able to witness history taking place. When the Apollo astronauts reached the Moon, (picture 6) billions of people saw the first human footstep ever taken on another world.

Over the last two centuries, communications have steadily improved, (picture 7), but the greatest changes have occurred in the last 30 years. Radio, television, and the telephone have come together with newer developments such as satellites, computers, and fibre-optic cables to form the technology of **telecommunications**.

We now live in a world where, at any time of the day or night, citizens of the developed countries can find out what is happening anywhere on Earth. Information can travel by electrical signals carried by wires stretching under the oceans, by radio waves transmitted to and from satellites far out in space, or by laser light flashing through cables of hair-thin glass. Sometimes it travels by combinations of all three. It may arrive in the form of moving pictures, on paper printed by a fax machine, or perhaps as a computer file downloaded from the Internet.

A person can watch a satellite view from space showing a hurricane moving towards the coast of America, (picture 8) or a swarm of locusts moving towards Egyptian farms (picture 9). More importantly, they can then issue a warning which may save lives or crops.

As the telephone is now something you can carry, someone stranded on a Scottish mountain can call for help before the weather closes in, or someone else can annoy an entire cinema when it rings during the film.

In the past, the time a message took to travel was always related to the distance it had to be carried. Now that we can send and receive messages almost immediately, the world seems to have shrunk. An event in China or Australia seems as real as something occurring in our own town. The world has become a **global village**, where everyone knows each other's business, and does business with everyone.

Picture 8

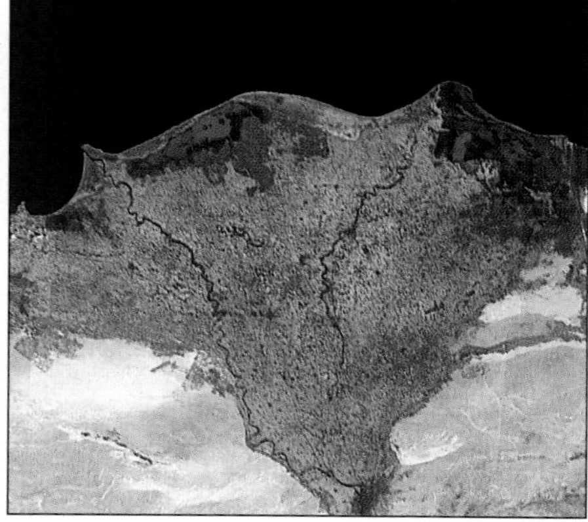

Picture 9

Picture 10 The future

At the centre of everything

Imagine your living room in the near future. There is a large flat cinema-quality screen with a CD standard digital sound system, linked to a computer and the phone. At the touch of a few buttons, or by using your own voice, you can finish watching a re-run of a favourite TV series and then open a menu of other activities.

You can choose any film ever made and it will be transmitted to your screen through the fibre-optic cable. The cost will be put automatically on your monthly bill. You can select from thousands of TV channels from all over the world, or buy the weekend groceries by 'virtual shopping' on screen.

You can ring an aunt in Australia and see her as you talk; browse through a catalogue of video clips of holiday destinations, and book with the travel agent's computer.

You can link up live to anywhere that has a cheap video camera attached to a fibre-optic link, for example a second division football match in Scotland. Your American cousin is staying with you, and he can watch his high school basketball team.

At school, your physics teacher has booked into a lecture from an astronomer in New Zealand, who is also calling up live pictures from the telescope in Hawaii. These are displayed on the classroom screen.

Your dad isn't feeling well. He fills in an interactive questionnaire on screen, which will be transmitted to the computer in the doctor's surgery. His prescription will be faxed to your home, or the doctor may decide to arrange an appointment. His computer checks his diary, and e-mails the details to yours.

Need help with your homework? You will have access to any encyclopaedia or dictionary ever published and it will include film and video sections to illustrate the subject.

The morning paper arrives, not through the letter box, but down the cable. It contains only the news topics that the family are interested in. You make a quick selection and while you shower, it is printed out ready to be read at the breakfast table.

In the near future your home will act as a control centre giving you access to more information and knowledge than previous generations could have dreamed of.

A2 Waves

Sound isn't the only thing that moves as waves. There are waves on water, light waves and earthquake waves.

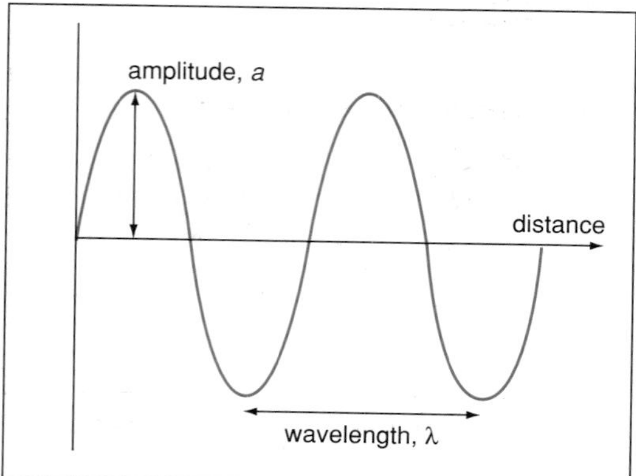

Picture 1

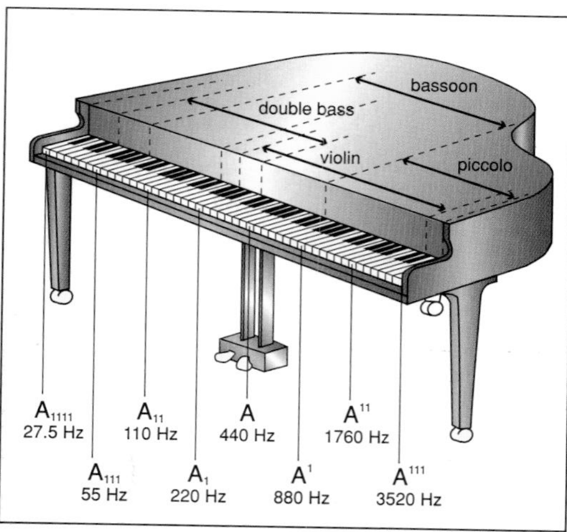

Picture 2

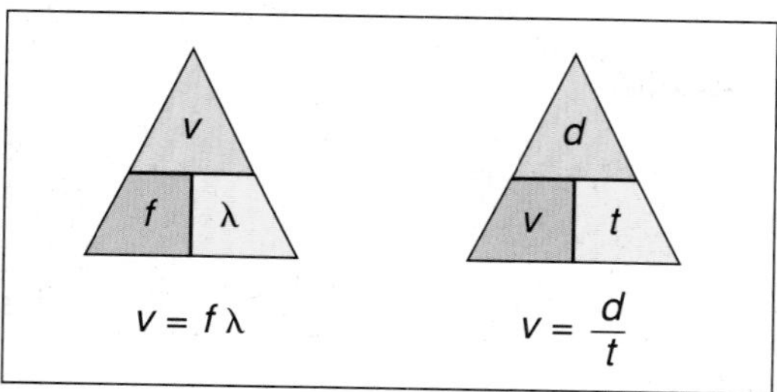

Waves in space

Light, and radio transmissions, travel through space as waves. Sound travels as waves through solids, liquids and gases (see page 12).

But whatever kind of waves they are, they are similar to each other. They all *move, carrying energy*. They all have a *pattern*, which *repeats itself*.

Picture 1 is a graph of a typical wave. It could be a water wave, a sound wave or a light wave. We can use it to explain the meaning of the key words we use to describe wave motion.

First, its **amplitude**. This is a measure of how much the wave vibrates the medium it passes through. It could be the height of a water wave, or the pressure of a sound wave.

The marked distance is the **wavelength** – the distance between equivalent points on the wave pattern. This could be from peak to peak, or from trough to trough. The symbol for wavelength is λ ('lamda').

The wavelength of a typical sound (say middle C) is about 133 cm. The wavelength of light is very much smaller. For yellow light it is about 600 billionths of a metre. Long wave radio broadcasts use a wavelength of over 1000 metres.

Frequency and pitch

Musicians use the word **pitch** to describe how 'high' or 'low' a note is. A high-pitched note is made by something vibrating very quickly. Something vibrating very slowly produces a low-pitched note. We use the word **frequency** to describe the rate at which something vibrates. It measures the number of vibrations per second, in a unit called a **hertz** (**Hz**).

When playing musical notes, for example on a piano, the frequency of the note **doubles** as we go up every eight notes. We call this an **octave**. Middle A has a frequency of **440 Hz**, while upper A has a frequency of **880 Hz** (picture 2). The same is true for the other notes on the keyboard, such as middle C at 256 Hz. One octave higher, C has a frequency of 512 Hz.

The human ear can hear sounds from sources vibrating at a rate as low as 20 vibrations per second (20 Hz) to as high as 20 000 Hz (20 kHz).

The wave speed formula

If a source of sound is vibrating 16 times a second it is producing 16 waves every second. At the end of that second the first wave has travelled 16 wavelengths away from the source. The wave speed is simply how far the waves move in a second. In this case it is obviously just 16 wavelengths. Picture 3 illustrates this.

If the sound source vibrated at 20 Hz, it would produce 20 wavelengths in a second. But sound travels at the same speed in air, whatever its frequency, so the waves are more squashed up – the wavelength is smaller. This is also shown in picture 3.

Thus, because the speed of sound is the same, however many waves are made each second they all have to fit into the same distance. This distance is 340 metres, in air. Looking at it mathematically:

$$\text{length of a sound wave} = \frac{\text{distance sound travels in a second}}{\text{number of waves made per second}}$$

or:

$$\text{wavelength} = \frac{\text{speed}}{\text{frequency}}$$

This is usually written more neatly as:

$$\textit{wave speed} = \textit{frequency} \times \textit{wavelength}$$

$$v = f\lambda$$

This formula applies to all waves.

As speed is also found by calculating $\frac{\text{distance}}{\text{time}}$, we can write

$$v = \frac{d}{t}$$

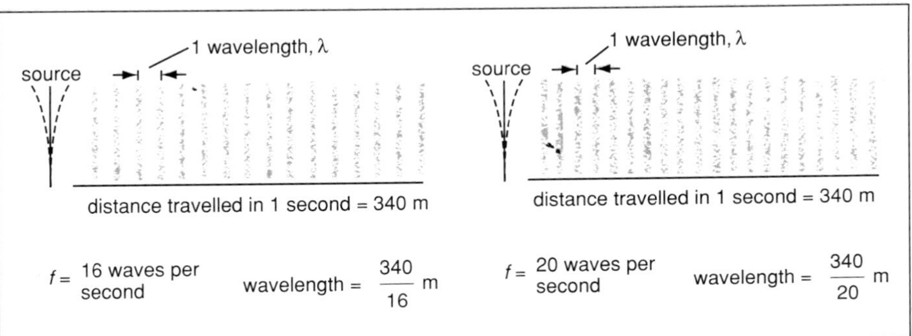

Picture 3 The speed stays the same, so wavelength gets less when frequency increases.

To and fro, up and down

Sound waves compress and expand the air. The particles of air move backwards and forwards in line with the direction the sound travels. Waves on a large-coil spring can also do this. These kinds of waves are called **longitudinal** waves.

When sea waves move, the water surface moves up and down as the wave moves along. Waves on a rope or a guitar string are also like this. Waves in which the carrier (medium) moves at right angles to the direction of wave movement are called **transverse** waves. Picture 4 shows these differences.

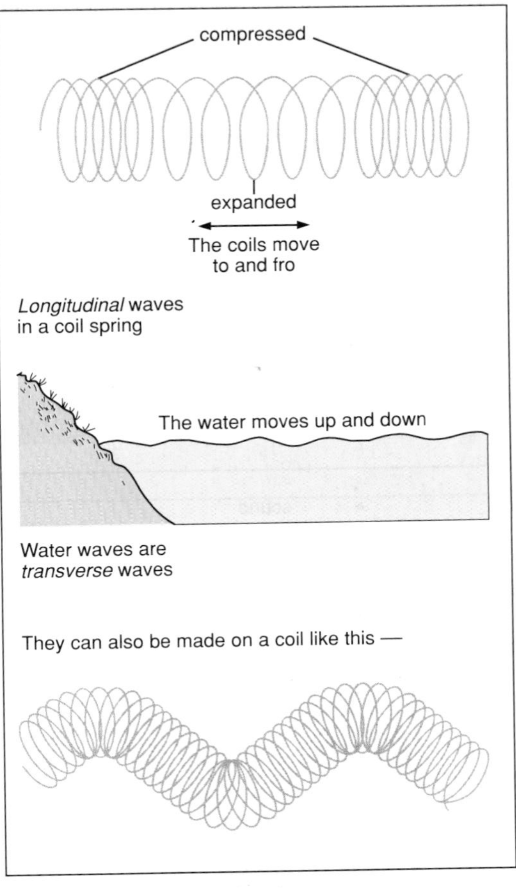

Picture 4 Longitudinal and transverse waves.

Waves through liquids

Sound waves travel well through water. Dolphins use sound waves as a sonar to hunt their prey. Sound travels through water because sound is a longitudinal wave. Transverse waves can travel along the surface of water but not through water. This is the case for all liquids. This fact has been used to prove that the core of the Earth is liquid, because the transverse earthquakes waves don't get across to the opposite side of the Earth.

Waves can carry energy

Picture 5 shows the coast of Norfolk at a place where the sea cliff is slowly disappearing. The energy for this has been carried by the sea waves continually beating on the base of the cliff. The worst damage is done in storms, when the sea waves are many metres high and carry a great deal of energy.

The bigger the amplitude of a wave the more energy it carries. In fact, the energy carried is proportional to the square of the amplitude. So doubling the wave height increases the energy carried four times. See Picture 6.

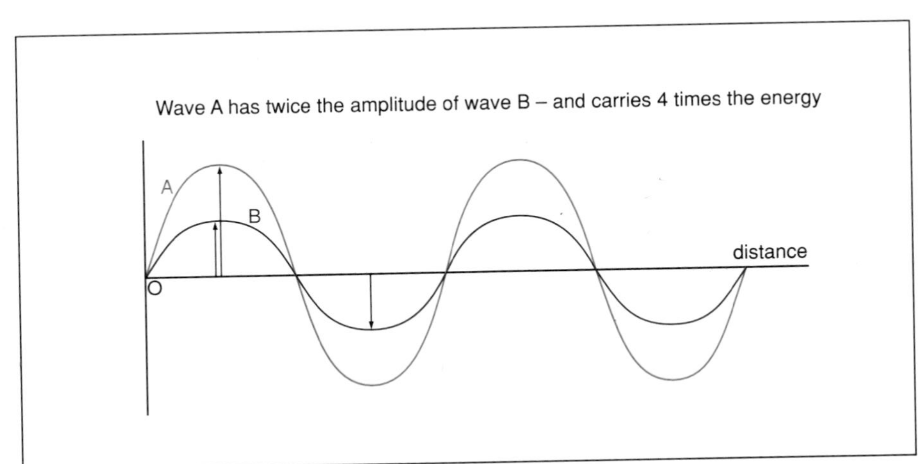

Picture 6 Energy and amplitude for a wave.

Picture 5

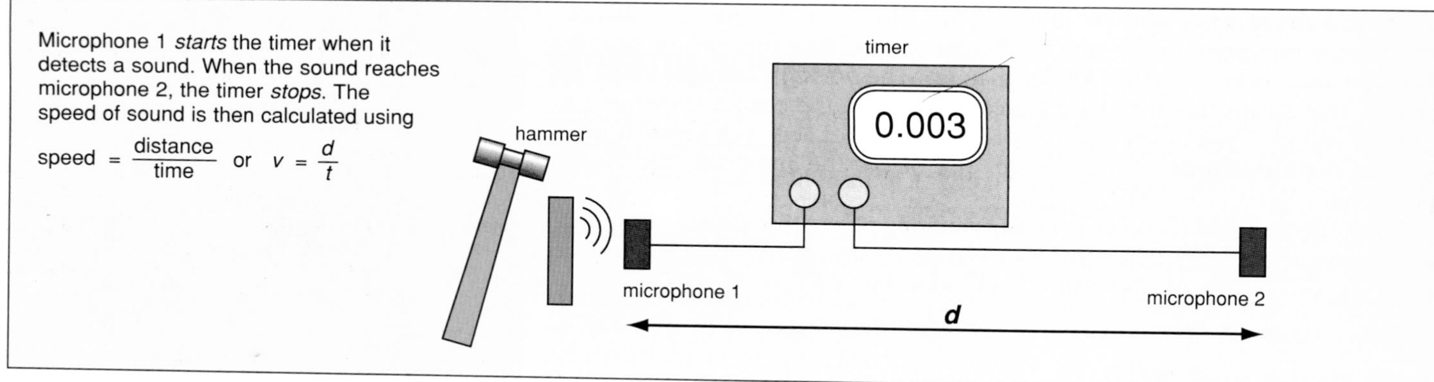

Picture 5 A method of measuring the speed of sound in the laboratory.

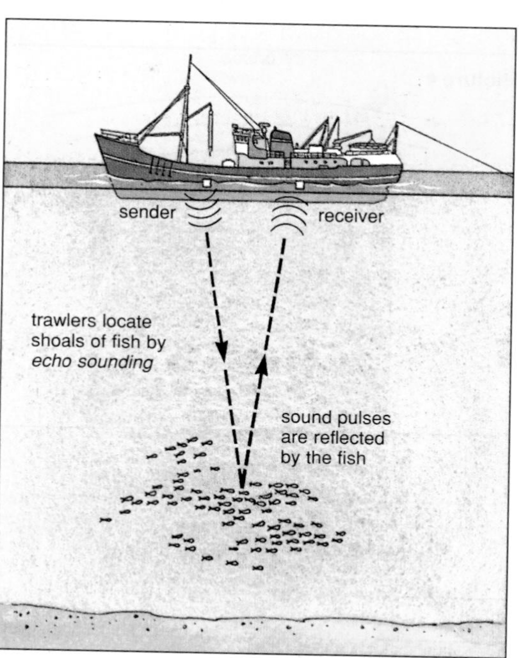

Picture 7 Using sound to find fish.

Echoes

Like other waves, sound can be reflected. We don't usually notice this, but we would find listening to music and speech in rooms and concert halls very strange if the walls didn't reflect sound.

Echoes are very obvious examples of sound being reflected. To hear a good echo, we must stand a few hundred metres from a cliff or hillside. When we shout, the sound travels to the reflector and bounces back (picture 6). If we are far enough away it means that we can finish a short sentence before the echo returns to us.

Echo ranging

If we make a short sharp sound we can time how long it takes for the sound to get to the cliff and come back again. We know that the speed of sound is 340 metres per second, so we can work out how far away the cliff is. Suppose it took 2 seconds for the sound to go there and back. This means it took 1 second to get there, so the cliff must be 340 metres away.

The same principle is used in **radar**, which uses radio waves to find the position of distant aircraft, for example. However, radio waves can't travel through water, so radar is no use under the sea. Instead, sound waves are used in **sonar** devices. They are used to find submarines, shoals of fish and to survey the bottom of the sea (picture 7).

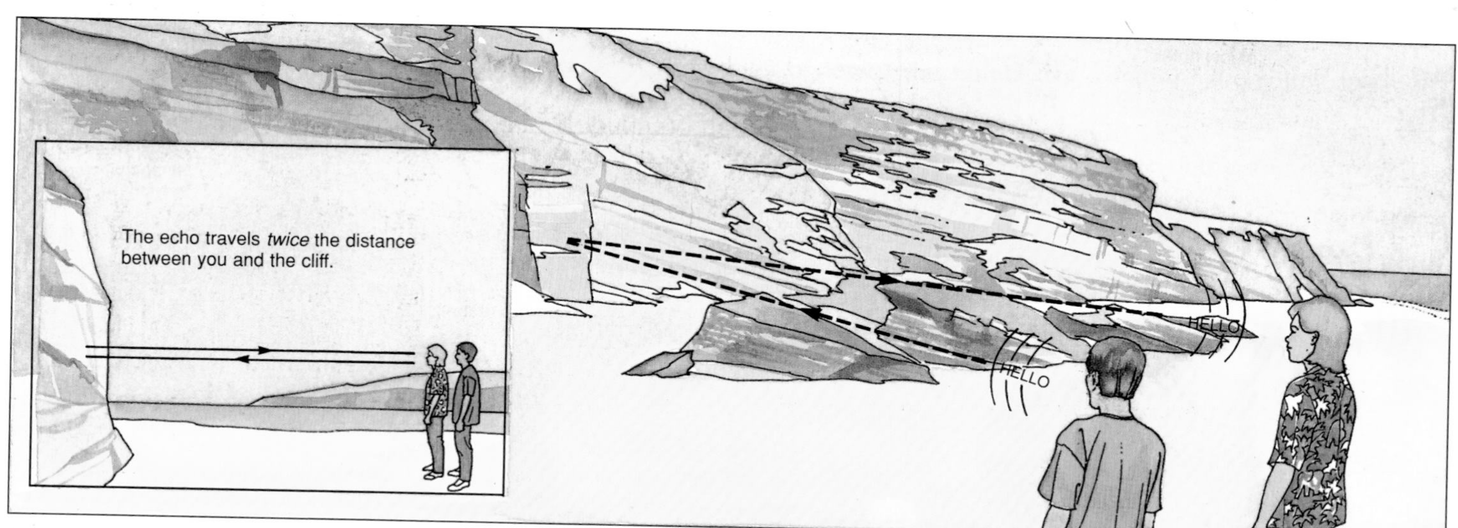

Picture 6 An echo is a reflected sound wave.

Flash and bang

Most people, when they were younger, have lain in bed at night during a thunderstorm with the covers pulled over their head. (Perhaps you still do!) First we see the flash of the lightning, then seconds later we hear the roll of thunder. The thunder is produced *by* the lightning strike, so why is there a delay? The answer is that light travels much faster than sound. As mentioned earlier (page 6), light travels at 300 000 000 metres per second, faster than anything else in the Universe. The flash from the lightning reaches us in such a short time that we can regard it as arriving instantly.

Sound travels at approximately 340 metres per second; the exact speed depends on the atmospheric conditions at the time. We could say that it covers *one kilometre* in roughly *three seconds*. If you wish to know how far away the last bolt of lightning was, start counting immediately after the flash. If you reach six seconds, then the lightning was two kilometres distant. If the time interval gets shorter, you know the storm is coming closer!

Of course a scientist will wish to be more precise. We know that:

$$\text{speed} = \frac{\text{distance}}{\text{time}} \quad \text{or} \quad v = \frac{d}{t}$$

Rearranging this (see the 'triangle rule' in picture 9), gives us:

$$d = v \times t = 6 \times 340 = 2040 \text{ m}$$

The scientist would use a stopwatch or other timing device to obtain an accurate time. If you do not have a stopwatch handy under the bedcover, most people can time reasonably accurately by counting 'one *elephant*, two *elephants*, ...' and so on.

This method applies to any situation where we see or detect the light from an event, and the sound wave reaches us later. Examples of this would be the flash and bang from a gun, or the bursting of a firework rocket followed by the boom of the explosion.

Picture 8 Light travels faster than sound.

The 'triangle' rule for speed, distance and time calculations

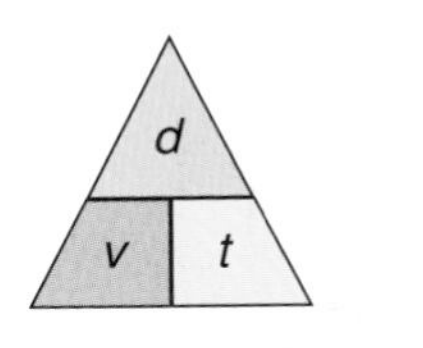

$$v = \frac{d}{t}$$

$$d = v \times t$$

$$t = \frac{d}{v}$$

Picture 9

Questions

1 The diagram shows part of a water tank in which models of ships are tested. The tank is 100 metres long and has a wave machine at one end. A depth scale is marked on the wall of the tank as shown.

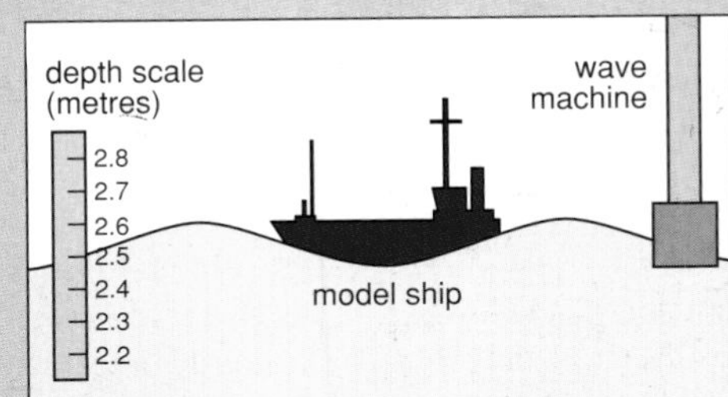

a The crest of a wave from the machine takes 25 seconds to travel from one end of the tank to the other.

Calculate the speed of the waves in the tank.

b The deck of the model ship in the tank moves between the 2.6 metre mark and the 2.8 metre mark on the depth scale as the waves travel along the tank.

Calculate the amplitude of the waves in the tank.

c The depth of the water in the tank is changed so that the waves have a speed of 3.8 metres per second. The wave machine operates at a frequency of 0.5 hertz.

Calculate the wavelength of the waves in the tank.

2 Two timekeepers Smith and Jones are timing a 100 m sprint.

Smith starts her stopwatch when she sees the smoke from the starter's gun. Jones starts his watch when he hears the bang from the gun. Both stop their watches at the instant the winner reaches the finishing line. Both timekeepers are 100 m from the starter.

a Which timekeeper records the shorter time for the winner? Explain your answer.

b The reading on Jones' watch is 11.3 s. What is the reading on Smith's watch?

3 At a fireworks display, John used a stopwatch to measure the time interval between the flash and the bang. The reading on his stopwatch was 0.7 s. John wants to calculate the height at which the fireworks were exploding.

a What other information would John need for his calculation?

b Explain why John's result for the height reached by the fireworks is likely to be very inaccurate.

4 The diagram shows a water wave travelling along a tank. The tank is marked as shown.

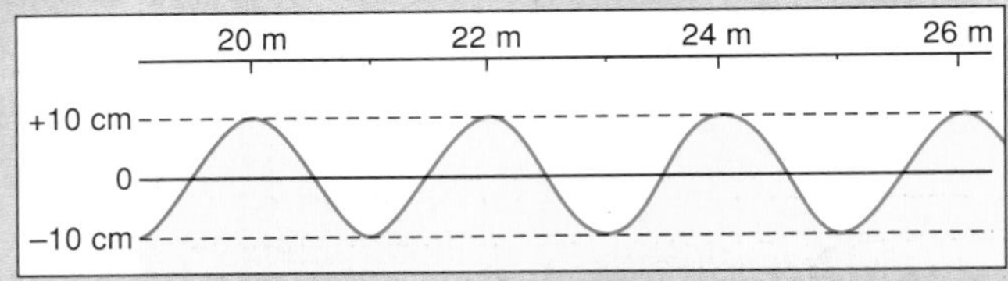

What is the wavelength of the wave?

A4
Signals through wires

Using electricity to carry messages revolutionised the speed and the range of communication.

It is difficult to imagine a time when a message might take a month to travel across the Atlantic Ocean, and another month might pass before a reply returned. Yet, when Queen Victoria came to the throne in 1837, Britain relied on exactly the same methods to carry messages as the Romans, two thousand years before: by foot, by horse, by signal tower, or by sailing ship (see page 16). The new science of electricity, however, was beginning to excite people's imaginations. They noticed that, when a switch was closed, a current seemed to flow *instantly* in a wire, regardless of the length of the circuit.

In Germany in **1825**, **Baron Schilling** used wires in jars of chemicals to send messages. When a current flowed in the wire, bubbles formed in the jar. Each letter of the alphabet had its own jar! In **1837, Cooke** and **Wheatstone** invented an **electric telegraph** which used swinging pointers to spell out a message (picture 1). This method was used by the British railways well into this century.

In the United States, a portrait painter called **Samuel Morse** worked with an American physicist called **Joseph Henry**. Their transmitter was a key switch which could be pressed to send bursts of current down a wire (picture 2). The receiver was a magnetic pen which wrote a series of dots and dashes onto paper – **Morse code**. This system only needed one wire to carry the signals, and the on/off nature of the code allowed a message to be sent quickly.

In **1844**, Morse sent his first message between Washington and Baltimore. After a while, operators grew so familiar with the buzzes produced by the equipment that they could remove the pen and translate a message simply by listening. A reasonably skilled telegraph operator could send roughly 40 words per minute. Henry's invention of the **electromagnetic relay** (see topic D2) made a long-distance telegraph possible. A signal transmitted over the largest practical distance could operate the relay switch, which was connected to a new set of batteries. It would send a fresh copy of the signal on the next stage of its journey. This was the first example of a **repeater stage**. Modern systems use sophisticated repeaters containing amplifiers (see page 18).

Picture 1 An early 'pointer' telegraph.

Picture 2 A Morse code transmitter and receiver. A quick press of the key produces a short burst of current in the wires and a note from a buzzer – a 'dot'. A longer press produces a 'dash'.

At that time, it took almost 180 days for a ship to carry a message from New York to San Francisco, on the other side of the United States. The telegraph followed the railways as the system extended across America. As the tracks were laid, telegraph poles were put up alongside. It is said that the telegraph and the railways were the two inventions that 'made America possible'.

Bridging the oceans

In September 1851, an underwater cable was laid across the English Channel, enabling telegraph communication between Britain and Europe. It was not long before the biggest challenge of all was attempted. On Tuesday 5 August 1858, a transatlantic cable was brought ashore in Ireland, linking America and Britain. Unfortunately, it did not work properly, and failed completely by 1 September.

Picture 3 The *Great Eastern*.

The cable was redesigned and the largest ship afloat, the *Great Eastern*, was employed to lay it (picture 3). After two more attempts, a working cable finally carried messages between the two continents in July 1866.

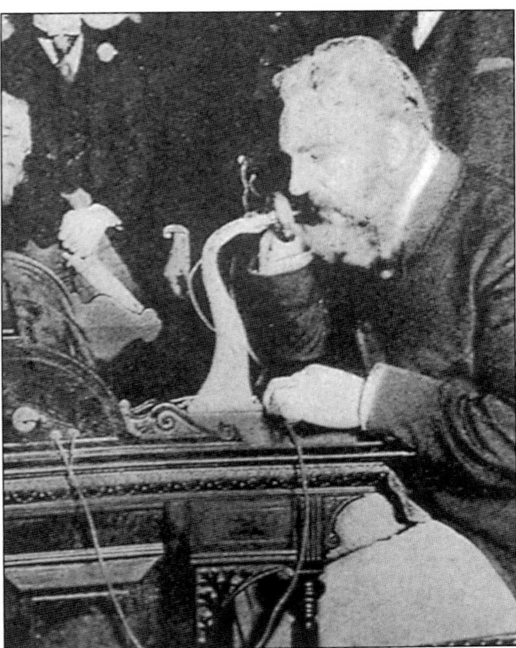

Picture 4 Alexander Graham Bell

Wires begin to speak

In 1876, the Chief Engineer of the British Post Office was asked if the new American invention of the telephone would be useful in Great Britain. His reply was, 'No sir, we do not need it; we have plenty of messenger boys'. The mayor of a large American city was much more enthusiastic, and thought it a marvellous invention, 'I can see the time when *every city may have one*,' he predicted.

Once invented, the telephone spread quickly. Within ten years there were over 100 000 telephones in the United States. As so often happens, its inventor **Alexander Graham Bell** had actually been trying to develop something else. Bell was a Scot from Edinburgh who emigrated to the United States, and was working on a way of sending several telegraph messages down one wire at the same time. By accident, he found that he could convert patterns of *sound* into matching *electrical* patterns. When these signals travelled down a wire, the electrical energy could be converted back into sound at the far end. He saw the possibilities at once, and went on to develop a device to transmit human speech. Picture 5 shows the patterns of the electrical signals in a telephone wire, displayed on an oscilloscope screen.

As we saw in the 'Sound' and 'Waves' sections, a *loud* sound has more energy than a *soft* sound, and so the sound wave has a greater **amplitude**. The electrical signal is shown as a wave pattern on the screen. A loud sound reaching the **transmitter** generates a signal which also has a high amplitude.

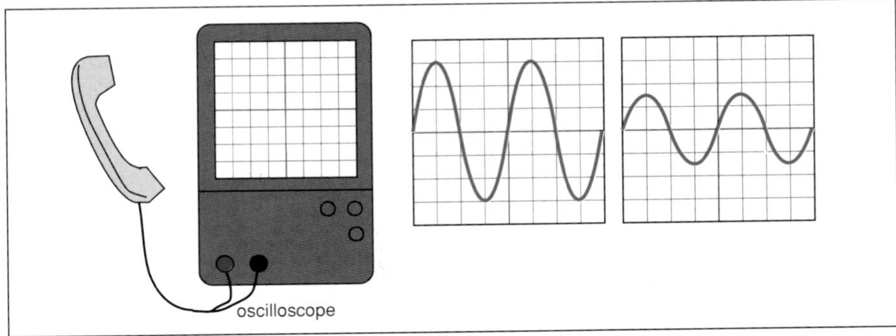

Picture 5 Loud sounds produce signals with greater amplitude.

When the signal is used to make an object vibrate (the **receiver**), a loud or soft sound results from a high- or low-amplitude signal.

A high-frequency sound produces more waves per second. As they arrive at the transmitter, each complete wave produces a 'peak and trough' of the electrical signal (picture 6). The frequency of the signal matches the frequency of the original sound, and reproduces it when fed into the receiver.

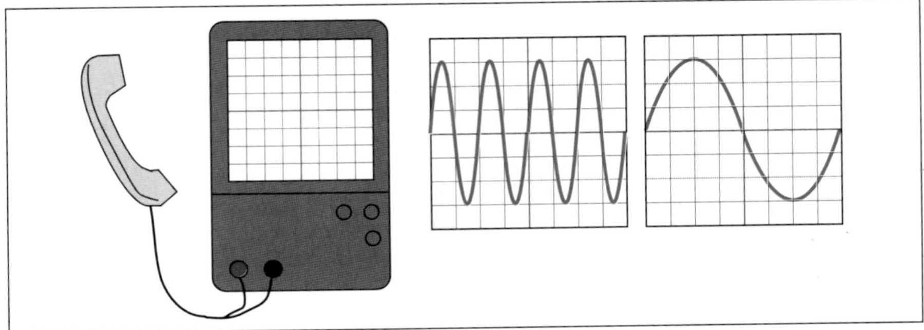

Picture 6 High pitched sounds produce high-frequency signals.

Bell's original transmitter and receiver were the same device, that is it worked both ways. It was not very efficient as a transmitter, and was eventually replaced by the **carbon microphone**. This was developed by another great American inventor, **Thomas Edison**.

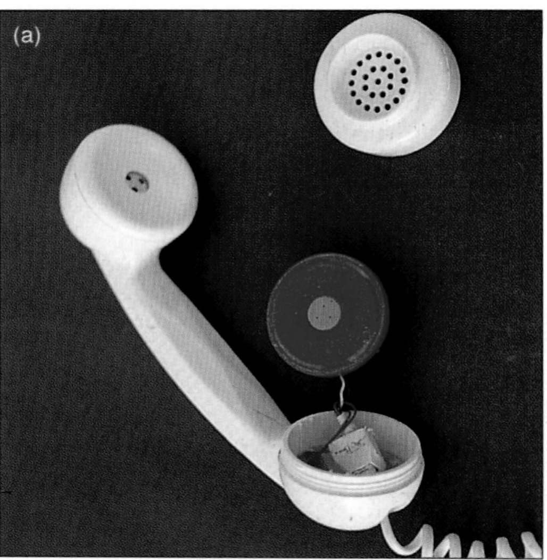

Picture 7 Carbon microphone

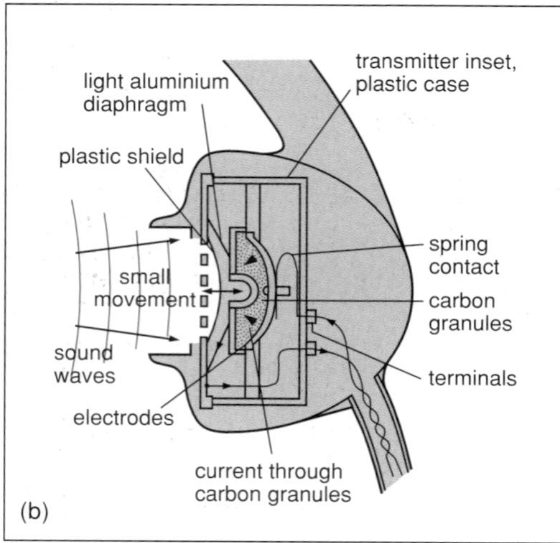

Microphones

Both microphones and loudspeakers are **transducers**. Transducers change information from one energy system to another. A microphone has the job of changing sound waves into a varying electrical current. The pattern of the changing signal has to be a close copy of the pattern of the sound wave. The speaker converts the changing current back into sound waves.

Picture 7 shows a typical microphone – the **carbon microphone**. It is still used in some older telephones, but modern ones use **electret microphones**. The key component in the carbon microphone is the capsule containing the carbon grains.

Carbon conducts electricity, and when the carbon grains are squashed together they let a bigger current pass. When they move apart, their resistance increases, and the current falls. When sound waves reach the microphone, they make a flexible piece of steel (the diaphragm) vibrate. The carbon grains are squashed together and moved apart in time with the vibrations. The current through the carbon grains changes in the same pattern as the sound waves striking the diaphragm.

Electret microphones use a very thin piece of plastic film with a charged metal coating. When sound waves vibrate the positively charged film, a negative charge flows to and fro in a metal plate. This signal is amplified and sent down the telephone line. Picture 8 shows the workings of an electret microphone.

Reaching its destination

Energy is needed to send a current through a wire and there is a limit to how far a useful strength of signal can be transmitted. Amplifiers are required at regular intervals to re-transmit the signal. In a copper cable, these amplifiers or **repeaters** are usually about 4 km apart. In a submarine cable carrying messages under the oceans, the repeaters must be very strong and reliable in order to work miles down on the seabed. The new technology of **optical fibres**, using light to carry messages (see page 31), only requires repeaters every 100 km.

Hearing the call

In wires or optical fibres, a telephone signal travels at about 200 000 km/s, which is so fast that we do not notice any delay when listening and replying on the telephone. When you take a call, the electrical signal in the wires must now be converted back into sound by the **receiver** in the handset – the **loudspeaker**.

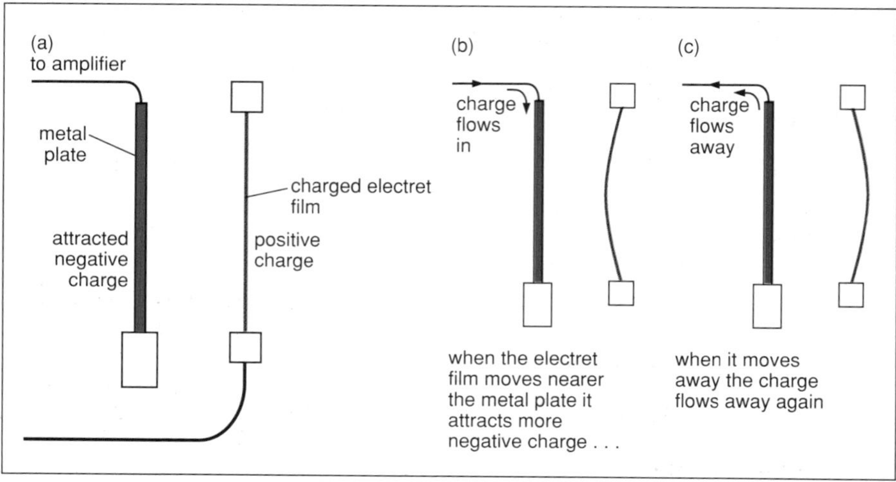

Picture 8

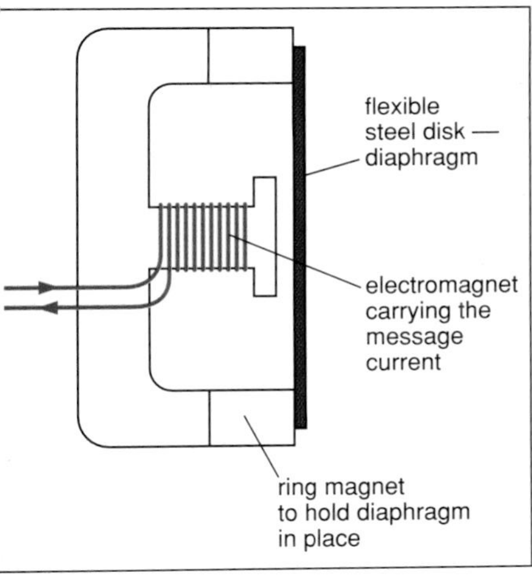

Picture 9 Telephone earpiece. The current in the coil is a copy (analogue) of the sound. It powers an electromagnet which makes the diaphragm vibrate to reproduce the original sound.

The key parts of the speaker in the earpiece (picture 9) are the electromagnet and the thin steel plate (diaphragm). The changing electric current changes the strength of the electromagnet, moving the plate back and forward. The vibrating metal plate produces a sound which is a copy of that picked up by the microphone in the caller's handset.

The telephone earpiece is good enough for conversations, but cannot reproduce musical sounds accurately. A better way of doing this is to use a **moving coil** loudspeaker (picture 10).

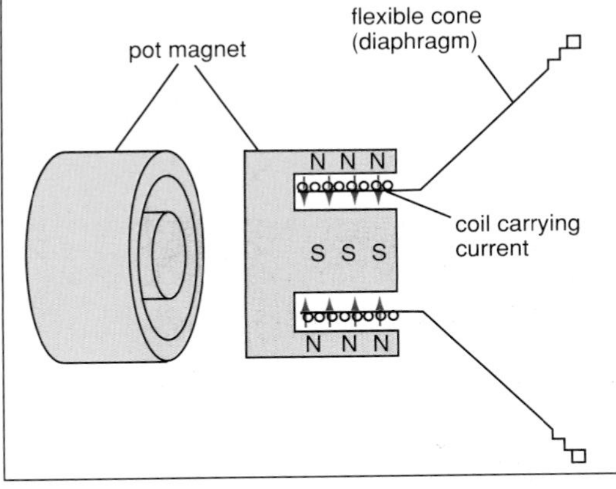

Picture 10 Moving coil loudspeaker.

Questions

1 Anne sets up the experiment below to measure the highest frequency Jim can hear.

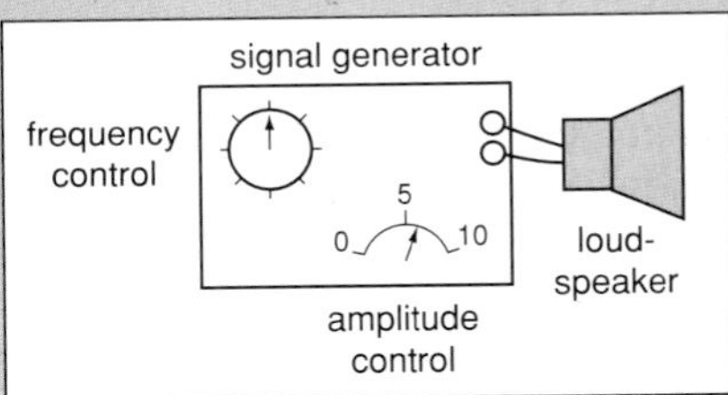

a What is the highest frequency you would expect Jim to hear?

b Anne now connects an oscilloscope across the loudspeaker. She sets the controls of the signal generator so that a **loud** sound of frequency 256 hertz is heard.

The trace on the oscilloscope is shown here.

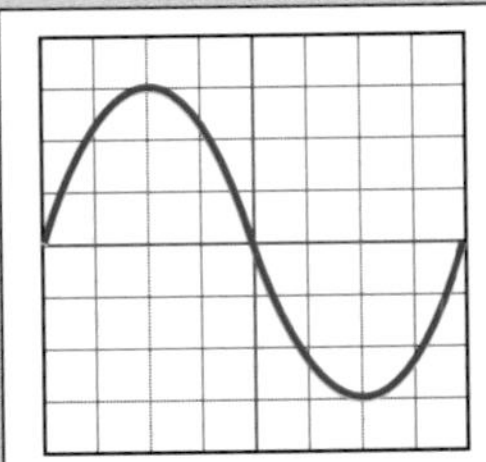

i) Anne then sets the signal generator to give a **quieter** sound **one octave higher**.

Copy the diagram to show the trace obtained on the oscilloscope.

ii) What is the frequency of this quieter sound?

iii) Anne asks Jim to calculate the wavelength of the note of frequency 256 hertz. She tells him that the speed of sound in air is 340 metres per second and that he can use the same formula as is used for water waves.

What value should Jim obtain for the wavelength of the note?

2a A telephone handset has an earpiece and a mouthpiece.

Copy and complete the following by inserting the missing words.

The earpiece contains a loudspeaker which changes .... energy to sound energy. In the mouthpiece there is a .... which changes .... energy to .... energy. The signal from the mouthpiece is transmitted along the wires at a speed of almost 300 000 000 metres per second which is the speed at which .... travels.

b A telephone cable between Scotland and America is 4800 kilometres long. How long will it take a signal to travel along the cable from Scotland to America?

3a In communication systems, what name is given to the part which sends out signals?

b Heather, Eric and Sharon wish to send a message in Morse code from one room to another. The circuit they use for their system is shown below.

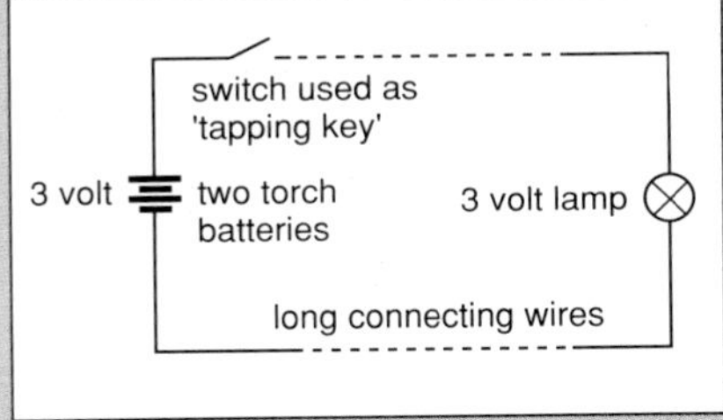

Describe how Heather could send the coded message to Eric and Sharon in the other room.

c When the circuit is set up, the lamp does not work, although all the components are in good working order.

They consider the changes they could make:

Eric suggests '*Leave one battery near the tapping key and put the other battery near the lamp.*'

Heather suggests '*Use one battery instead of two.*'

Sharon suggests, '*Use connecting wire with less resistance.*'

The pupils try each of the suggested changes and find that only **one** works.

i) Who made the correct suggestion?

ii) Explain why this change was suitable.

iii) Explain why the other two changes were not suitable.

A5 Radio

Communication without wires revolutionised our world.

Picture 1

Radio

Create a disturbance by throwing a stone into a pond. The splash creates waves which spread out over the surface. If they reach a a floating log, it starts to move up and down. The movement energy of the stone has been transferred to the water. The waves have carried the energy across the pond, and some of it has been transferred to the log (picture 1).

In 1888, while working with static electricity, a German scientist called **Heinrich Hertz** was producing electrical disturbances – sparks. He noticed that whenever he generated a spark, another spark would be produced in equipment on the other side of his laboratory. Energy from the electrical disturbance was being carried across the space, and transferred to the totally separate apparatus (picture 2).

Hertz had confirmed a theory put forward 15 years earlier by a famous Scots physicist called **James Clerk Maxwell**. Maxwell's theory described the behaviour of light waves, but it also predicted the existence of other waves. Light was one member of a whole 'family' of **electromagnetic** waves, and Hertz gave the first proof of the existence of a different section of that family – **radio** waves. Modern society would be crippled if it did not have radio transmissions for communication, but at the time Hertz could think of no practical use for his discovery! Hertz is honoured by having the unit of frequency named after him.

Marconi (see page 7) used a spark transmitter to send the first radio messages, but only simple on/off codes, such as Morse could be used.

If we display the signal from a spark transmitter on an oscilloscope, (picture 3) we see that it is a jumble of different frequencies. This is similar to the wild splash produced by the stone thrown into the pond. It was only when radio waves of a set frequency could be generated by transmitters that voice messages became possible.

Picture 2 A later version of Hertz's apparatus. The curved metal sheets direct the radio waves.

Transmitting

A microphone converts a pattern of sound waves into an electrical signal, which has the *same frequency* as the original sound. The range of sound frequencies that we can hear are called **audio** frequencies. The microphone gives out an electrical signal that has an audio frequency. Radio waves have much *higher* frequencies than audio signals.

If we connect an oscilloscope to a radio transmitter when there is no audio signal being broadcast, we see a constant radio frequency signal. This is called the **carrier** wave. Different radio stations have different carrier wave frequencies.

If an audio signal is added to the carrier wave, a peak of the audio signal will make the carrier wave stronger, and its *amplitude* increases. A trough will subtract from the carrier wave, lowering its amplitude. The *pattern* of the audio signal is now overlaid on the carrier wave (picture 4). We have changed or **modulated** the amplitude of the carrier wave. This method of transmission is therefore called **amplitude modulation** or **AM**.

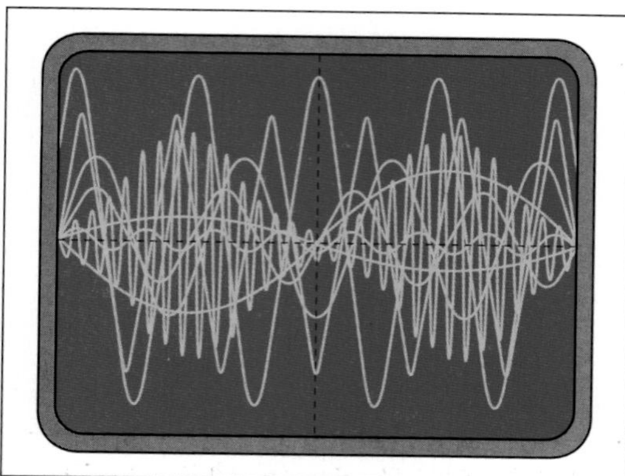

Picture 3 The jumbled signals from a spark transmitter.

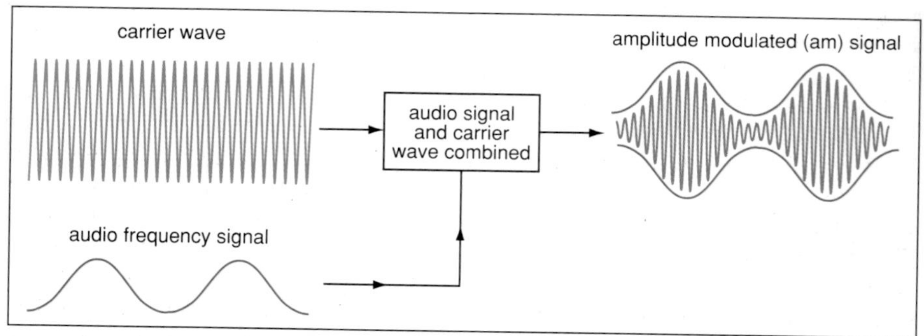

Picture 4 How an AM signal is produced.

Detecting a signal

As a float in the water bobs up and down at a particular frequency, it produces water waves with that frequency. When the waves reach another float, they transfer energy to it. It moves with the *same* frequency as the source.

When we feed a changing electrical signal into a wire or other metal conductor, we produce an **alternating current**. The electrons in the wire move back and forward, speeding up and slowing down. As they do this, they emit **radio waves** which spread out from the conductor – the **transmitting aerial.**

When the waves reach a metal **receiving** aerial, they cause the electrons to move back and forward at the *same* frequency as the radio waves. The energy in the waves has been transferred to the electrons in the metal, producing a changing current – an electrical signal which is an *exact copy* of the original in the transmitting aerial.

Radio waves will affect the electrons in any metallic conductor. If we place a radio receiver and aerial in a metal cage, most of the energy of the radio waves is either absorbed by the electrons in the metal frame, or reflected back. The same process occurs if we wrap the radio in metal foil. This is why a car radio needs an external aerial – the metal car body stops radio waves reaching the radio receiver. Some buildings have a metal framework which causes poor indoor reception.

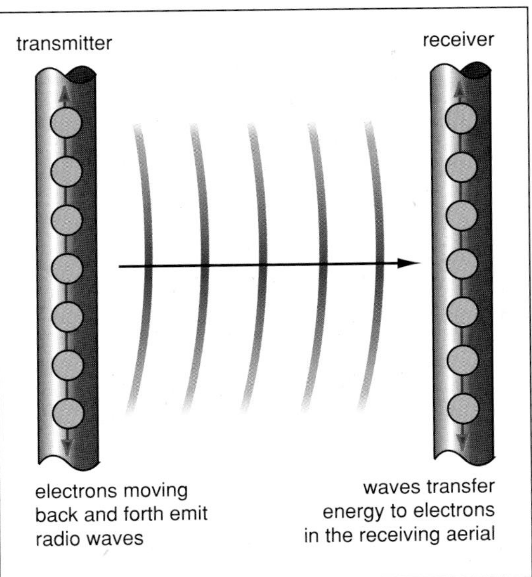

Picture 5 Moving electrons generate radio waves. These waves cause the electrons in a metal aerial to move.

Picture 6 Energy must be transferred at the correct frequency.

Tuning in

Imagine you are pushing a small child on a rope swing (picture 6). If you try to add energy by pushing halfway through the backswing, the rope jolts and shudders to a halt. The child and rope have a natural frequency. You can only add energy successfully if you time your push to match each complete swing. The frequency of the push must match the frequency of the swinging child.

The circuit in picture 7 lets current flow back and forth at a particular frequency. If we feed in a signal at a different frequency, it will not fit the natural 'rhythm' of the circuit. Just like the child and swing, the signal being received must match the natural frequency of the circuit – it is **tuned** to a particular frequency. The aerial of a radio receiver will pick up many different signals. When these are fed into the tuned circuit, only the signal that matches the circuit frequency is accepted. Of course, a radio that can only pick up one station is not very good value for money! By using a variable component called a **capacitor**, the natural frequency of the circuit can be changed, so that it can detect different stations. The tuner *selects* the station we wish to listen to.

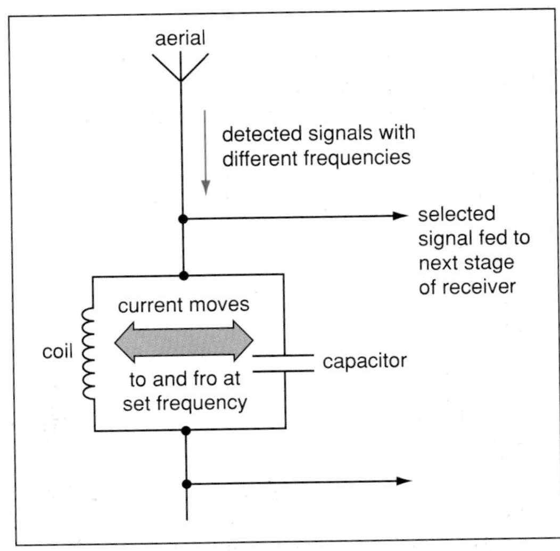

Picture 7 Only a frequency which matches the natural frequency of the circuit is accepted.

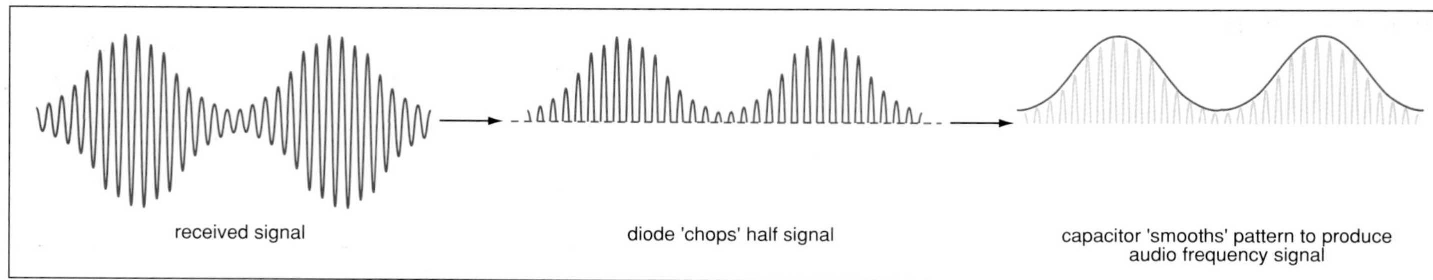

Picture 8 The audio signal must be separated from the carrierwave by the decoder.

Decoding the information

If we tune our radio to a station's carrier wave frequency, we will receive a signal that changes in strength (amplitude). To reproduce the audio information, we must **decode** the signal to separate the radio and audio frequencies. This can be done by feeding the signal through a **diode**, a component which only allows current to flow in one direction. As we can see in picture 8, this 'chops' out the bottom half of the signal. By using another capacitor, we can 'smooth' the pattern until we have retrieved the original audio signal.

Amplification

In the early days of radio, radio broadcasts could be listened to using a receiver called a 'crystal set'. This was basically an aerial, a tuned circuit, a primitive diode, and an earpiece.

The diode was constructed from a fine wire and a crystal. The wire was referred to as the 'cats whisker'. The tiny amount of energy in the radio waves could power the earpiece! A weak radio signal is totally incapable of driving a modern loudspeaker, so the decoded signal must have energy added to it. As we are increasing the amplitude of the signal, this is referred to as **amplification**. The amplifier section draws energy from a battery or the mains supply. It increases the strength of the audio signal before sending it to the **loudspeaker**, which converts it into sound.

(For more on amplification, see topic D9.)

Picture 9 The stages of radio transmission and reception.

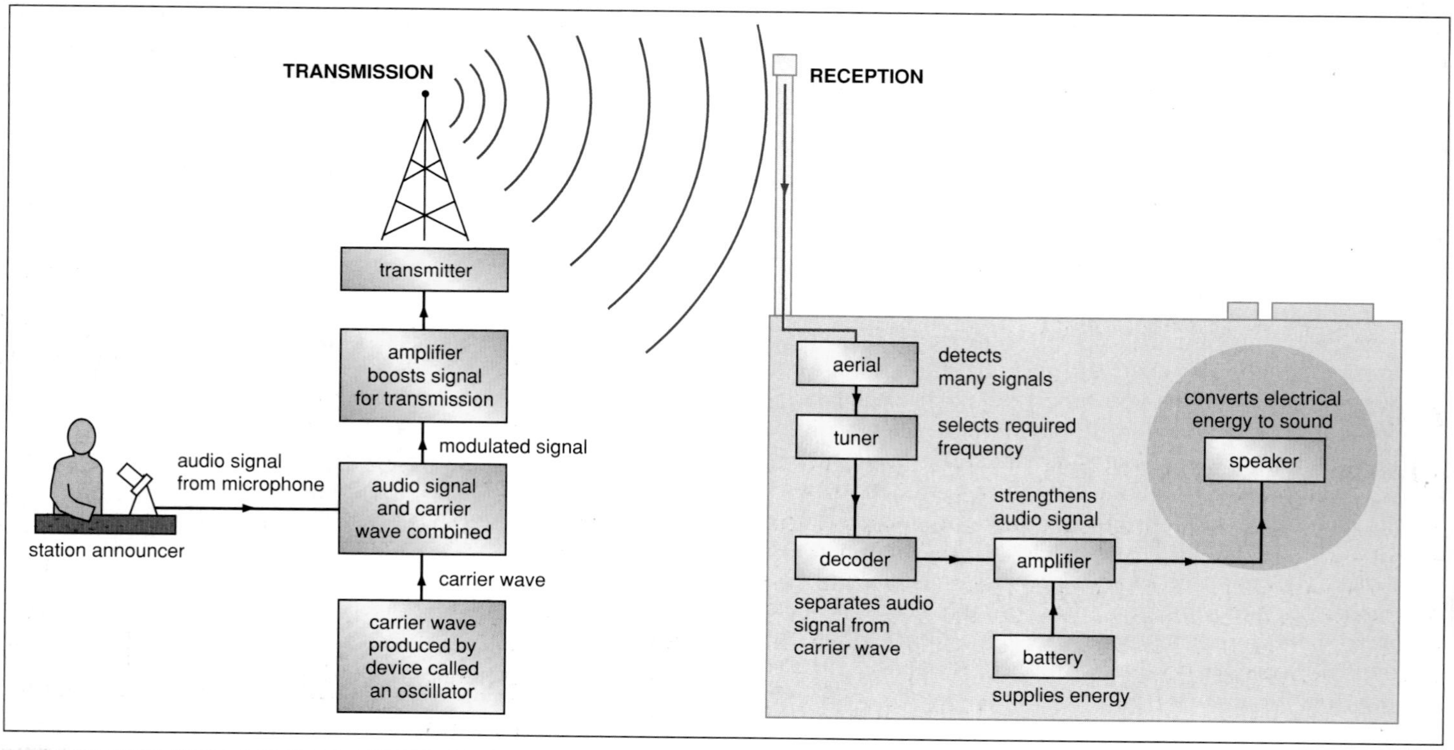

Different frequencies

Look at the tuning controls on a radio receiver. You will usually see a choice of at least three different 'bands' of radio stations. They are normally labelled LW, MW, or FM. The first two stand for **Long Wave** and **Medium Wave**. The markings show that the MW band has *smaller* wavelengths than LW. If the tuner is marked in frequencies, you will notice that the MW band has *higher* frequencies than the LW.

Radio waves, like light, are electromagnetic waves. *All* electromagnetic waves travel at the speed of light, which is 300 000 000 metres per second. They obey the wave equation, $v = f\lambda$, which can also be written as: $\lambda = v / f$ (picture 10).

As v is always the same, this means that as frequency f *increases*, then the wavelength λ will get *smaller*. In other words, the higher the frequency, the shorter the wavelength.

MW and LW stations use frequencies measured in **kilohertz** (1000 Hz = 1 kHz). Your radio might also have a short wave (SW) band on it, which is used for international transmissions such as the BBC World Service. These are measured in megahertz (1 000 000 Hz = 1 MHz).

FM stations are Very High Frequency or VHF transmissions. **FM** stands for **Frequency Modulation**, which means that it is the *frequency* of the wave that is changed to carry a signal (picture 11). FM is very suitable for high-quality stereo broadcasts, and suffers less from interference.

Radio waves behave differently according to their *frequency*. This affects how far they will travel round the Earth. In 1901 Marconi sent a Morse code signal across the Atlantic. If radio waves behave like light, then we would expect them to travel in straight lines. Due to the curve of the Earth, Marconi's signal should have travelled out into space without reaching America.

The mystery was solved by the discovery of a layer in the upper atmosphere called the **ionosphere**. Just as light reflects from a mirror, this layer reflects radio signals back and forth to Earth, (picture 12) allowing them to travel large distances when conditions are right.

In 1928, short waves were used to provide a radiotelephone service between London and New York. The wavelengths used were between 16 and 32 m.

Radio transmissions which use reflection are called **sky waves** (picture 13(a)). Longer low-frequency waves bend naturally round the curve of the Earth and travel closer to the ground, so they can be received directly without being reflected. They lose energy more easily, however, and only have a range of roughly 1000 km. These waves are called **ground waves** (picture 13(c)).

Waves with frequencies above 30 MHz are called **space waves**, as they are *not* reflected and pass out into space. To receive them, you must be in a straight line of sight from the transmitter (picture 13(b)). If you are below the horizon from the transmitter, you will not receive the signal. FM stations operate in this frequency range, and so can reach roughly 40–50 km. This is why FM is used for local commercial radio, such as Radio Clyde and Radio Forth. BBC Radio Scotland has to have several transmitters around Scotland, to cover the whole country with the same programme. Each of these transmitters broadcasts the same signals on a slightly different frequency.

UHF

Television pictures are carried by Ultra-High Frequency (UHF) waves, in a band from 300–3000 MHz. Because these frequencies have short range, many transmitting stations are needed to give TV coverage to the whole of Scotland. Each transmitter uses a different frequency to prevent problems caused by signals overlapping. To receive BBC 1 you must tune your set to different frequencies in different parts of the country. If you live near Glasgow, you will probably receive BBC 1 from the Blackhill transmitter, which broadcasts in the 623.25 to 631.25 MHz band.

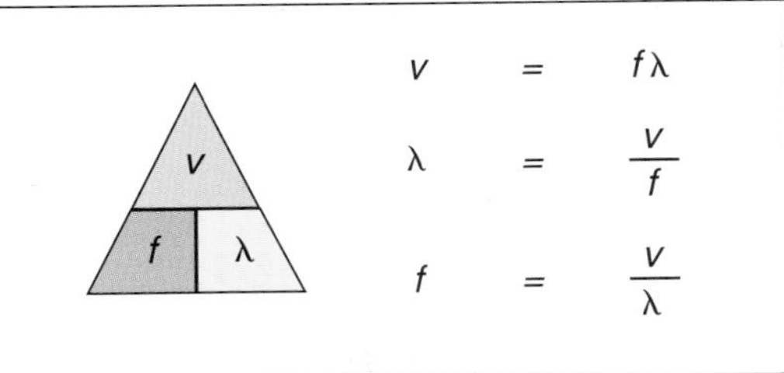

Picture 10

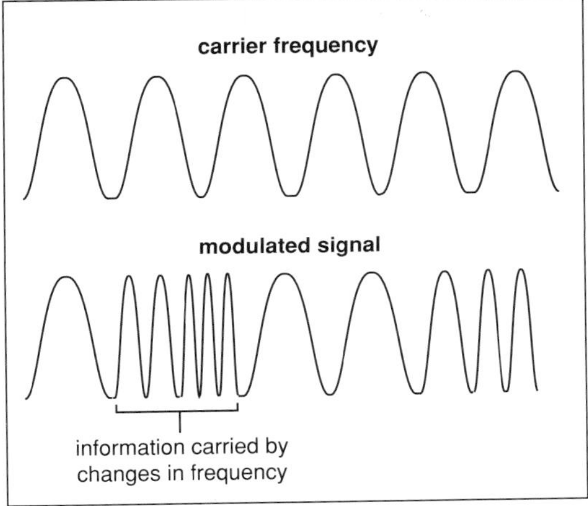

Picture 11

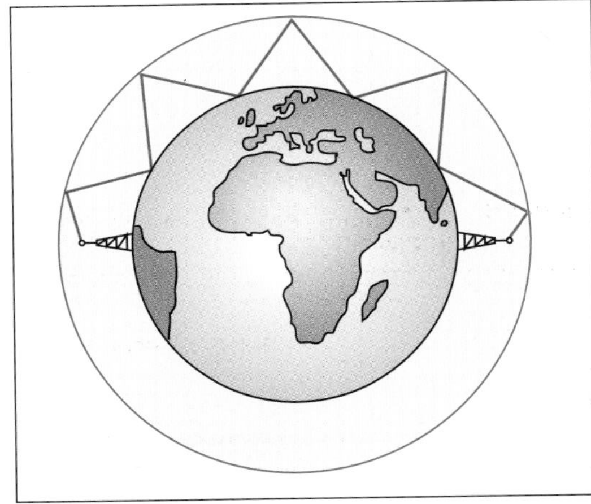

Picture 12

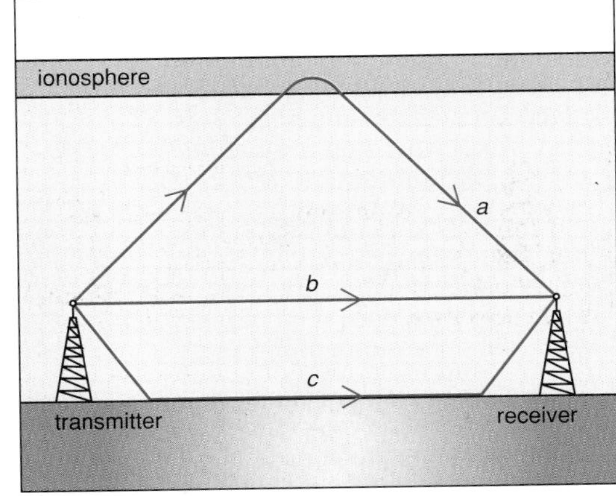

Picture 13

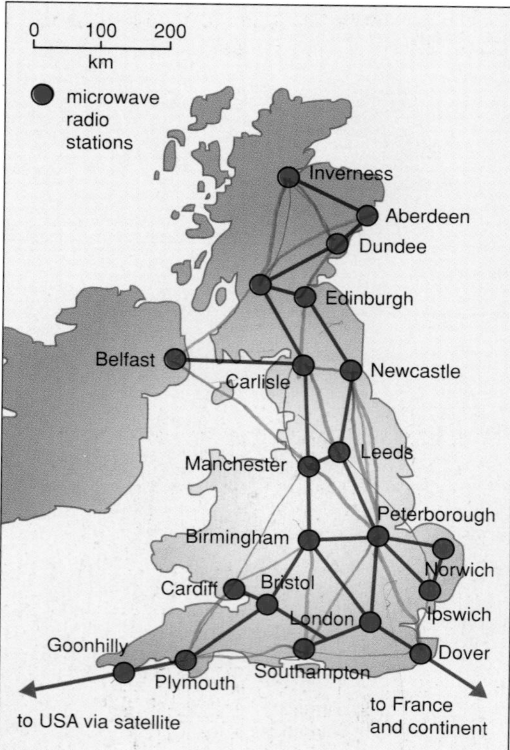

Picture 15

Picture 14

Microwaves

When we talk about microwaves, we usually think first of microwave ovens. These use radio waves whose frequency is particularly suited for transferring energy to the water molecules in food.

For *communications* purposes, microwaves are useful because they can be transmitted in narrow beams which travel in straight lines from the transmitting aerials (picture 14). Signals are passed along a chain of repeater stations which must be in line-of-sight from each other (picture 15). They can carry information across areas where it may be impossible or very expensive to lay cables, for example in island regions. Microwaves also pass through the ionosphere, so that they are suitable for satellite communications.

The higher the frequency of radio waves, the more information that they can carry, and the better the quality of the signal. Microwaves can be used for **digital** transmissions, where the signal is converted into a series of coded pulses. This is ideal for transmitting large amounts of information very quickly.

Bending waves – diffraction

When water waves pass an obstacle, such as a harbour wall, they bend round slightly when they pass. This effect can be seen in a ripple tank when water waves pass a barrier, and is called **diffraction** (picture 1).

Low-frequency waves diffract *more* then high-frequency waves. Radio waves behave in the same way. This is why low frequency (LW) signals bend round the curve of the Earth.

When radio waves encounter an obstacle such as a mountain, *high-frequency* waves such as UHF television transmissions do not diffract as much as MW radio broadcasts. People living in hilly rural areas can get reasonable MW radio reception, but FM reception may be poor. They may also need a communal TV aerial on a nearby hill to supply their village.

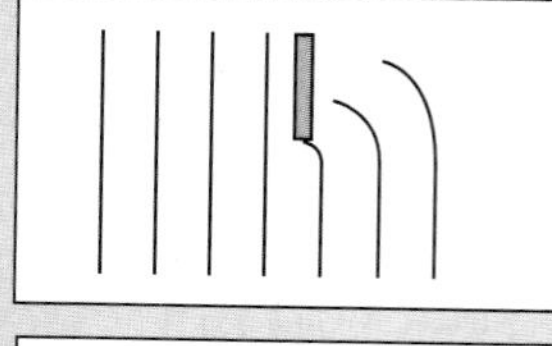

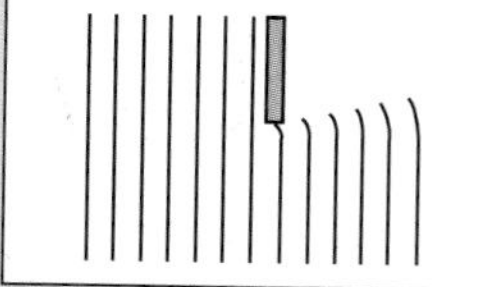

Picture 1 High frequencies diffract less

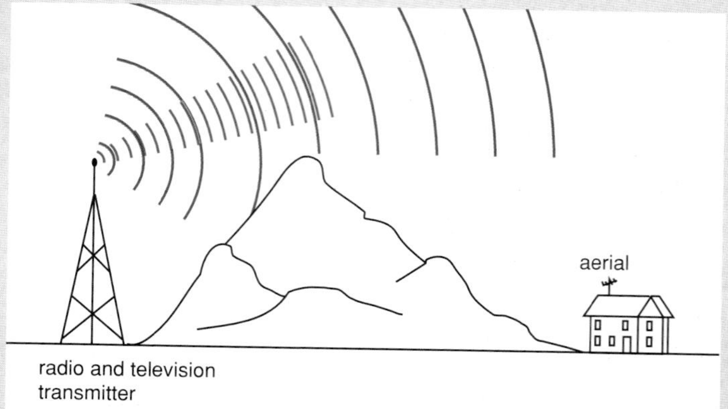

Picture 2

Frequency	Band	Examples of use
150–550 kHz	long wave	national radio (Radio 4)
550–1660 kHz	medium wave	national radio (Radio 1)
2.2–30 MHz	short wave	international radio (BBC World Service)
87.5–100 MHz	very high frequency	international radio (BBC World Service)
30–300 MHz	very high frequency	military, shipping, taxis
300–3000 MHz	ultra-high frequency	radio phones, television, satellites
1–300 GHz	microwave	telephones etc., space vehicles, radar

Table 1 Use of different frequency bands.

Questions

1a A number of different stations can be heard on a radio.

Which electronic part of the radio allows you to choose the station you wish to hear?

b The block diagram of a radio is shown below.

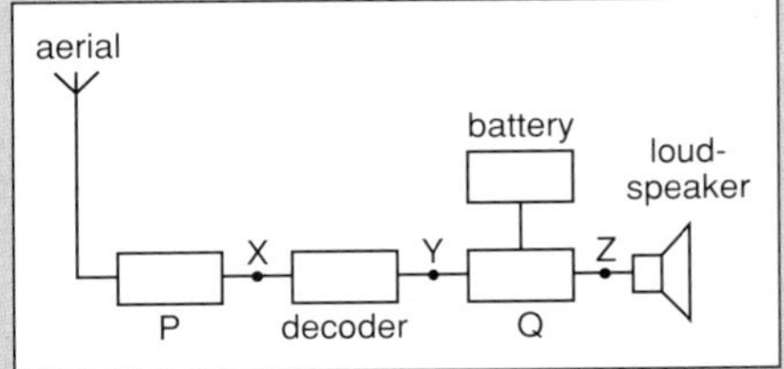

i) Name parts P and Q on the block diagram.

ii) Oscilloscopes are connected at X, Y and Z to examine the waveforms of the electrical signals at these points.

Draw the waveforms at X, Y and Z.

iii) The power of the signal received by the aerial of this radio is very small. The power from the loudspeaker is much larger.

What provides this extra power?

2 Mary is sitting in the crowd at a rock concert being held at Wembley stadium in London. Mary's seat is 150 m from the loudspeakers as shown. Her brother John is listening to a live broadcast of the concert on his personal radio in their Edinburgh home.

a Explain why John hears the music before Mary.

b Calculate how far radio waves will travel in the time it takes the sound from the speakers to reach Mary.

c The concert is being broadcast on both the medium wave and FM radio wavebands. FM radio waves have higher frequencies than the radio waves used on the medium waveband.

i) In which of these wavebands do the radio waves have the longer wavelength?

ii) Explain why people who live in hilly country may have no choice but to listen to the medium wave broadcast of the concert, even if their radios are designed for both medium wave and FM.

3a The diagram below shows the display panel on a radio. The pointer on the display is set so that the radio is tuned to receive a medium wave (MW) broadcast from Radio X.

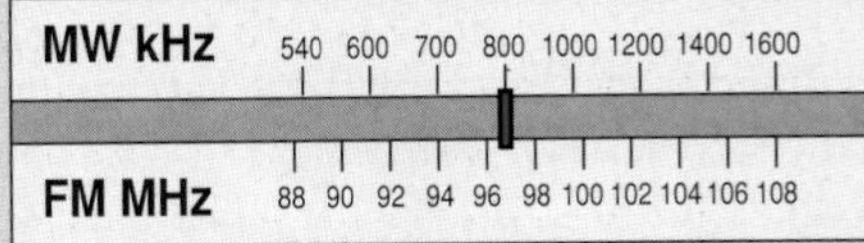

i) On which frequency does Radio X broadcast?

ii) Calculate the wavelength of the broadcast from Radio X.

b An engineer is checking the operation of the transmitter of Radio X. A test audio signal is produced for transmission. The modulated electrical signal in the transmitter is displayed on an oscilloscope as shown in the diagram below.

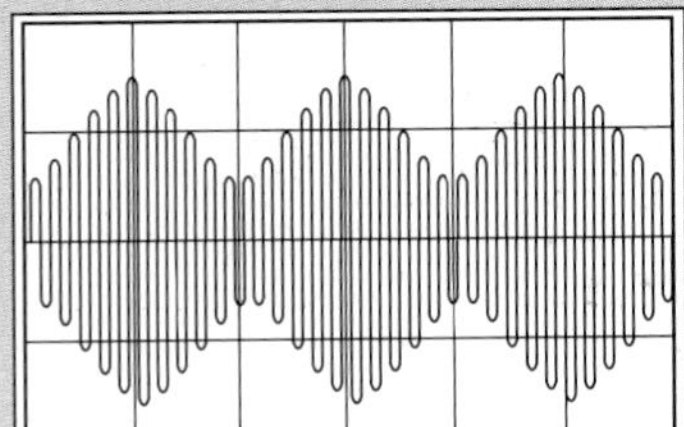

Without adjusting the controls, the engineer uses the oscilloscope to display the traces of the three signals described in parts (i), (ii) and (iii) below.

Draw the trace which would be observed for each signal if:

i) The audio signal only is displayed.

ii) The unmodulated signal used to produce the radio carrier wave is now displayed.

iii) Radio X can also broadcast on the Long Wave (LW) band. The same test audio signal is produced for transmission on LW.

The trace of this modulated signal is displayed.

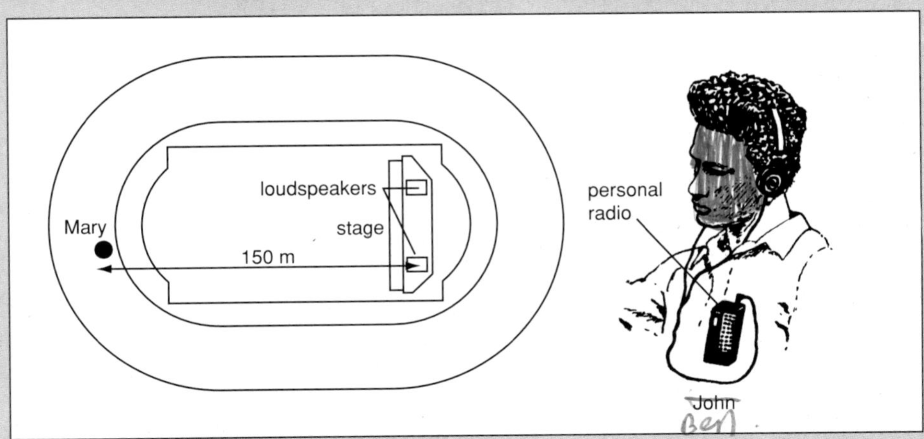

A6
The moving image

How does a picture arrive on the TV screen in our home?

As we have seen in the section on radio, a television signal is carried by radio waves in the Ultra-High Frequency (UHF) range. A television picture contains a large amount of information, which requires high frequency transmission. Sound information must be transmitted to go with the picture, and this is broadcast as part of the same signal. UHF transmission allows this sound to be of very high quality, and many TV receivers now offer stereo sound.

We have seen how a microphone can change sound waves into an electrical signal. An image is made up of light. How can we covert light into an electrical signal?

In the TV studio, light from the scene being transmitted enters the TV camera. It is then focused to produce a picture on a screen (picture 1). Modern TV cameras use a screen built up from miniature parts called **charge coupled devices**, or **CCDs**.

When light falls onto a CCD, it produces a tiny electrical current. The greater the amount of light, the stronger the current. The currents from all the CCDs are combined to produce a signal representing the pattern of brightness falling on the screen.

A colour camera produces signals for the three primary colours of light: red, green and blue. When a signal is ready to be transmitted, it contains coded information describing the colour and brightness of each point on the picture. The picture and sound signals are then used to modulate the transmission signal before it is broadcast (picture 2).

The principle of TV reception is similar to radio. The aerial detects the signals, a tuner selects one, and this is decoded and amplified. The major difference is that we have to separate the signal into its *video* and *audio* parts. Picture 3 shows the block diagram representing the different sections of a TV receiver. Separate circuits handle the video and audio signals. As in a radio, the sound signal is fed to a loudspeaker. The video signal must be fed to the **picture tube**.

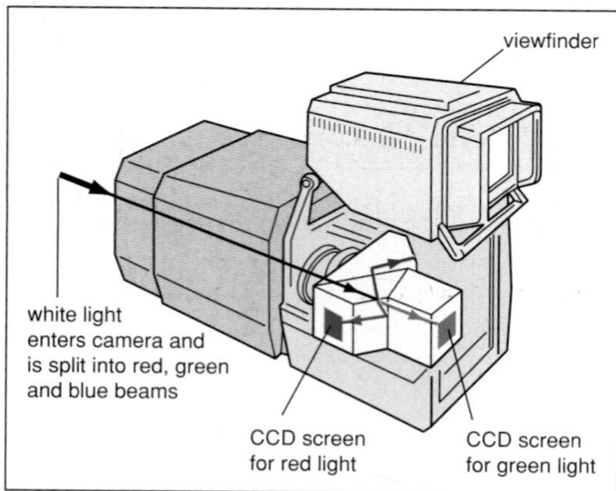

Picture 1

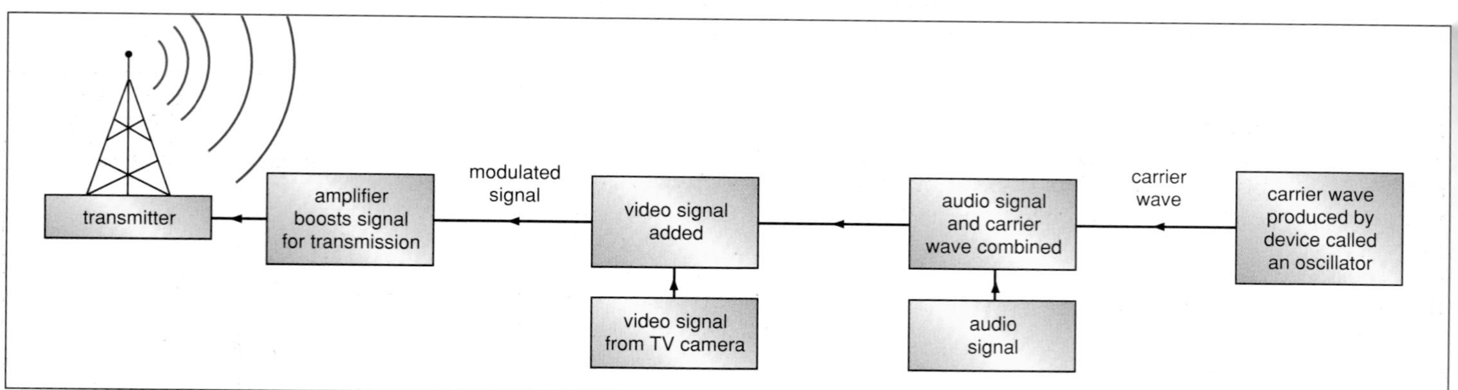

Picture 2 How a TV programme is transmitted.

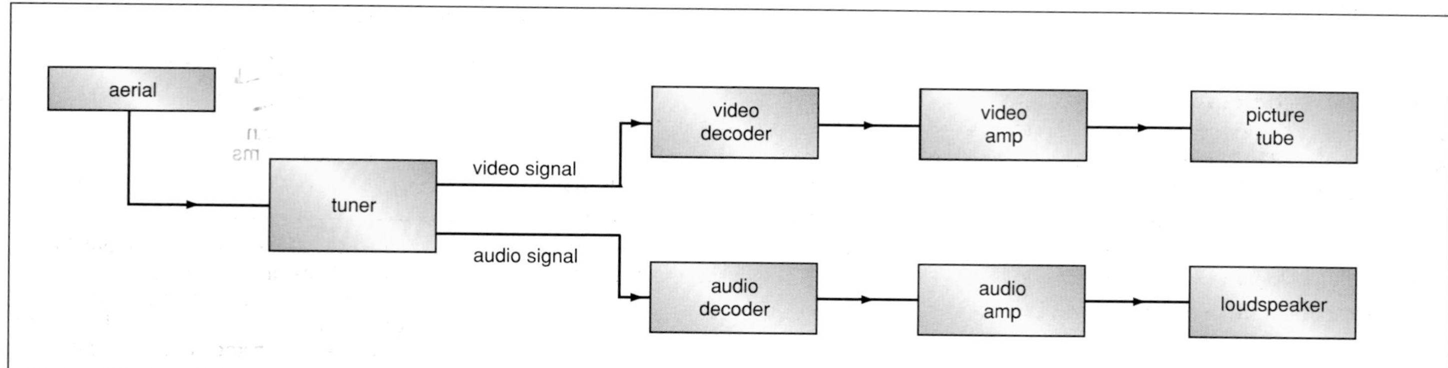

Picture 3 Stages of TV reception.

Inside the picture tube

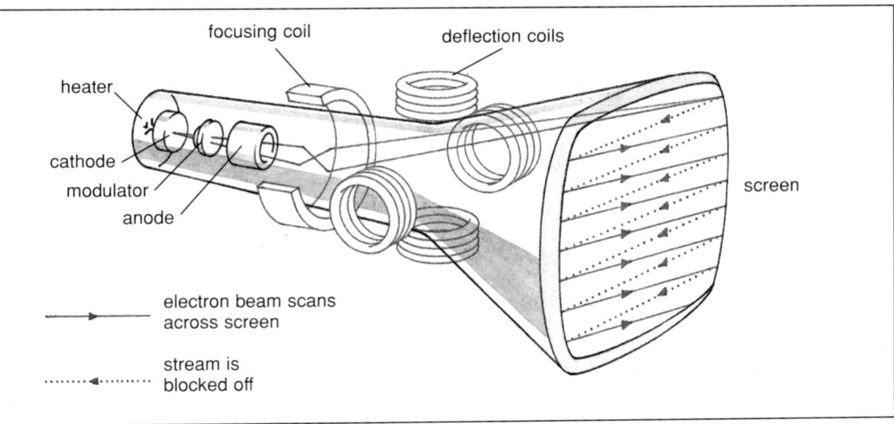

Picture 4 Only a few scans are shown – there are actually 625 in each 'screenful'.

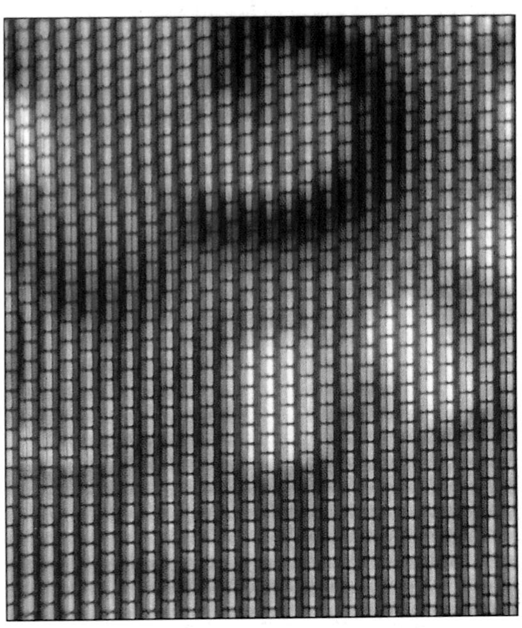

Picture 5 The 'pixels' in a TV screen.

The electron gun

In earlier studies of electricity, you will have learned that an electric current is made up of tiny negative charges, called **electrons**, moving through a wire. A TV picture is produced by a stream of electrons which 'draw' the picture on the inside of the screen. A TV tube is mostly empty space (picture 4).

The picture screen is covered on the inside by **phosphor**. This is a chemical which glows when it is hit by electrons. The electrons are fired from the narrow end of the tube by a device called an **electron gun**. The space inside the tube must be completely empty of any gas, otherwise the electrons would collide with the gas molecules. The stream of electrons is focused into a narrow beam which has to be very accurately aimed so that the phosphor screen glows in exactly the right places at exactly the right times to make a picture.

Making the picture

The picture is made by **scanning** the electron beam across the screen in a series of lines which are moved from top to bottom of the screen. In a black and white TV, the signal from the TV station instructs the gun when to switch *on*, making a *bright* dot on that part of the line. When the gun is *off* there is a *dark* dot. There are 625 lines in a screenful, and the screen is completely scanned by the beam in 1/25 of a second. When the picture is completed the beam starts again at the top of the screen. It takes about a twentieth of a second for your eye–brain system to wipe away a picture. The beam produces 25 pictures a second, so one picture merges neatly with the next. Better pictures can be made with more lines in a screen, and the new 'high definition' TV sets use many more lines.

Controlling the colours

In a colour tube there are three electron guns which hit three separate picture cells (**pixels**). The pixels glow red, blue or green (picture 5).

A **shadow mask** is a metal mesh with holes in it, positioned so that when the 'red' electron gun fires, its electron beam can only strike the red pixels. The 'blue' and 'green' guns fire at slightly different angles, so that each gun can only 'see' the pixel colours it is supposed to hit (picture 6). The signal from the transmitter contains separate instructions for each gun.

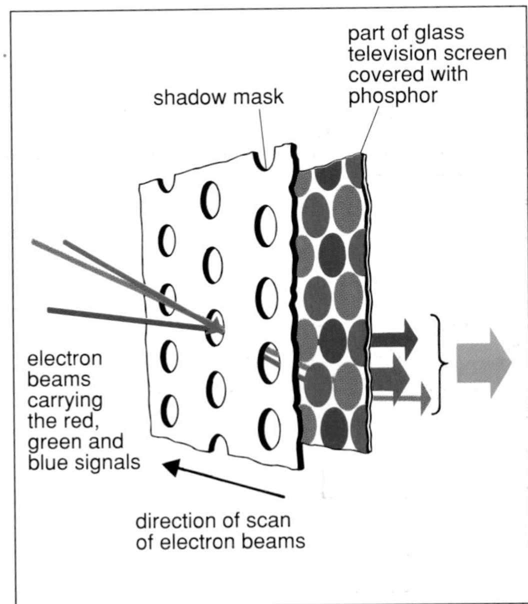

Picture 6 The picture tube screen has more than 300 000 coloured phosphor dots arranged in groups of three on its surface. A metal mask behind the screen has holes which keep each of the three electron beams in line with its own colour dots and away from dots of other colours.

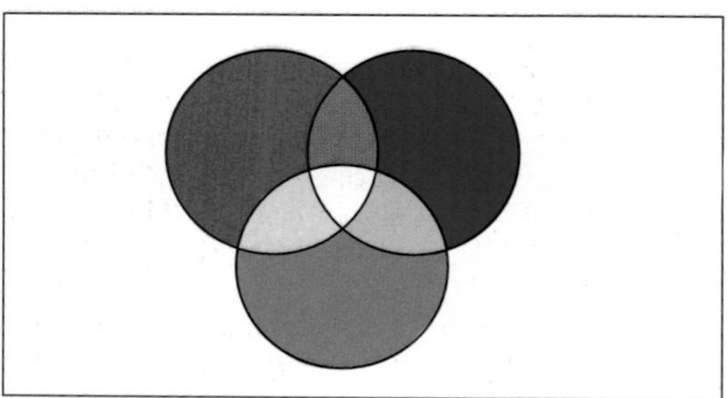

Picture 7 The primary colours combine to produce secondary colours.

Red, blue and green are the **primary** colours (picture 7). These three colours can be combined to give the illusion of all the colours of the rainbow. Different brightness combinations of the three colours of pixels give different colours on different parts of the screen.

Controlling the electrons

The electron guns affect the *strength* of the electron beam, to control the screen brightness. The beam is *aimed* by a strong magnetic field. In picture 8 you can see the coils of wire that produce this field. The field strength is controlled by the signal sent out by the TV station and picked up by the TV aerial.

Electrons are the lightest known objects in the Universe, so they change direction very quickly. The magnetic fields have to change very quickly to produce a new picture 25 times a second, but the electrons are light enough to follow the changes.

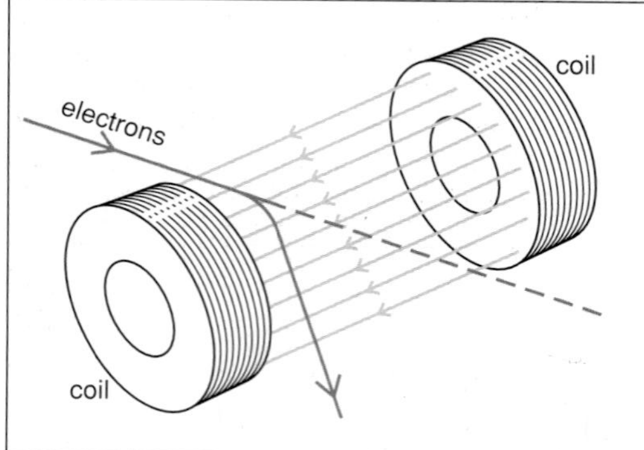

Picture 8 In the magnetic field of the coils, electrons are deflected as shown.

The cathode ray oscilloscope

Another way of changing the direction of a stream of electrons is to make use of electric forces. This is the method used in the measuring and display instrument called a **cathode ray oscilloscope** or **CRO** (picture 9).

The electron gun in a CRO fires its beam between two pairs of metal plates (picture 10). A positively-charged plate attracts the negatively-charged electrons. The plates are arranged at right angles so that the electron beam is deflected either up or down or from side to side.

The plates that move the beam *vertically* are called the **Y-plates**. The **X-plates** move the electrons *horizontally*. In a CRO the X-plates are used to move the beam steadily across the screen from left to right. This is done by a steadily increasing positive voltage applied to the right-hand plate. The steady movement of the beam across the screen is called a **time base**. It is like the 'time axis' you might draw on a graph. The signal to be studied is applied to the Y-plates. If the time base is switched off, we see a vertical line as the beam moves up and down. If we use the time base, and adjust the horizontal speed of the beam, we can observe the shape of the signal (picture 11). A CRO can be used to measure the voltage of a *signal*, or its *frequency*.

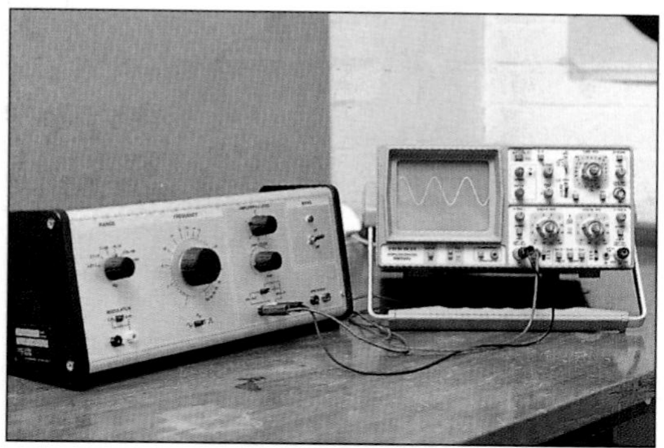

Picture 9 A cathode ray oscilloscope is a very useful instrument.

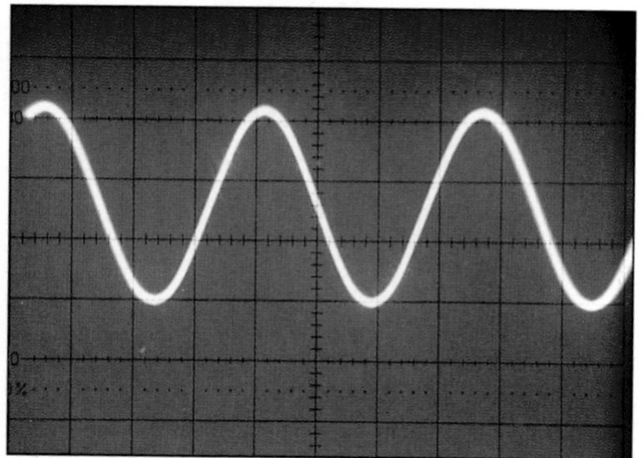

Picture 11 A combination of up and down and sideways movement can draw out a graph.

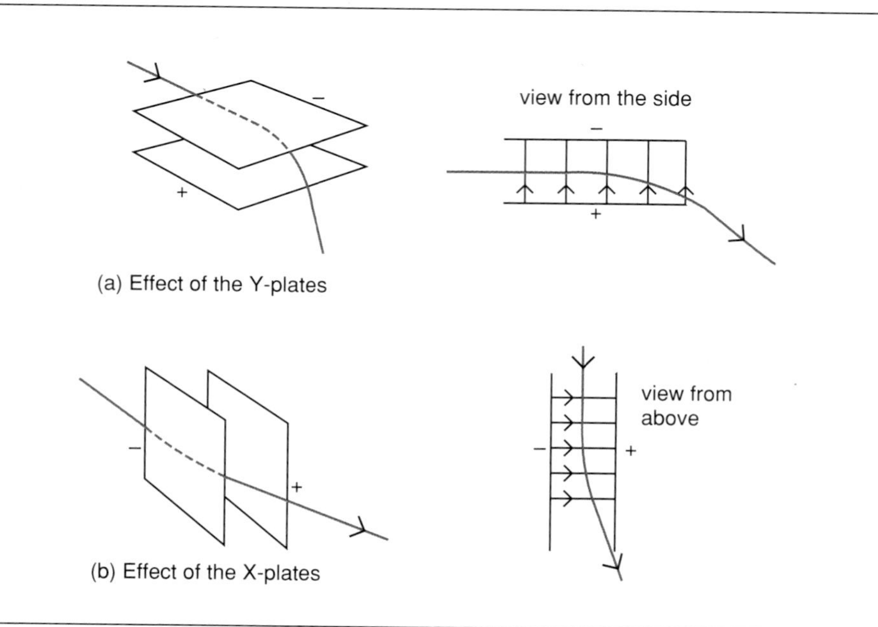

Picture 10 Using electric fields to control beam direction.

Questions

1 A remote control device for a television set has buttons which are used to produce signals to change the channels, the brightness and the colour of the picture. The remote control has a transmitter as shown in the diagram below.

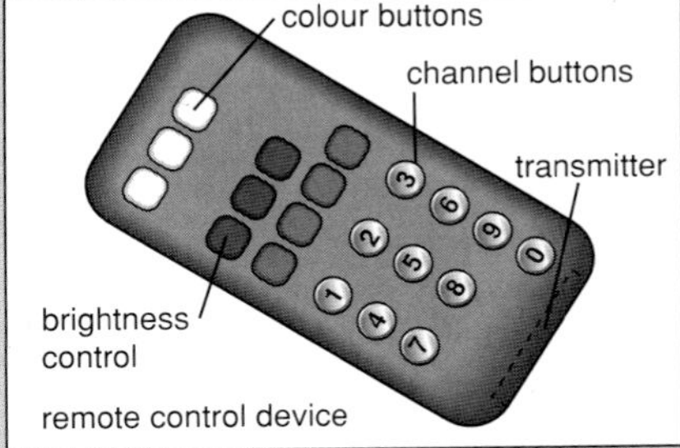

The signals are carried from the transmitter to a detector on the TV set.

a The channel buttons on the remote control are used to change to different stations on the TV.

Which part of the TV circuit selects one particular station?

b Describe what happens inside the tube of the TV set when the brightness control button is pressed to increase the brightness of the picture on the screen.

c The screen of a colour TV is made up of red, green and blue phosphor dots which glow to produce colours on the screen.

Which phosphor dots will glow if the screen is

i) white

ii) yellow?

d Describe how different shades of yellow are produced on the screen.

2 While on holiday in the Highlands with her family, Kirsty notices that a radio and television transmitter is situated on the other side of the hill from the cottage where she is staying.

a On checking the local paper, Kirsty finds that the radio programme she wishes to listen to is transmitted at a frequency of 1089 kHz and that the television programme she wishes to see is transmitted at a frequency of 623 MHz.

Which of these two transmissions has the longer wavelength?

b Kirsty notices that, although she can get good reception on her radio, the television reception is very poor.

Use your answer to part *a* to explain this difference in reception.

c Kirsty tries playing a video cassette and finds that she gets a perfect picture on the television screen.

Explain why this can happen when the television reception is so poor.

A7
Pulses of light

Communication by light has come a long way since people used mirrors to send messages by flashes of light.

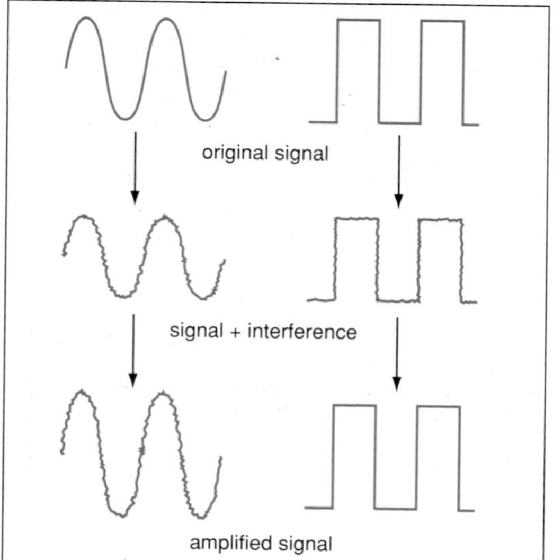

Picture 1 Transmitting analogue and digital signals.

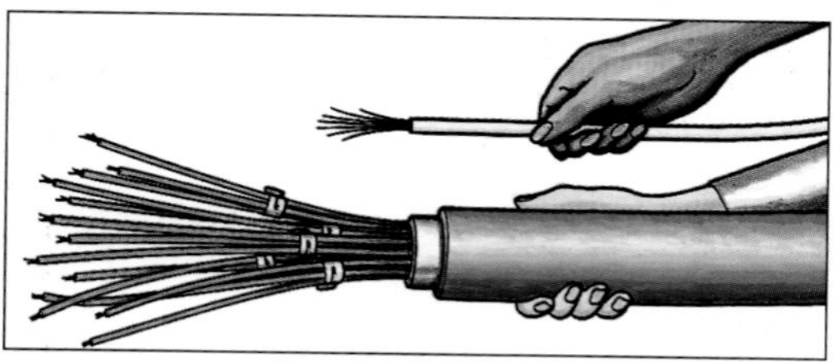

Picture 2 Modern communications are going back to using light – for very good reasons.

Picture 3

Digital codes

So much information is being sent from place to place, that it is hard to find room for it. The world is getting more and more crowded with radio and TV signals, criss-crossing each other and getting in each other's way. Telephone lines can carry only so many conversations at once, even when they are specially coded.

Computers now carry and store a large part of the information necessary for our everyday lives, and are also used to control our communication systems. Communication systems are gradually converting to the same code that computers use to handle information – they are becoming **digital**. Information can be stored digitally using a simple on/off, two-number code. Patterns of information are stored as numbers, which can be transmitted as pulses. These can then be converted back into the original pattern. A compact disc, for example, stores music in digital form, which is then converted into an electrical signal and sent to a loudspeaker. There are many advantages to digital coding. Information can be compressed, which cuts down transmission time, and many more signals can be sent at the same time.

Consider the two telephone signals being boosted in picture 1. The familiar wave pattern signal is called an **analogue** signal. (For more on analogue and digital signals, see topic D2.) Interference has affected the signal, and when it is amplified, the interference is also amplified. This can cause errors, particularly in complicated computer data. (You would not like this to be a signal to your bank's computer about your savings!)

The digital signal has also picked up some interference, but when *it* is amplified the equipment simply counts whether a pulse is present or not. This pattern of numbers is used to generate new pulses. The interference is gone.

We saw earlier that the higher the frequency of a radio wave, the more information could be carried. *Light* is a higher-frequency electromagnetic wave than radio, and is not affected by electrical interference. By using light to carry messages, and encoding the message digitally, we could have a very powerful communications method.

If light is used to carry signals, it must be of *one* particular frequency, not a mixture of different frequencies such as ordinary white light. We need to use **laser** light, and reflect it down a 'cable' of glass so pure that we could see straight through a mile thick block! How this is done is described in the section on **fibre optics** on the page opposite.

There is no doubt that fibre optics has started to revolutionise communications. In topic A4, we learned that a reasonable Morse code operator could send 40 words per minute down a single telegraph wire. The transatlantic fibre-optic telephone cable, TAT-9, can carry 80 000 conversations simultaneously. This means it could carry the entire contents of the Encyclopaedia Britannica across the Atlantic in a *single second*.

Picture 3 shows another use for fibre optics. A cable several kilometres long can be used to carry control signals for remotely operated vehicles, such as the miniature submarines that discovered the wreck of the *Titanic*.

It can also used in this way in modern aircraft. The flight computers of the Airbus 340 send signals through fibre optic cables to the machinery that operates the steering control surfaces on the wings and rudder of the plane.

Fibre optics

Thin glass fibres carrying 'light' signals are much better for carrying information than almost any other medium. The messages are **digitally** coded.

The 'light' used does not quite travel at the same high speed as light in air, but can travel much further. It is produced by a laser, which gives a very pure form of light.

The light is coded electronically. When you speak into a telephone the sounds you make are first changed into a varying electric current. This is a copy (analogue) of the sounds you make. An **analogue-to-digital** converter changes the signal to a set of binary pulses. In turn these are used to switch the laser beam on and off in the same digital pattern.

At the listener's end the pulses are changed to an electric signal again. This can be put back into analogue form electronically and used to make the earpiece work.

Optical fibres are very thin, and are made of very pure and transparent glass. The light is fed in at one end and cannot escape. This is because of **total internal reflection** (see picture 3). A simple fibre works as shown in picture 1. The light bounces off the inside of the fibre. But this produces a distorted signal after the signal has travelled a few kilometres down the fibre.

A better design uses glass in which the speed of the light changes gradually from the inside out. This means that the light path curves gently as shown in picture 2.

Even so, the signal gets distorted sooner or later. **Repeater stations** are built into the line to reshape and amplify the signals. In a modern telecommunications system using fibre optics the repeater stations can be 100 km apart. This compares with having them just 4 km apart when copper wires are used to carry messages electrically.

Another advantage is that optical fibres can carry many conversations at the same time. This needs quite complicated electronics, but a typical optical fibre system can allow 11 000 pairs of people to talk to each other simultaneously. The old copper wire system could only carry about 1000 conversations at once.

Optical networks can also carry TV signals and computer data more cheaply and accurately than wire systems can.

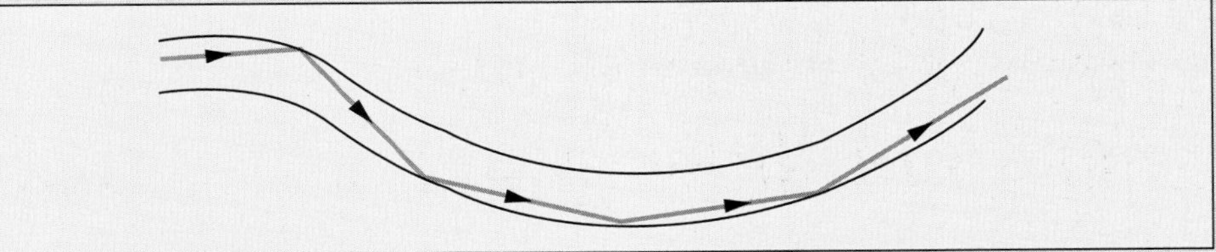

Picture 1 A simple optical fibre.

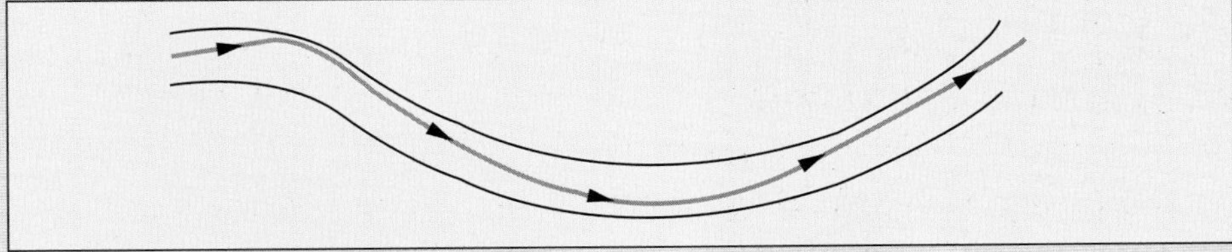

Picture 2 A more sophisticated fibre.

Thus useful things like home shopping and banking are much more practicable.

Copper, used as telephone wire, is an expensive metal, and may become scarcer in the future. Although fibre-optic cable is not cheap, it is more economical because it carries more information than a piece of copper wire costing the same amount.

When homes are connected, there is some disruption and inconvenience because the cable is laid underground. In future however, house owners can receive satellite TV channels without having a satellite dish on the wall of their house, and there will be no need for telephone wire strung between houses and poles.

The diagram shows how light behaves when it travels from glass into air. The light moves through a semi-circular glass block, and escapes from the horizontal surface.
The ray of light striking the boundary between glass and air is called the **incident** ray, and the angle it makes with the dotted line is called the **angle of incidence**. As the angle of incidence increases, more light is reflected back.
Beyond a certain angle, called the **critical angle**, no light can escape.

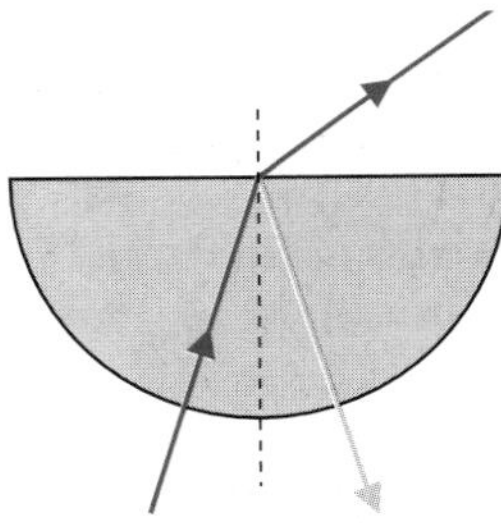

Small angle of incidence – most light escapes, a small amount reflected.

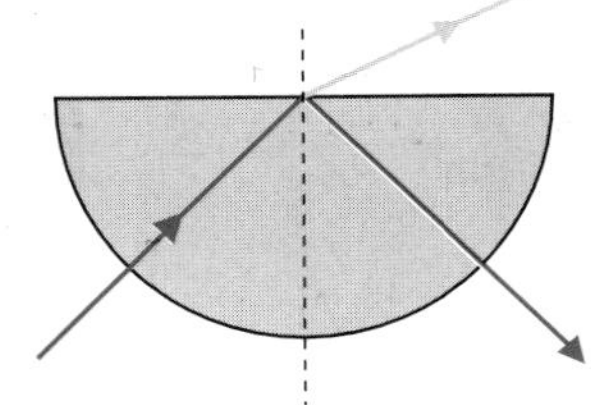

Larger angle of incidence – most light reflected back at the boundary.

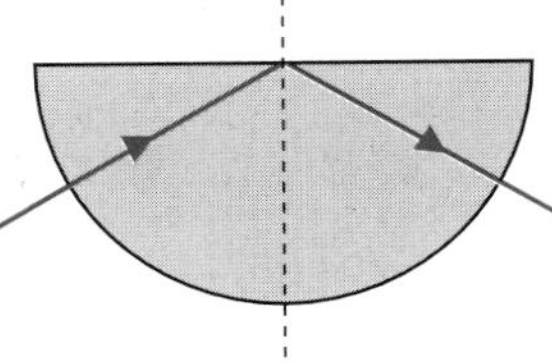

Angle of incidence greater than a critical size – all light reflected back at the boundary. No light can escape, so we have **total internal reflection**.

Total internal reflection in a glass rod. Light entering one end cannot escape, and is reflected from one internal surface to another, until it reaches the end of the rod.

Picture 3 Total internal reflection.

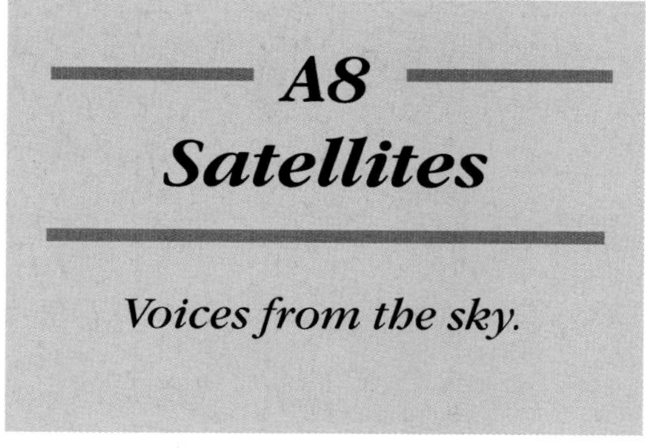

A8 Satellites

Voices from the sky.

The first ever artificial satellite was launched by the Soviet Union in 1957, and was called Sputnik (see topic G6, page 202). It went round the Earth in roughly 90 minutes, because it was in a low orbit.

Earlier, in 1945, the famous science fiction writer Arthur C. Clarke put forward the idea of a worldwide communications network based on just *three* artificial satellites (picture 1). These satellites would be in a high orbit, at a distance of 34 000 km, so that they would circle the Earth in twenty-four hours. This is the time it takes for the Earth to spin *once* on its axis, (that is, one *day*). This meant that a satellite positioned over a particular point on the globe would keep pace with the Earth as it turned. To an observer on the ground at that point, the satellite would always be overhead. It would appear to be stationary in the sky above that part of the Earth – a **geostationary** satellite (see picture 2).

Sputnik could be tracked by radio aerials which had to turn to follow it during the brief time it was passing above a region of the Earth. With a geostationary satellite, the aerial could be permanently pointed at one area of the sky. Clarke suggested that a radio message could be beamed up to the satellite and then re-transmitted back to a destination on the Earth. If the message was intended for the far side of the world, it could be passed from the first satellite to the second or third, and then down to Earth.

Rockets which were powerful enough to place a satellite in such a high orbit had not been developed by the early 1960s. The first ever transatlantic TV broadcast, in July 1962, was relayed from a satellite called **Telstar**. It circled the Earth several times a day, and could provide a service for only short periods. The first geostationary satellite, **Syncom 1**, was launched in 1963, and in 1964 **Syncom 3** was able to relay live pictures of the Tokyo Olympics. It could only carry one black and white TV channel. **Early Bird**, later renamed **Intelsat 1**, could carry one TV and and 240 telephone channels. The latest Intelsats are designed to handle several colour TV channels and over 100 000 phone links!

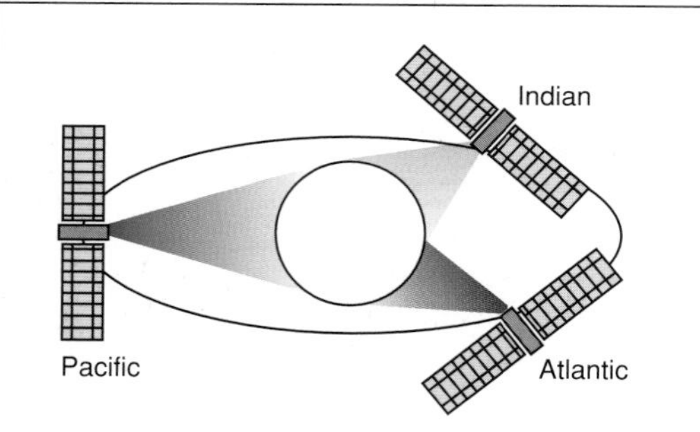

Picture 1 Worldwide coverage with three satellites.

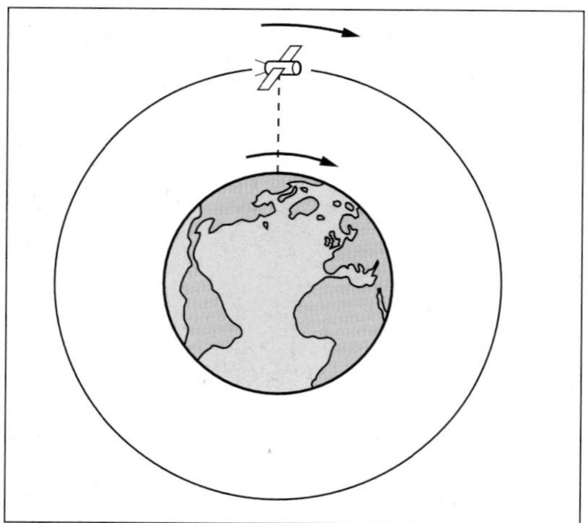

Picture 2 A geostationary satellite.

Picture 3 An Intelsat satellite.

Picking up a signal

Many homes nowadays also make use of signals from **Direct Broadcast Satellites** (DBS), which send their transmissions directly to a small satellite 'dish' fitted to the wall or roof of a house.

The energy of the signal received from a satellite is very low. If we used a simple aerial, the waves would be too weak to produce a usable signal.

In picture 4, we can see what happens when light reflects from a curved mirror. The rays of light all converge on a single point – the **focus** of the mirror. This means that all the energy of the light waves is concentrated at this point.

Radio waves behave in the same way as light – they will reflect from a curved surface and converge at the focus. Radio telescopes make use of this to detect faint signals from incredibly distant objects in space (see topic G3). Fortunately, satellite dishes do not have to be as large as radio telescopes! A satellite dish has

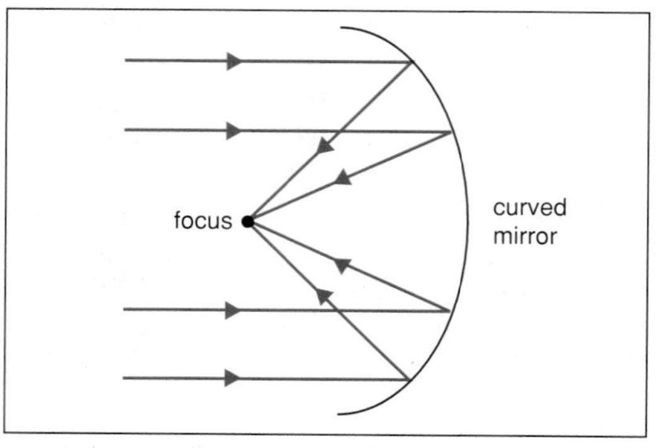

Picture 4 Light focused by a curved mirror.

a receiver placed at the focus of the dish. Radio waves that would have passed by the receiver strike the dish and are reflected back to the focus (picture 5(a)). This means that *all* the energy in the signal is picked up by the receiver.

The same method can be use for sending signals. A transmitter at the focus of a dish sends out waves which are reflected as a narrow beam (picture 5(b)).

Both these techniques are used on the satellite itself. Different dishes are used to receive and transmit. To avoid confusion between the received and transmitted signals, different frequencies are used. The signals received by the satellite may have a frequency of 6 or 14 GHz. By the time it has reached the satellite, the signal is very weak. Solar panels use the energy of sunlight to provide electrical power to the satellite. This is used to amplify the received signal and beam it back to a **ground station** on Earth, at a frequency of 4 or 11 GHz (picture 6).

Ground stations use large adjustable dishes to aim accurately at the satellite. Picture 7 shows what happens when a signal is received. It may be fed across a land line to a microwave link, then sent through a submarine cable, beamed up to another satellite, relayed to another ground station, and finally be answered by someone at a telephone on the other side of the world.

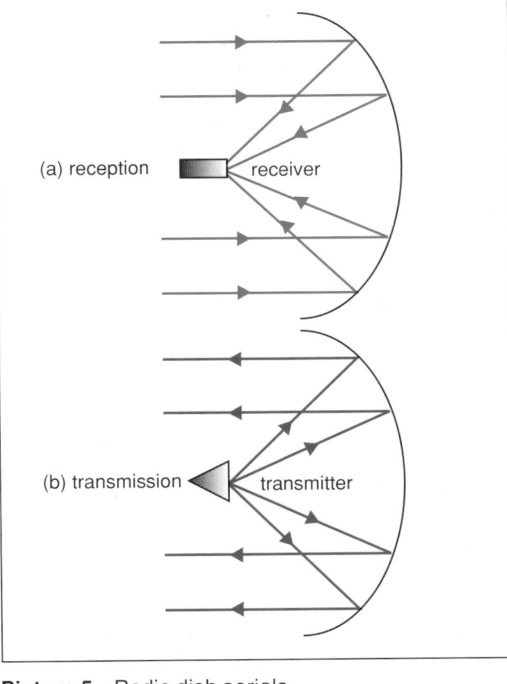

Picture 5 Radio dish aerials.

Picture 6

Telephone calls can be carried across the world by Comsats with only a few seconds' delay.

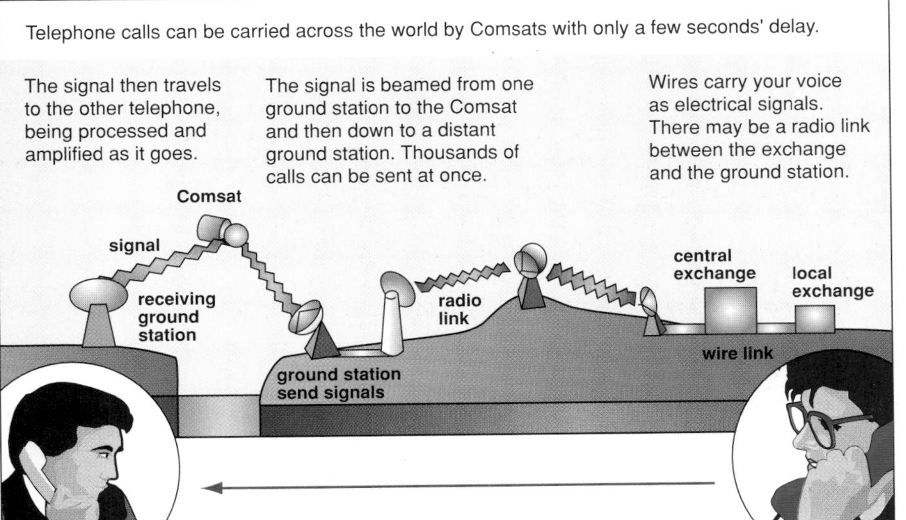

Picture 7 Calling across the world.

Questions

1 The 1996 Olympic Games were held in the city of Atlanta in the United States of America (USA).

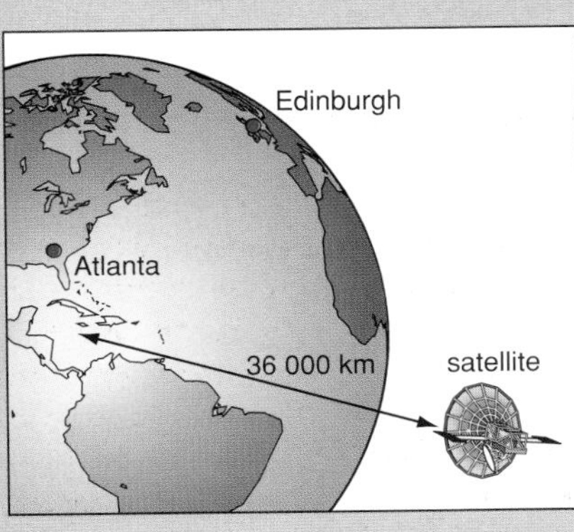

a Television pictures of the Games were transmitted from the USA to Britain. The TV signals were carried by microwaves. The microwaves travelled from the USA to Britain via a geostationary satellite positioned 36 000 km above the surface of the Earth as shown in the diagram (left).

i) What is meant by saying that the satellite is geostationary?

ii) The frequency of the microwaves used in the transmission was 12 GHz.

Calculate the wavelength of the microwaves used in the transmission.

b Newspaper reporters at the games were able to fax their reports back to Britain by a telephone link. The telephone link uses an 8000 km length of glass optical fibre. The telephone signals are carried by light which is transmitted through the glass fibre at 2×10^8 m/s.

How long does it take the telephone signals to travel from the USA to Britain?

2 A TV signal is transmitted from an aerial in Aberdeen at a frequency of 480 MHz.

i) Calculate the wavelength of the signal.

ii) How long would it take this signal to travel directly from Aberdeen to Dundee, a distance of 88 km?

iii) Such a signal from Aberdeen cannot usually be received in New York, USA. Give **two** reasons for this.

iv) A system consisting of a small aerial and a large curved dish is used to transmit the TV signal to a satellite. With the aid of a diagram, explain the purpose of the curved dish.

B1
Using electricity safely

Electricity can be very dangerous; in fact it is probably the most dangerous thing you let into your home.

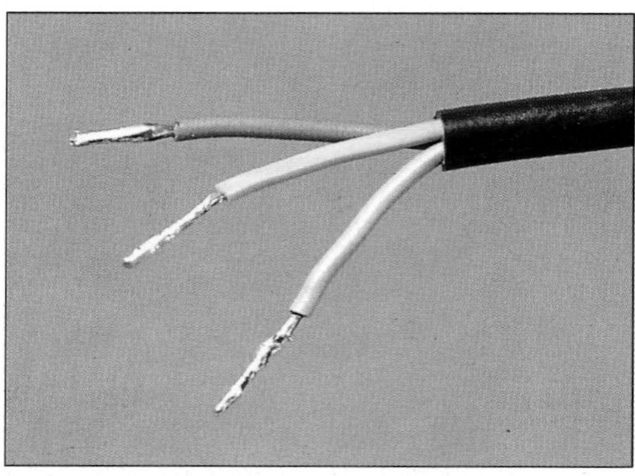

Picture 1 A three-wire cable.

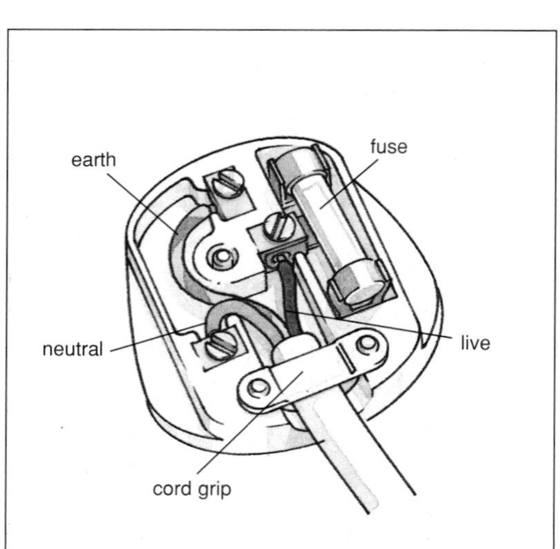

Picture 2 A correctly wired three-pin plug.

Stick to the rules!

There are very strict rules about how houses should be wired and how electric appliances should be made. This is because electricity can give a strong electric shock which may kill. It can also cause fires. Most of the fires started in homes and buildings are caused by electrical faults. How can we guard against these dangers?

The three-wire system

The mains supply uses three wires (picture 1). One pair carries the current 'out and back'. These are the **live** and **neutral** wires. The household supply is **alternating**. The '230 volts' of the mains supply is actually a kind of average of the alternating voltage. Actually, mains voltage swings from +325 volts to –325 volts 50 times a second.

All household devices would work perfectly well with just these two wires, but there is a third wire, the **earth** wire. This is for safety. The three wires are colour coded, as shown in picture 1.

If an electric appliance is properly made and connected using a three-pin plug (picture 2) it should be impossible for you to get a shock, or for a fire to start, even if something goes wrong.

The earth lead connects the metal case of an appliance to the ground inside or just outside the house. If a fault occurs which would make the case live, electric charge will flow harmlessly into the earth. This stops the charge going through you to earth, or through another part of the appliance which might get too hot (picture 3).

Fuses and circuit breakers

The path to earth has a very low resistance, so that as soon as a fault occurs the current that flows is very large. This could be dangerous, because it could make the conductor too hot and start a fire. To guard against this a **fuse** or **circuit breaker** is built into the circuit. Modern wiring systems have both.

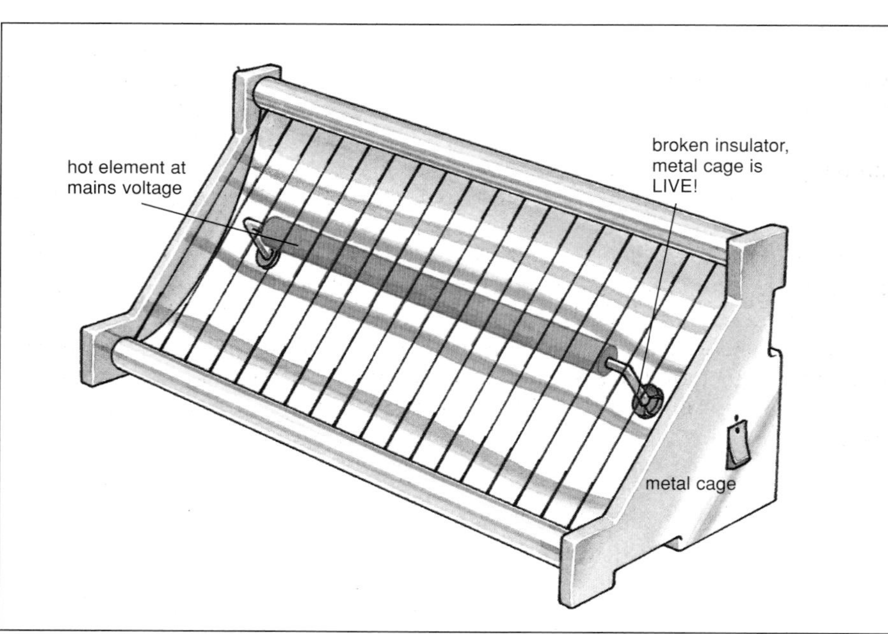

Picture 3 What happens if the case of this electric fire is not earthed? (What would have happened if it was earthed?)

There is a fuse in each three-pin plug, and many devices have fuses built into them as well. A fuse is simply a short length of wire inside a protective case (picture 4). The wire is made of an alloy with a low melting point. A current larger than its 'rated' value will make the wire hot, and it melts. This breaks the circuit and current stops flowing.

A circuit breaker is usually built into the central distribution board where the mains supply enters the house. It is usually near the fuse box. There are quite small ones that fit into mains sockets (picture 5) so that you can use them to protect you whenever you use especially dangerous equipment. You should use them for electrical devices used out of doors, such as lawn mowers.

Circuit breakers use an electromagnetic or electronic device to cut off the current if it gets too large because of a fault, or if current is leaking to earth. They are very sensitive and can detect quite small faults. They work much more quickly than a fuse. They give extra protection because even a small current going through the wrong part of a device can cause overheating, with the risk of fire. An ordinary fuse might not 'blow' under these conditions.

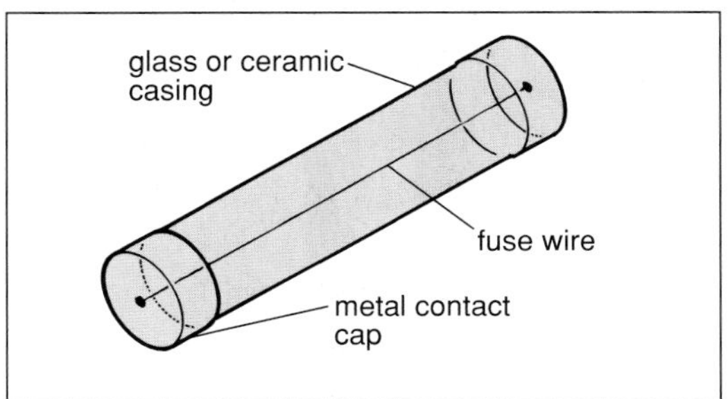

Picture 4 A fuse.

Picture 5 A 'portable' circuit breaker.

Electricity and the human body

The human body is quite a good conductor of electricity – once the electricity gets inside it. This is because the human body is largely water, with all kinds of salts dissolved in it.

Luckily, when the skin is dry it is quite resistant to electricity. Also, if you are wearing rubber or plastic soled shoes the charges can't get out easily. So people may touch bare wires at mains voltage and still survive, although they will certainly feel the shock and it's not a lot of fun.

The most dangerous condition to be in is to have a wet skin and bare feet (picture 6). This makes bathrooms very dangerous, electrically, and special care is needed. To start with, all switches in bathrooms have to be operated by 'remote control', using lengths of insulating cord. Heaters with bare wiring are banned. Bathrooms are not the places to watch TV or listen to mains radios! The makers of electric showers have to make sure that the water is kept totally insulated from the mains electricity.

What happens when you get an electric shock?

The nervous system of the body works by means of electricity. Muscles are controlled by electrical messages from the brain or from nerve sensor cells. When a current enters the body it can override the nerve signals. You lose control of muscles. This means that you might be unable to let go of a live wire, your body might quiver uncontrollably, and you might be unable to speak. This can happen with a current as small as 15 *thousandths* of an ampere.

If the current is larger it could cause burning, due to its heating effect. But the real danger is that the heart stops beating. The heart, like any other muscle, is controlled by electrical nerve pulses. If these are overridden by an electric shock the heart might stop beating, and you will also stop breathing. Death follows in a very short time.

Thus the first aid treatment for electric shock is similar to that for drowning – heart massage and mouth-to-mouth resuscitation. But first-aiders must be careful to switch off the electricity first, otherwise there would be two patients to deal with.

Picture 6 Water conducts electricity well: wet bodies are at risk. Why are bathroom light switches safer than an ordinary switch?

Picture 7 Danger! This is a serious fire risk.

Good advice

The local electricity company produces pamphlets which give very good advice on the safe use of electricity. They can be got free from any showroom. The most common dangers are due to old, frayed wiring, or cuts in new wiring.

Everyone should know how to fit a mains plug correctly, and to use the right fuse in it. Appliances should come with the plug already wired and with the correct fuse fitted.

It is dangerous to 'overload' a circuit. This might be done by connecting high-current appliances (like heaters or even TV sets) to low-current lighting circuits. Instead they should be connected to the correct **'ring-main'** circuit. This is the circuit that has three-pin sockets with wiring that is thick enough to carry the current without overheating. Even this circuit can be overloaded if you use adaptors which allow you to connect too many appliances. Picture 7 shows a selection of dangerous fittings.

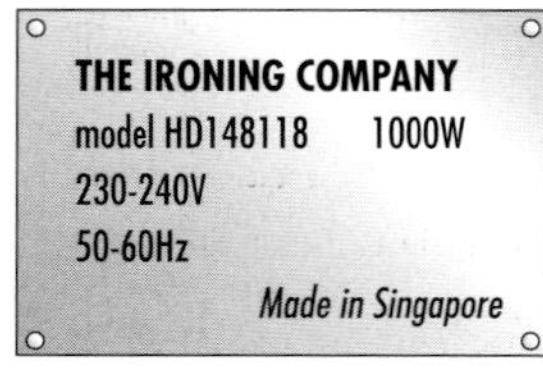

THE VACUUM COMPANY
model AB-167
230V 50Hz 200W
Made in EEC

The PC Company
Assembled in Singapore
100-230V 50-60Hz
1.3A max
model AP 1120

Picture 8 Rating plates give you information about the appliances you use.

How can you check ?

You may have bought a second hand appliance from a friend. How can you make sure that it is safe? Most appliances have a small plate, called the rating plate, fitted somewhere on the casing. Some examples are shown in picture 8. The technical information that you may need is shown on this plate.

The power of an appliance is shown in **watts** (W) or **kilowatts** (kW), and the current is measured in **amperes**, (A), or 'amps' for short. The most powerful appliances are those that use most energy every second and so take the most current.

A good general rule for choosing a fuse for an appliance is:

- power rating **below** 700 W – **3 A** fuse,
- power rating **above** 700 W – **13 A** fuse.

Some appliances, for example fridges and vacuum cleaners, are exceptions to this rule. They use electric motors which take a 'surge' of current when first switched on, so they are usually supplied with a 13 A fuse.

Later in this section we will learn how to calculate how much current is flowing in an appliance, if we know the power rating. It is important to choose the **lowest** value of fuse that will carry the normal current. If the current rises, the fuse will melt before it reaches a dangerous level.

Table 1 Different appliances require different types of flex to operate safely.

Power rating (W)	Flex current rating (A)	Approx. flex conductor diameter (mm)
720	3	0.8
1440	6	1.0
2400	10	1.12
3240	13.5	1.26
3840	16	1.38

Flexes

Many appliances, such as cookers and fires, rely on the fact that heat is given off whenever a current flows in a conductor. A fuse works because too high a current results in enough heat to melt it. This can also happen in the wires of the connecting flexes which carry the electricity from the socket to the appliance. If the wires are thin, they will heat up when overloaded, and the plastic insulation may melt. This could cause a short circuit and perhaps a fire. The table on the opposite page shows the types of flex that should be used with different appliance power ratings.

Double insulation

Many items of electrical equipment (picture 9) are now produced without external metal parts. The workings of a power drill are completely encased in a tough plastic covering, which is an exceptionally good insulator. This is called double insulation, and means that no earth wire is required. The plug can be wired using suitable two-core cable. If an appliance is double insulated, this is shown by a symbol on the rating plate.

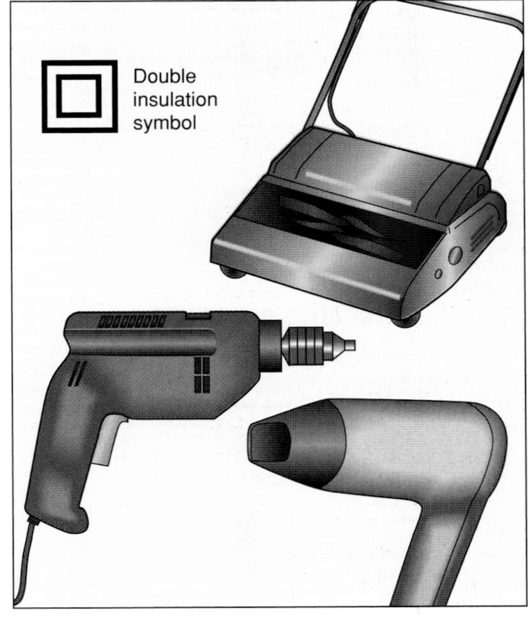

Picture 9 Some examples of double-insulated appliances.

Questions

1 Cartridge fuses are normally available as 3 A, 5 A, or 13 A.

a What would probably happen if you used a 3 A fuse in the plug for a 3 kW electric heater?

b Why is it bad practice to use a 13 A fuse in the plug for a 60 watt desk lamp?

c What happens when a fuse 'blows'?

d You buy a second-hand hair dryer, in good condition, but without a plug fitted. The dryer is labelled '240 V, 800 W'. What fuse would you choose to put into the plug? Explain how you worked out your answer.

2 The diagram below shows the inside of a plug which is connected to a TV.

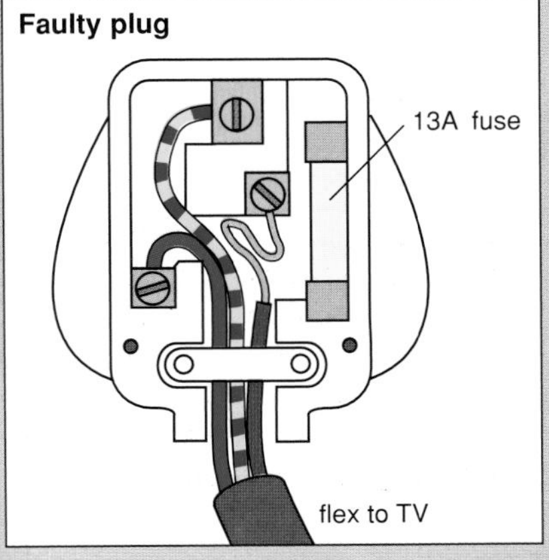

a List **three** faults in the plug.

b Explain why it would be very dangerous to touch a faulty plug with wet hands.

3a A diagram of a rating plate on a hair dryer is shown below.

Electronic Model No.272
230V ~ 50Hz
⧈ 1200W

A suitable flex has to be connected to the hair dryer.

Which **one** of the following flexes, P, Q, R and S, is the most appropriate for connection to the hair dryer?

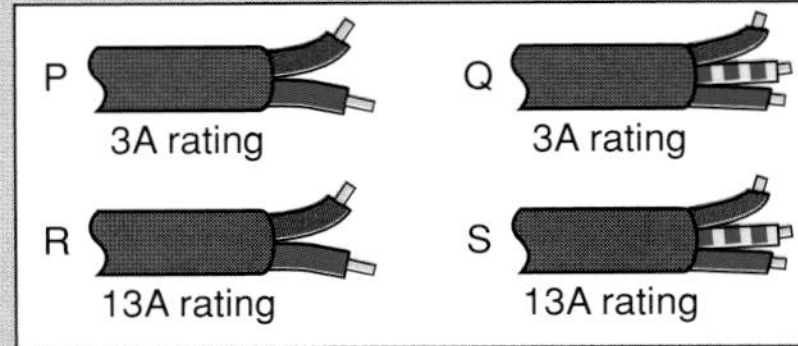

b Give **two** reasons for your choice in part (a).

c The rating plate for a food processor is shown below.

Type 162 Code 210
360W
230V ~ 50/60Hz
Made in U.K.

State the rating of the fuse which should be in the plug of the food processor.

4a A lawnmower is connected to the mains supply by a **two core** flex.

Name the two wires in the flex and give the colours of their insulation. In your answer make it clear which colour applies to each wire.

b An electric iron is connected to the mains supply by a **three core** flex.

i) Name the additional wire in this flex.

ii) Explain how this additional wire acts as a safety device when a fault occurs in the iron.

B2
Electricity from frogs?

To the ancient scientists all electricity was 'static'. Then by accident, an electric current was discovered ...

The first electric current

When electricity was 'rediscovered' 300 years ago it was 'static' electricity. But in 1780 an Italian doctor, Luigi Galvani, discovered a way to produce a continuous flow of charge – the first electric **current**.

Galvani, who experimented with electrical equipment in his home, was preparing some frog's legs for his sick wife. When they were laid out ready for cooking, his wife noticed that whenever a spark was produced by a nearby 'electric machine' the frog's legs twitched!

A missed meal

Galvani started experimenting with them to find out why they twitched. He found that it happened when the leg nerves were stimulated by electric sparks. Then, to his great surprise he found that the legs twitched even when the machine was not working. But this only happened if the nerve ends were touched by metals. *He then drew the wrong conclusion.* He thought that the electricity came from the frog's leg. It just needed the metals for it to be conducted away. After all, if you can get electric eels (picture 2) why not electric frogs?

It took 14 years for the *true* cause of 'frog electricity' to be explained by another Italian, Alessandro Volta. He showed that the electric current was caused by the fact that Dr Galvani had used *two different metals, in the presence of salt water*. The frog's legs had been preserved in salty water, Dr Galvani had used a zinc dish and steel scalpels, and he had also touched the legs with copper wires.

Volta used this idea to make the first **battery**. He made it from alternating pairs of zinc and copper discs separated by cloth soaked in salt water (picture 4). This produced a continuous flow of what he called 'artificial electricity'.

Picture 1 'You cannot be serious!'

What is needed for electricity to flow?

For this to work, three things are needed:

- electric charge which is free to move – electrons,
- energy to move the charge,
- a material that charges can move through – a conductor.

Picture 2 An electric eel.

Picture 3 Dr Galvani experimented with frog's legs.

The basic plan of any electrical device is quite simple: it is a collection of **circuits**. A simple circuit (picture 4) has the energy source (a battery), a switch, some wires and, say, an electric buzzer. The wires are made of a metal which is a good conductor – usually copper.

Luckily, the electric charges are already in the conductor! A metal contains many millions of charged particles that are free to move. These particles are called **electrons**. All atoms contain electrons.

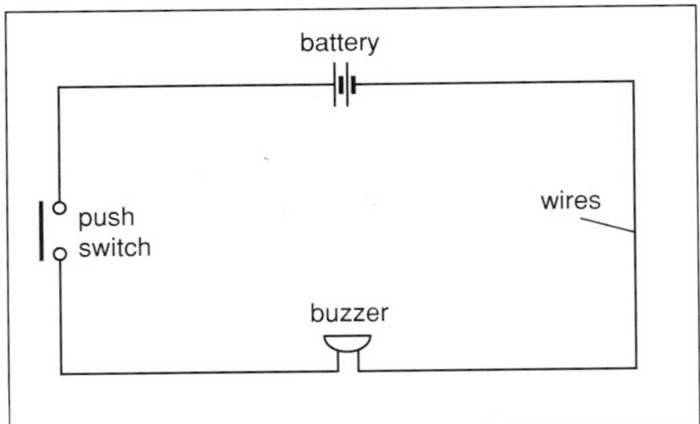

Picture 4 A simple circuit.

Electric charge and electric current

An electric current is a flow of charged particles. If you buy sugar in the shops, you do not count out the individual grains – this wouldn't be a very efficient way to buy such tiny particles! Usually, you buy a 1 kg bag of sugar. You could say that a 1 kg bag is the standard amount, or a practical *unit* for shopping. Similarly, the charge on a single electron is extremely small. It takes many millions of moving electrons to carry the charge that flows through an ordinary torch bulb in just one second. This large number is hard to think about and work with, so we need a more sensible unit of charge – the **coulomb** (C). We can think of the coulomb as our 'bag' of charge.

The size of a current depends on the rate at which charges move through a wire.

If **1 coulomb** of charge flows in **1 second**,
then we have a current of **1 ampere**.

Charge, current and time are linked as follows:

$$\textbf{current} = \frac{\textbf{charge}}{\textbf{time}}$$

For example, 6 coulombs flowing for 2 seconds gives a current of 3 amperes.

- The symbol for current is I, and it is measured in **amperes** (A).
- The symbol for charge is Q, and it is measured in **coulombs** (C).
- The symbol for time is t, and it is measured in **seconds** (s).

So we can write:

$$I = \frac{Q}{t}$$

Picture 5 shows the 'triangle rule' giving the different versions of this formula.

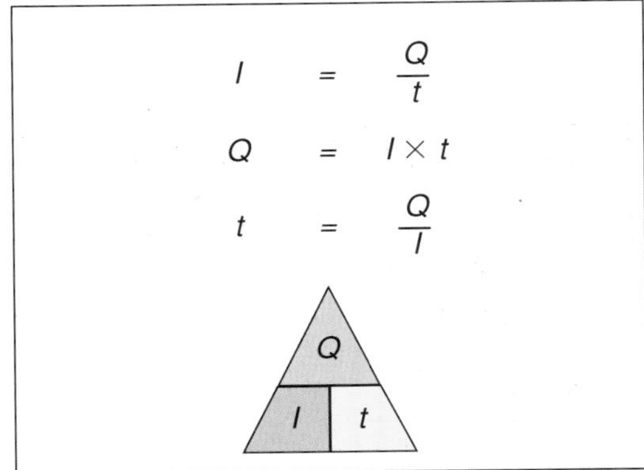

Picture 5

Voltage

We read on page 38 how Volta made the first battery (picture 6). The most common batteries use carbon and zinc, separated by a solution of ammonium chloride. Other batteries use metals such as nickel, iron, cadmium and mercury.

We measure the 'strength' of a battery by its **voltage** (named after Volta). A battery is used to make current flow round a circuit. To make anything move, we must supply energy. The **chemical** energy in a battery is used to supply **movement** energy to the electrons in a wire. We can measure the strength of a battery by measuring how much **energy** it can supply to a set amount of **charge**.

The unit of **charge** is the **coulomb** (C) and the unit of **energy** is the **joule** (J), so we can say that:

when **1 joule** of energy is given to **1 coulomb** of charge,
the supply is **1 volt** (V).

So we can write:

$$V = \frac{E}{Q}$$

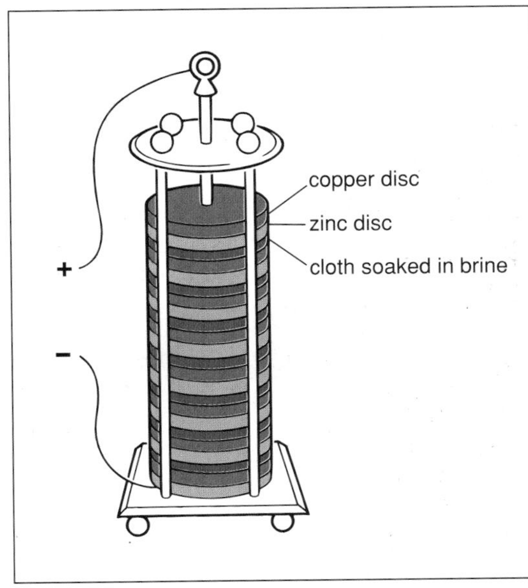

Picture 6 The first battery used zinc, copper and salt water.

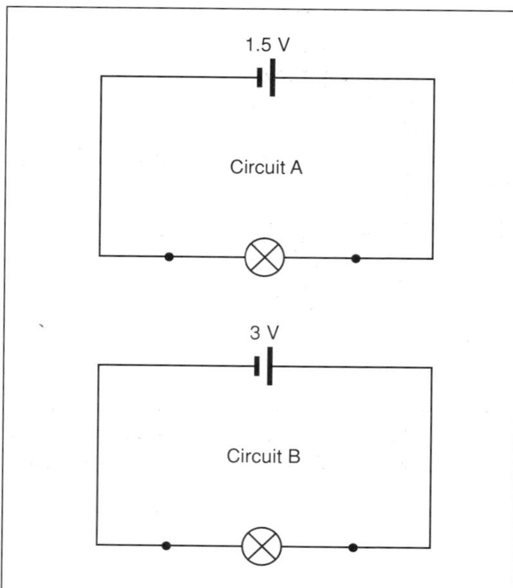

Picture 7 The bulb in circuit **B** receives energy at a greater rate than the bulb in circuit **A**.

Similarly, a 3 volt battery supplies 3 joules of energy to every coulomb of charge which flows in a circuit.

Picture 7 shows two circuits that are almost identical. Circuit **A** uses a **1.5 V** battery and circuit **B** uses a **3 V** battery. As charge moves through the lamps, energy is transferred to the lamp filaments, which glow.

Each coulomb of charge moving in circuit **B** can deliver 3 joules of energy, *twice* as much as those in **A**. The lamp in **B** is being supplied with energy at a greater rate from the battery and so gives out more heat and light.

In these circuits we have used the electric current to **transfer** energy from the battery to the bulb – we have used electricity as an **energy carrier**. We can think of each coulomb of charge as delivering a little 'parcel' of energy which it picked up from the battery. Those in circuit **B** delivered a *larger* load to the bulb. Of course, in practice some of the energy is used to keep each coulomb moving along the wire.

Alternating and direct current

If we connect a battery to an oscilloscope we can measure its voltage. The line on the oscilloscope screen moves up from the centre position. The screen is divided into centimetre squares and the oscilloscope can be adjusted to show different values of voltage for every centimetre of movement. If the line (called the *trace*) moves by *three* squares when the oscilloscope is set to 0.5 V/cm, then the battery voltage is 1.5 V (picture 8(a)).

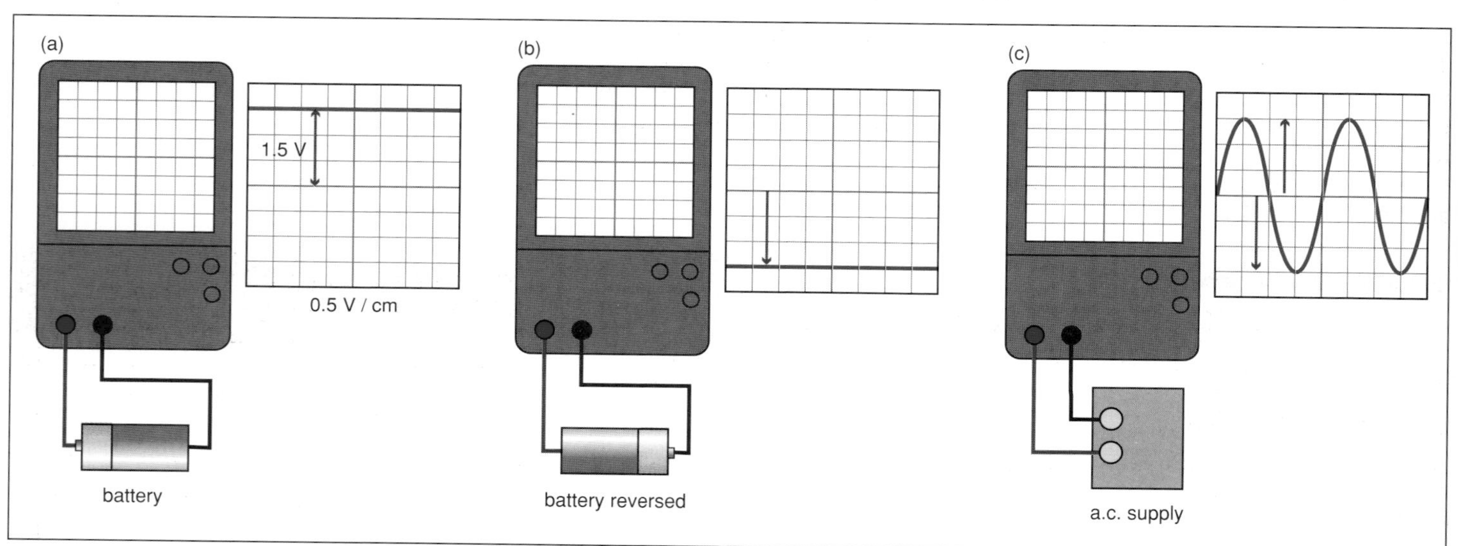

Picture 8 (a), (b) and (c) d.c. and a.c. voltage traces on an oscilloscope.

A battery produces **direct current** (d.c.). This means that the battery 'pushes' charge in one direction. Electrons move out of the *negative* terminal of the battery and travel towards the *positive* end. If we reverse the battery, we see that the trace moves down, as in picture 8(b). This shows that the battery will now push charge in the *opposite* direction.

A laboratory power pack has a pair of yellow terminals. If we connect these to an oscilloscope, the trace moves above *and* below the centre line in a regular pattern (picture 8(c)). The voltage from these terminals is obviously changing direction rapidly, or **alternating**. In fact, the power pack terminals supply electricity at the same frequency as the mains socket – **50 Hz**. If connected to a circuit, the alternating voltage will move charge to and fro at the same frequency – it will produce an **alternating current** (a.c.). Later in this section we will discover why using a.c. in the mains supply makes it easier to deliver electricity to our homes. The power pack supplies a voltage which is safe to use in the science lab. Mains electricity has a *much* higher voltage. If you look at the rating plates of appliances (page 36), you will see that they are all designed to work at a mains voltage of **230 V**.

Picture 9 Peak a.c. voltage has a higher value than a d.c. voltage producing the same effect.

Picture 9 shows two identical bulbs, one in a d.c. circuit, the other in an a.c. circuit. The power pack has been adjusted until both bulbs have the same brightness. The oscilloscopes show the voltages supplied to the bulbs. We can see that the *peak* a.c. voltage is much higher than the d.c. voltage. Of course, the a.c. voltage only stays at its peak for an instant and is always changing.

The *effective* voltage, the value that would produce the same result as a d.c. voltage, is roughly 7⁄10 of the peak voltage. This is called the **r.m.s.** value. We can write this as:

$$\mathbf{V_{r.m.s.} = 0.7\ V_{peak}}$$

If both bulbs operate at 6 V, then the *peak* voltage in circuit 2 is roughly 9 V. The r.m.s. value of an a.c. voltage is used in everyday practice. For example, the voltage control on the power pack is marked in r.m.s. values, so that if we connect a 12 V heater, it will produce the same result as when it was connected to a 12 V battery.

Mains voltage is 230 V r.m.s., which means that the peak mains voltage is approximately 325 V.

Questions

1 Copy the table and complete it by using the formula ***I***, ***Q*** and ***t***.

Device	Current *I* (A)	Charge *Q* (C)	Time *t* (s)
bulb		9	60
iron	10	3600	
battery	0.2		300
toaster		2000	400

2 The voltage settings for each oscilloscope screen are shown.

a State the type of current and the *maximum* voltage being measured.

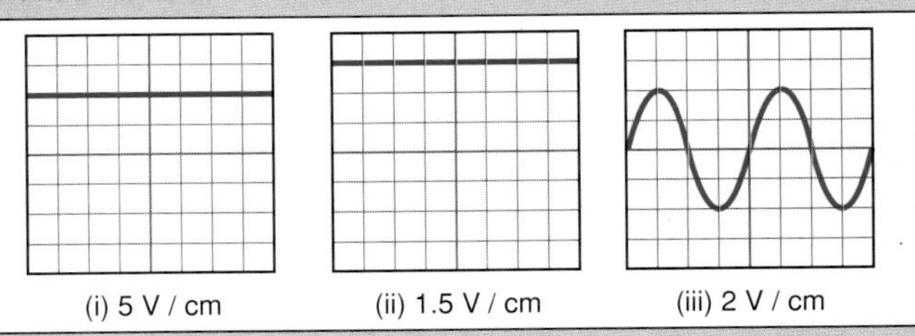

b State the r.m.s. voltage of the supply in (iii).

3 The diagram below show the rating plates attached to a musical keyboard and to a television.

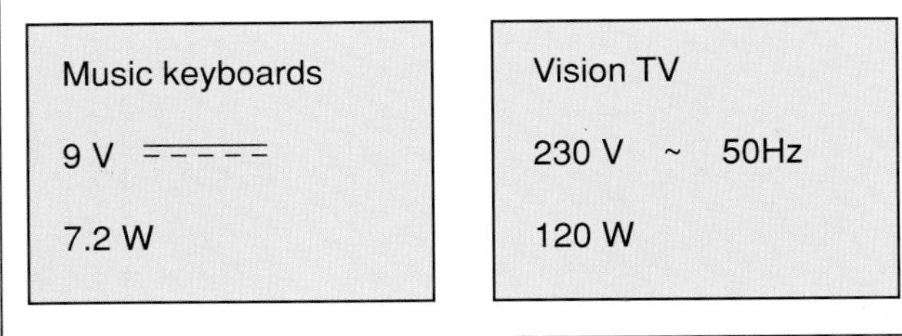

a Which appliance should be connected to an alternating current supply?

b Explain, in terms of current, the difference between direct current and alternating current.

B3 Controlling electricity: current and resistance

To make the best use of electricity, we need to be able to control it. We can also use electricity to control other things.

Picture 1 Resistors – the main way we control electricity.

Resistance and resistors

If we use a battery which has a set voltage, the size of current that flows in a conductor depends on its **resistance**. The bigger the resistance of a conductor, the harder it is for electric charge to flow through it. If the bed of a river is smooth, the water can flow downhill easily and more can get through in a given time. But if the bed of the river is rocky, the water can't flow so easily or quickly. A lot of energy is wasted – you can hear the noise and see the water being thrown up in the air. We get a similar effect in a conductor with a high resistance. It cuts down the flow of charge, and energy is released. The conductor gets hot.

A **resistor** is a special type of conductor, as shown in picture 2. It is made from carbon, or perhaps a high resistance metal or alloy.

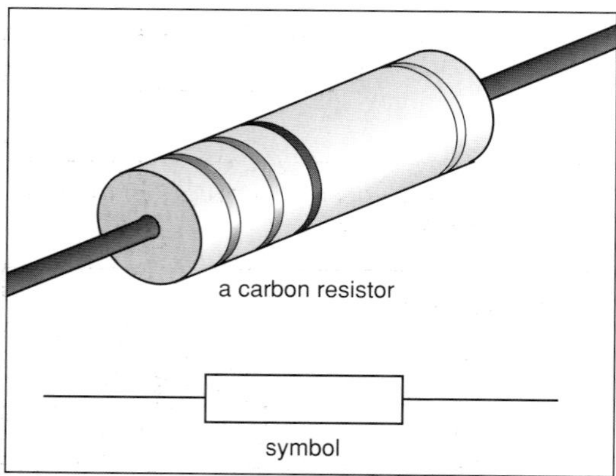

Picture 2 A carbon resistor and its symbol.

Ohm's Law

Table 1 shows a set of results from an experiment to measure the change in current in a resistor as we alter the voltage across it (picture 3).

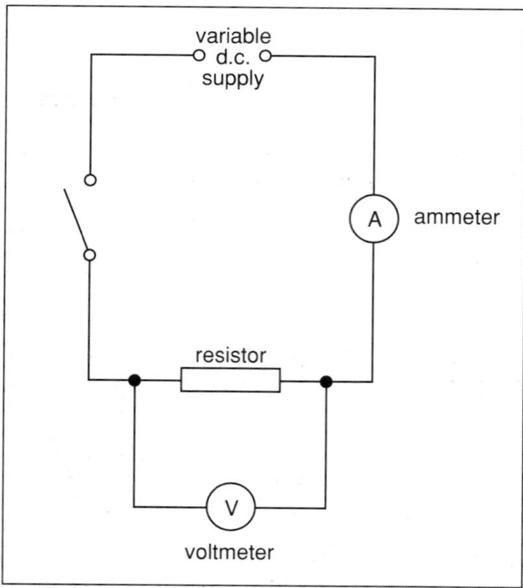

Picture 3 A circuit for measuring resistance.

Table 1

V (volts)	2	4	6	8	10
I (amps)	0.25	0.5	0.75	1	1.25
V/*I*	8	8	8	8	8

The experiment was then repeated with a different resistor.

Table 2

V (volts)	2	4	6	8	10
I (amps)	0.125	0.25	0.375	0.5	0.625
V/*I*	16	16	16	16	16

We can see that, for both resistors, the current increases *in proportion* to the voltage. For many useful conductors there is a simple rule which connects current, voltage and resistance. If we double the applied *voltage*, the *current* is doubled. If we halve the voltage, the current is halved.

This effect doesn't work with all conductors, but it is true for metals and for carbon, *if they don't get too hot*.

The rule is: *at a constant temperature, the current in a conductor is proportional to the applied voltage*. This is known as **Ohm's Law.**

Points to notice:

- The second resistor gave us *half* the current for the *same* voltage. We can assume it has a resistance *double* the first one.
- For each resistor, when we divide the voltage by the current we *always* get the *same* number, as shown in the third row of the tables.
- When we calculate V/I, we get 16 for the second resistor and 8 for the first. In other words, V/I gives us a value we can use to *compare* different resistors – we have calculated the **resistance, *R***.

We can write this as the formula $R = V/I$, where R is a constant value for a particular conductor. Picture 4 shows different versions of this formula.

Resistance is measured in units called **ohms (Ω)**. A 16 ohm resistor would have *twice* the resistance of an 8 ohm resistor. We can use version (b) of the formula to calculate the size of the current that will flow if we connect a resistor to a particular supply voltage.

(a) $R = \frac{V}{I}$

(b) $I = \frac{V}{R}$

(c) $V = IR$

V
I R

Picture 4 The triangle rule for I, V and R.

Voltage drop across a resistor

We have talked about voltage as a measure of the amount of energy supplied by a battery as it moves charge through a conductor. On pages 39–40, we saw how some of that energy is transferred to the conductor. For example, in a torch bulb, some of the energy supplied by the battery is given off as heat and light.

When charge moves through a bulb it transfers energy to the atoms in the filament. We can imagine electrons bumping into atoms and giving up some kinetic energy to make them vibrate more. Then the electrons speed up again to hit more atoms, and so on. The result is that the filament gets hot. The energy transferred per coulomb of charge (electrons) equals the voltage drop across the resistor.

Think about the two 5 Ω resistors in picture 5(a). The current in each resistor is the same, so the quantity of energy transferred to heat them will be the same and there will be a voltage drop of 3 V for each.

Picture 5 (b) shows a 10 Ω and a 5 Ω resistor. It is twice as difficult to move charge through the 10 Ω resistor as the 5 Ω, so it will require twice as much energy per coulomb. This means voltage drops of 4 V and 2 V. Notice that the size of the total voltage drop equals the supply of voltage from the battery. The supply voltage is divided up *in proportion* to the size of the resistors – this is a **voltage divider** circuit (see below).

If we know the current flowing through a resistor, we can calculate the voltage drop using version (c) of our formula:

$$V = IR$$

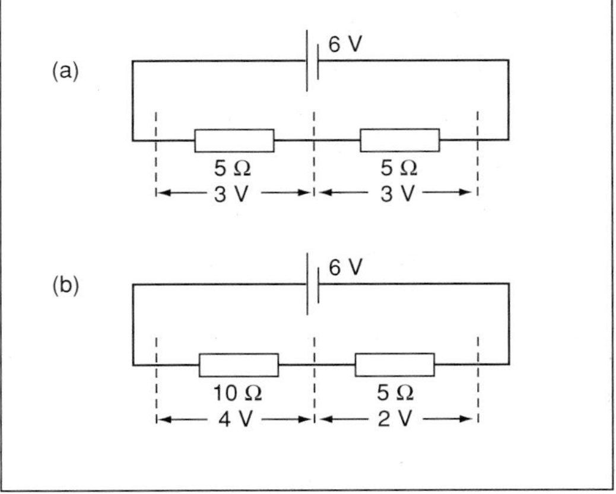

Picture 5 The drop in voltage depends on the value of the resistors.

Controlling current

Picture 6 shows an example of a very useful type of resistor. By moving a sliding contact, more or less resistance material is put in the way of the current, so making the current smaller or larger. This is a *variable* resistor.

When used in simple circuits to change the size of a current, variable resistors are called **rheostats**, but they are most often used to control the size of a **voltage**.

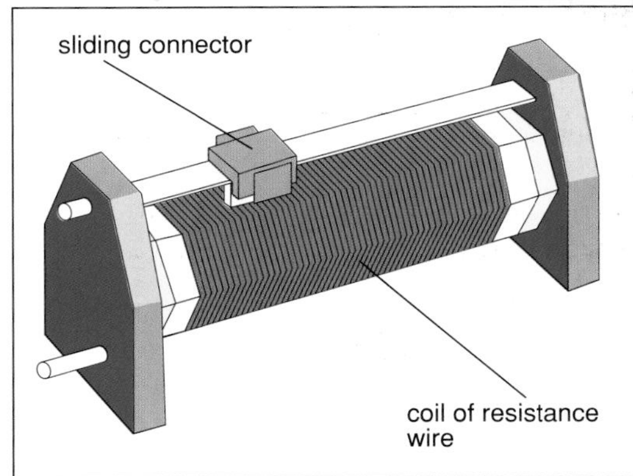

Picture 6 A rheostat – 'flow controller'.

Controlling voltage

When you turn the volume control of a radio or cassette player you are using a variable resistor to control the voltage somewhere in the amplifier circuit. When used like this, a variable resistor is called a **potential divider**. It divides up the total voltage into smaller amounts.

In picture 7, AB is a variable resistor with a sliding contact S. When AB is connected to a battery, current flows through it. The voltage across the resistor is the battery voltage, say 6 V. S is three-quarters of the way to A from B. The voltage between S and B is thus three-quarters of the whole 6 V, which is 4.5 V. Half way it is 3 V. By sliding S up and down the resistor AB, we can get any voltage we like between 0 V and 6 V.

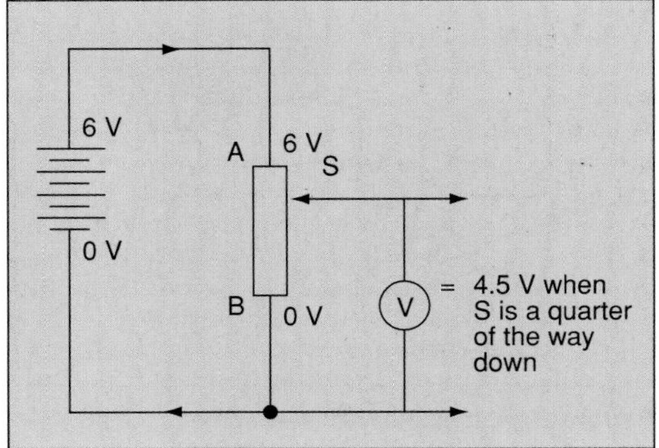

Picture 7 The potential divider.

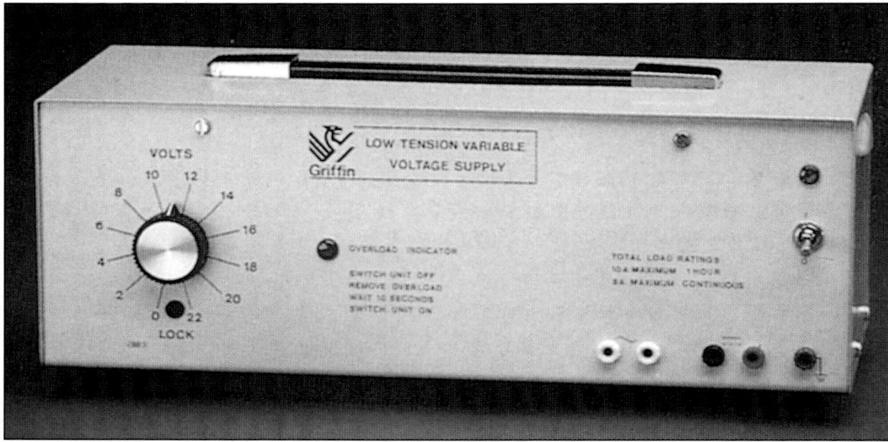

Picture 8 A variable power supply.

Picture 9 An ammeter will read the current going through it.

Variable power supplies

Picture 8 shows a typical low-voltage power supply. Its output can be changed, using a control knob, from 0 to 22 V. The main part of the power supply gives a fixed voltage. The control knob is connected to a variable resistor which changes the output to anything between zero and the maximum, using a voltage divider.

Imagine we do not have a variable power supply. Instead we have a battery which gives 6 V. If we connect it to a 2.5 V bulb, the bulb will 'blow'. We need to connect the bulb in **series** with a resistor, so that there is the correct voltage of 2.5 V across the bulb. How can we work out the size of the resistor we should use? The voltage across the resistor must be 6 – 2.5 = 3.5 V. The normal current through the bulb is 0.25 A, which will *also* flow through the resistor. We use:

$$R = \frac{V}{I} = \frac{3.5}{0.25} = 14\ \Omega$$

A 14 Ω resistor will allow us to safely use the bulb with the battery.

Measuring current and voltage

Current is measured with an **ammeter**, and voltage with a **voltmeter**. Both of these instruments look much the same, and may in fact work on exactly the same principles. This can be confusing, because what they measure is very different. Also, they are placed differently in circuits.

Ammeters tell us how much electric charge is passing though a circuit per second. Remember that **1 ampere** is a flow of **1 coulomb** of charge **per second**. Ammeters have to be put directly in the path of the current, so that they can check everything that goes through the circuit (see picture 9).

Voltmeters are trickier. They take a sample of the current in a device or circuit and then *calculate* the voltage that must be across it. They have to keep the 'sampling current' small if they are not to change the circuit too much. This means that they have high resistances and are connected *across* the device being tested (see picture 10).

The meters illustrated are moving coil or **analogue** meters. Often you will use **digital** meters, which display the reading as numbers on a screen. They can be switched between different uses as ammeters or voltmeters, and can be used as **ohmmeters** to directly measure the resistance of a component.

Picture 10 A voltmeter samples some of the flow and 'works out' the voltage between two points (A and B).

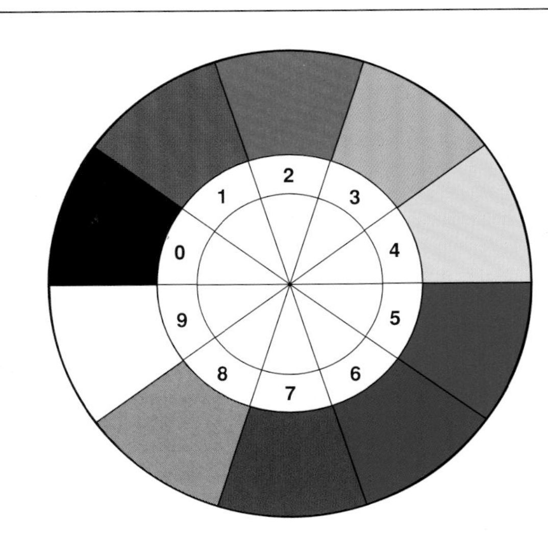

The first two stripes give you the first two numbers of the resistor's value.

The third tells you how many 0s to add onto the numbers.

The fourth stripe at the far end tells you the tolerance or accuracy to which the resistor is manufactured. If there is no colour, this is 20%, silver is 10%, and gold is 5%.

A 100 Ω resistor with a silver stripe could therefore have a value between 90 and 110 Ω.

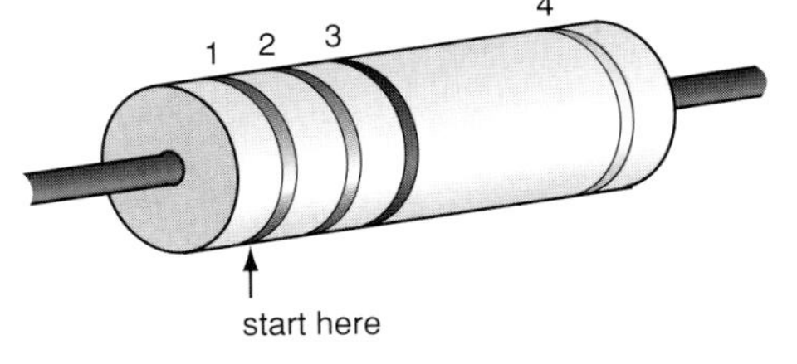

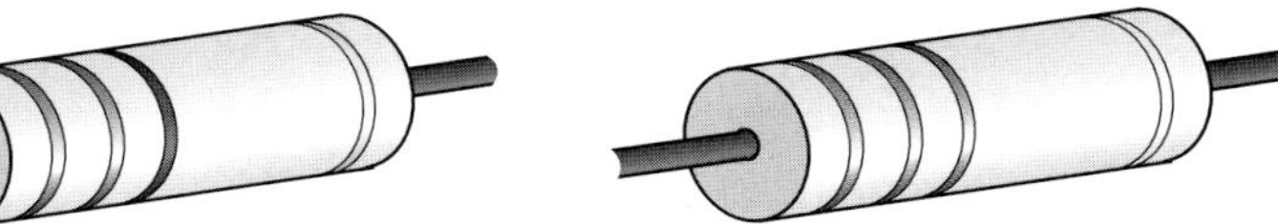

Picture 11 The resistor colour code.

Questions

1 A lamp is connected in series with a resistor to a 12 volt supply as shown. The current in the lamp is 0.2 ampere and the voltage across it is 3.5 volts.

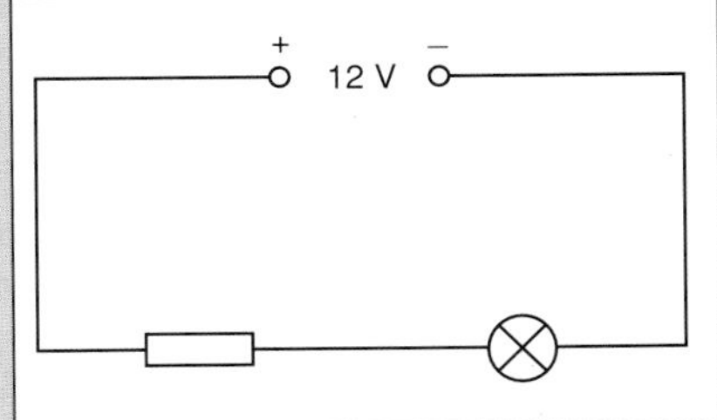

a What is the current in the resistor?

b What is the voltage across the resistor?

2 A variable resistor is used in the speed controller for a model railway engine. The variable resistor controls the current in the motor of the model engine. The motor is connected in series with the variable resistor and supply as shown below.

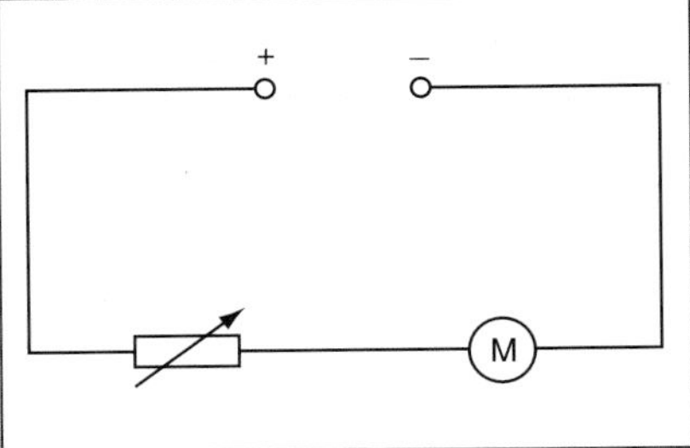

a At one particular speed, the voltage across the variable resistor is 4 volts and the current in it is 0.5 ampere.

i) Calculate the resistance of the variable resistor.

ii) What is the value of the current in the **motor**?

b The resistance of the variable resistor in the speed controller is increased. State what happens to the speed of the train. Give a reason for your answer.

c Give **one** other practical use for a variable resistor.

3 You are supplied with a resistor, an ammeter, a voltmeter, a variable power supply and leads.

a Copy and complete the diagram below to show how the components would be connected to obtain a value for the resistance of the resistor.

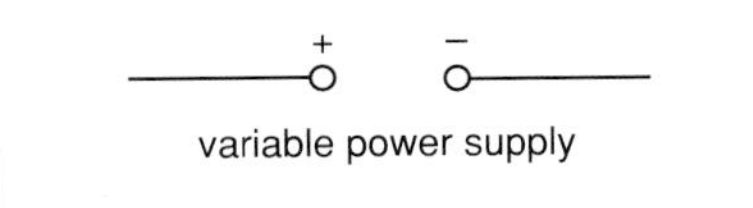

b A pupil uses the above components correctly and obtains the following measurements.

Reading on voltmeter (volts)	Reading on ammeter (amperes)
2.0	0.1
4.0	0.2
6.0	0.3
8.0	0.4

i) Calculate the resistance of the resistor in the circuit.

ii) In setting up the circuit, the pupil had the choice of ammeters X, Y and Z shown below.

Which ammeter could **not** have been used to obtain all the current readings shown in the table?

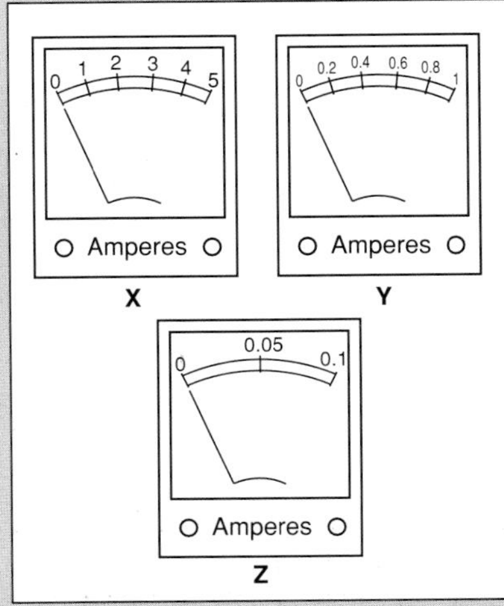

B4

Using electricity: heating and lighting

Electricity is useful because it can carry energy from one place to another and we use it to do many different jobs.

Electric heating

When electrons flow through a conductor they collide with the atoms in the conductor. As they do this they give energy to the atoms. The energy is simply movement energy, transferred from the moving electrons to the atoms. The atoms are fixed, and just vibrate a little more (picture 1). We feel this extra vibration as a rise in temperature – the conductor warms up.

The electrons soon speed up again after the collisions, pushed on by electric forces. These forces are provided by a battery, or a cycle dynamo or the generators in a large power station. Most of the work done by electrical devices in homes and factories uses the energy from fuels burnt in power stations – see page 148.

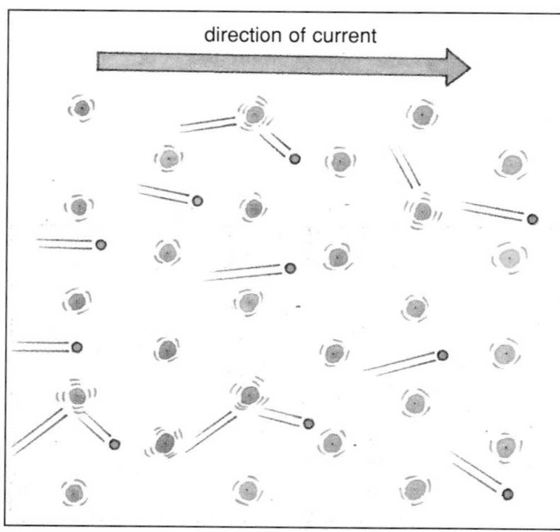

Picture 1 Electrons give energy to atoms in a conductor by colliding with them.

Resistance wires

Electric heaters need special kinds of wire as conductors. The wire in an electric fire element is usually an alloy of different metals. The alloy needs to have the right properties:

- a high resistance,
- a high melting point (to stand the high temperatures produced),
- chemical stability (so that it doesn't burn or corrode at high temperatures in air).

Types of heater

Picture 2 shows four types of electric heating device. Only one of them gets to be red hot, with a temperature of 600 to 700 °C. This is the ordinary electric fire, which radiates energy as electromagnetic waves from the hot coil of wire.

An electric kettle has an element which doesn't need to get hotter than about 100 °C, the boiling point of water. If it does, perhaps when the kettle boils dry, an automatic switch cuts off the current.

The night storage heater is very heavy because it is full of special bricks which can store a lot of energy when they get hot. They take a long time to heat up, but take an equally long time to cool down. This is why they are so useful. They release their energy to heat up the room slowly, so that the room is heated over a long period of time. Inside the bricks there is an electric heater, which heats up the bricks at night. Electricity is cheaper at night – see page 155.

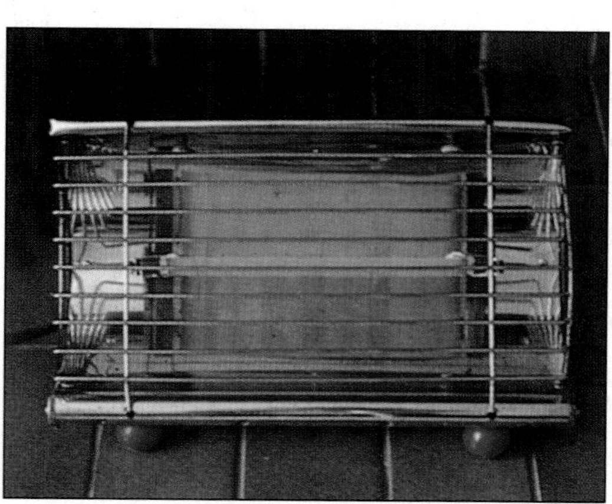

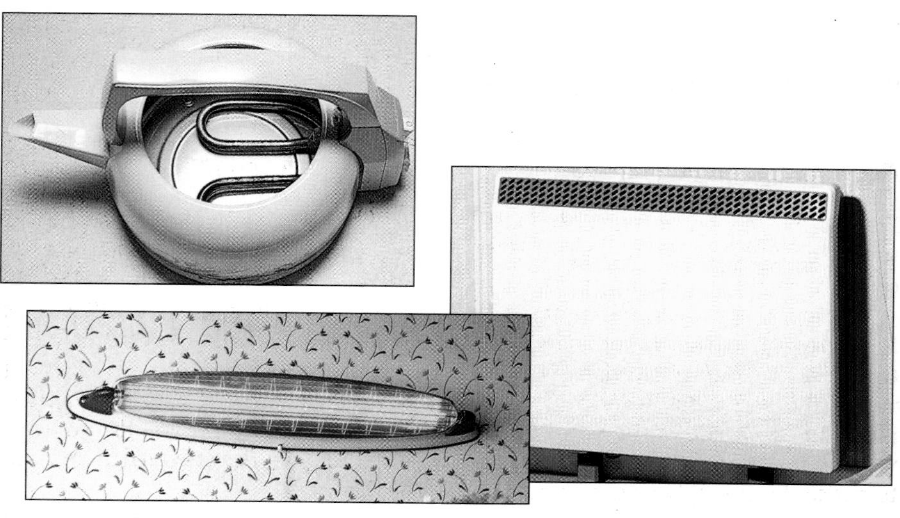

Picture 2 Different ways of using electrical heating.

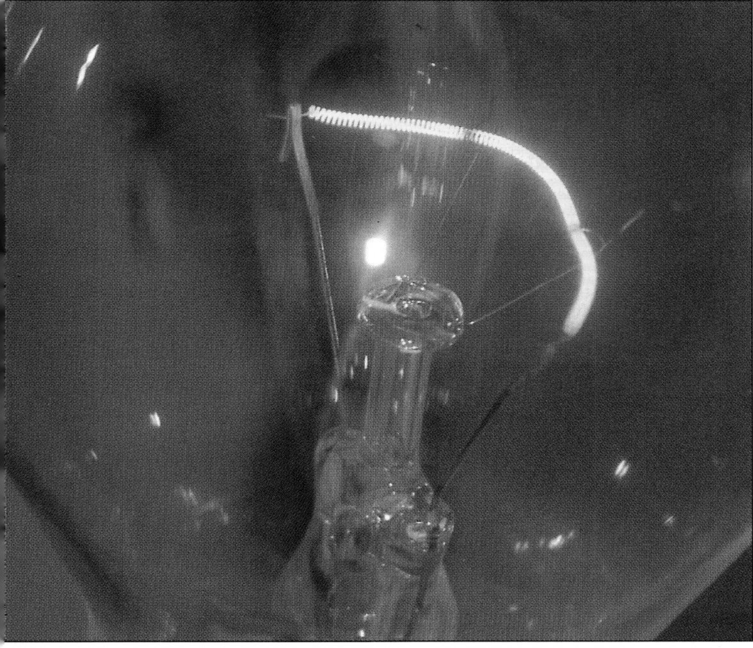

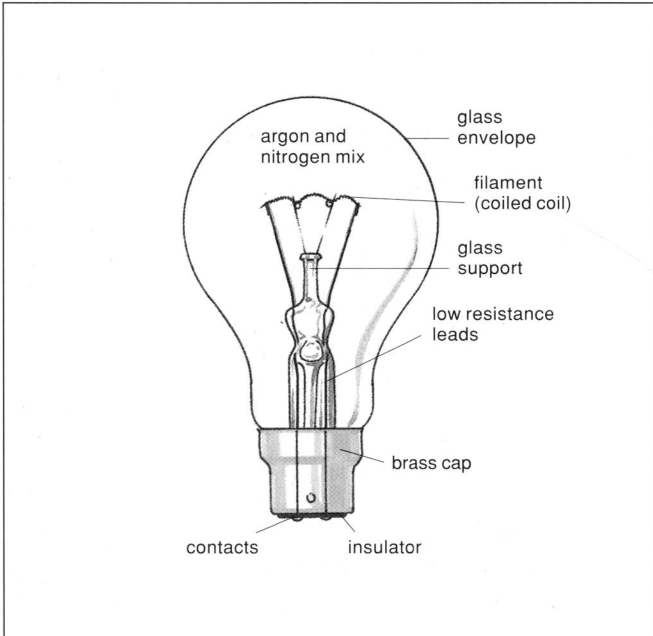

Picture 3 The parts of an ordinary filament lamp.

Infra-red heaters are another kind of low temperature heater. Unlike ordinary electric fires the hot wire is embedded in a special glass. This means that it can't be touched, and so these heaters are safer for use in bathrooms where the danger of electric shock is greatest.

The glass gets hot, but the heater relies on the fact that radiation energy can get through the glass. It is this **infra-red** radiation that warms up the room and the people in it.

Electric lighting

There are two main kinds of lighting used in the home. The oldest is the filament lamp (picture 3). This contains a very thin and long piece of wire (the 'filament'). It is made of a metal, tungsten, that can be heated to such a high temperature that it becomes white hot but doesn't melt. At this temperature it would burn in air, so it is kept inside a glass bulb filled with gases that don't react with it, such as argon and nitrogen.

Although it is glowing white hot, and sending out a lot of energy as radiation, most of the energy comes out as invisible (infra-red) radiation. You can feel this if you put your hand near the bulb. In fact, only 2 or 3% of the energy supplied to the lamp is turned into visible radiation (light).

Fluorescent lamps

Fluorescent lamps are more efficient. A 40 W fluorescent lamp produces as much light as a 150 W filament lamp – and far less heat (picture 4). They work on a completely different principle.

The lamps are filled with a gas (mercury vapour) at low pressure. Electrons flow through the gas and collide with the gas atoms. When collisions take place the mercury gives out invisible (and dangerous) ultra-violet radiation. But don't worry, this radiation doesn't escape from the lamp. It hits a special **phosphor** paint on the inside of the lamp and makes it glow white. It is much the same as what happens in a TV tube (see page 27), where high-speed electrons are used to make the phosphors glow with different colours.

Picture 4 Fluorescent tubes being checked.

When we buy a light bulb in the shops, we usually ask for a 60 W, 100 W, or 150 W bulb. The power of the bulb is measured in watts, just as the power of an appliance is shown in watts on its rating plate (see page 36). The greater the power rating, the brighter the bulb. This is because more heat and light energy is being given off. Of course, this means that more electrical energy has to be converted. **Power** is the amount of **energy** transferred every *second*.

For example: in one second a 60 W light bulb converts **60 J (joules)** of electrical energy into heat and light energy. A one-bar electric fire supplies 1000 J of heat to a room every second. Its power rating is therefore 1000 W or **one kilowatt (kW)**.

We can perform power calculations using:

$$\textbf{power} = \frac{\textbf{energy transferred}}{\textbf{time taken}}$$

or in symbol form:

$$P = \frac{E}{t}$$

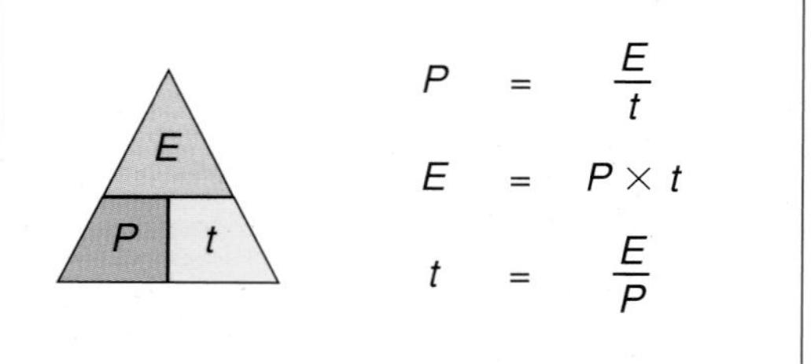

Picture 5

Picture 6 shows the triangle rule for the different versions of this equation. As an example of this type of problem, consider how much energy is used if a 100 W bulb is left switched on for 5 minutes:

$$E = P \times t = 100 \times 300 = 30000\ \text{J}$$

Power, current and voltage

We know that the current in a conductor is equal to the number of *coulombs* of charge flowing *per second*. We also know that the voltage is the number of *joules* of energy carried by each *coulomb*.

Suppose a current of 2 A is flowing in a bulb. This means that 2 C of charge travels through the filament each second. If the voltage is 12 V, then each coulomb is delivering 12 J of energy. After the 2 C have moved through the bulb, they will have delivered 24 J in one second (picture 6). This means that the power is 24 W. We have found the *power* by multiplying *current* and *voltage* together.

$$\textbf{power} = \textbf{current} \times \textbf{voltage}$$

or:

$$P = IV$$

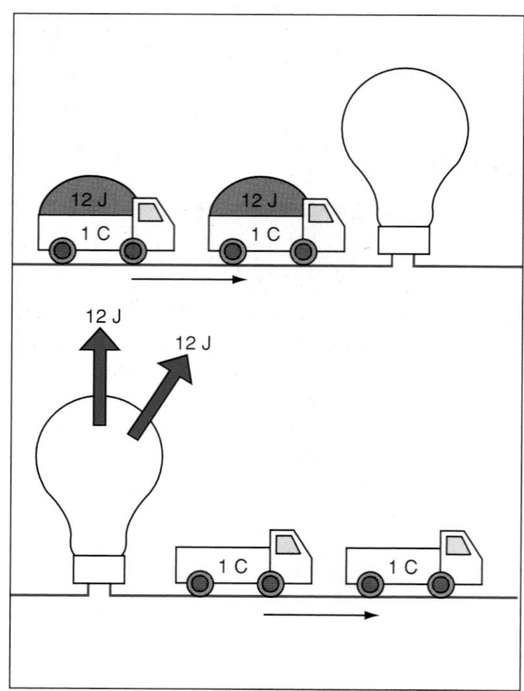

Picture 6 Each coulomb of charge delivers a quantity of energy.

If an iron uses 5 A at a mains voltage of 230 V, then its power rating is given by:

$$P = I \times V = 5 \times 230 = 1150\ \text{W}$$

This is particularly useful if we wish to make an accurate calculation of the current flowing in an appliance, to make sure we use the correct size of fuse. On page 36 we learned a simple rule in order to choose between a 3 A or 13 A fuse. Sometimes we wish to use a fuse which is closer in value to the actual level of current, to provide a greater margin of safety. Imagine we were using a 2000 W appliance. We can rearrange the formula (picture 7) to give us:

$$I = \frac{P}{V} = \frac{2000}{230} = 8.7\,A$$

In a case like this, we would use a 10 A fuse.

$$P = I \times V$$

$$I = \frac{P}{V}$$

$$V = \frac{P}{}$$

P
I V

Picture 7

On page 46, we saw that many heating appliances use resistance wires. If you are asked to design a 2.5 kW kettle, which will operate at mains voltage, you will need to know what resistance to use for the heating element in the kettle (picture 8).

Luckily, we know from Ohm's Law that $I = \frac{V}{R}$

This means we can write $P = I \times V$ as:

$$P = \frac{V}{R} \times V = \frac{V^2}{R}$$

which gives us: $R = \frac{V^2}{P} = \frac{(230)^2}{2500} = 21\ \Omega$

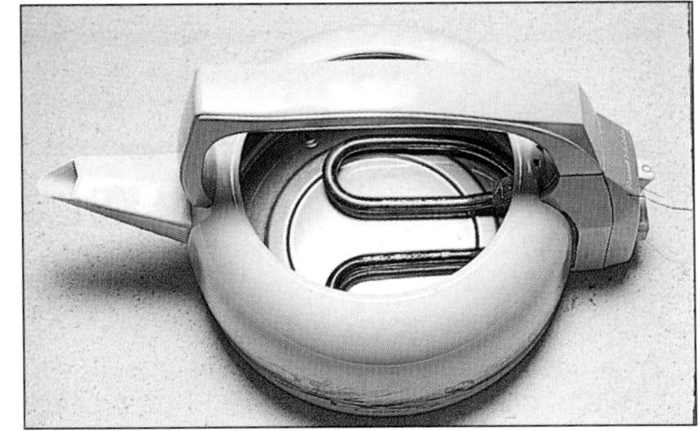

Picture 8

Similarly, if we wish to connect a 100 Ω resistor in a circuit carrying 0.5 A, then we may need to find how much energy will be transferred as heat. Overheating can pose a safety problem, or cause damage (picture 9).

Again, from: $I = \frac{V}{R}$ and $V = IR$

We can write

$$P = I \times V \text{ as:}$$
$$P = I \times (IR) = I^2R$$

The power is given by: $P = I^2R = 0.25 \times 100 = 25\ \text{W}$

So the resistor is heated at a rate of 25 W.

This can all get very confusing! You should try to remember each version of the power formula and use it to construct a 'triangle' rule. You can then rearrange it to suit whichever calculation you need to perform. The box below summarises the different equations and when you should use them.

Picture 9 Some electrical equipment must be cooled to stop components getting too hot.

For any power, energy, and time calculation

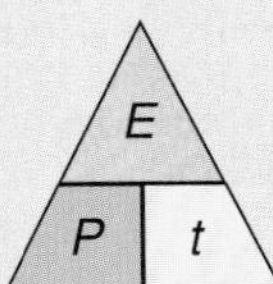

$$P = \frac{E}{t}$$

For any power, current, or voltage calculation:

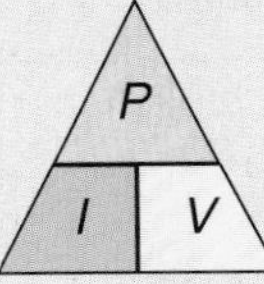

$$P = IV$$

For any power, current, or resistance calculation:

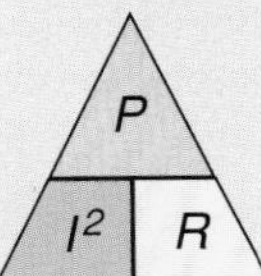

$$P = I^2R$$

For any power, resistance, or voltage calculation:

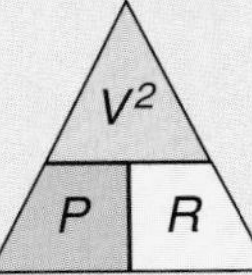

$$P = \frac{V^2}{R}$$

Questions

1 An electric motor does 120 000 joules of work raising a lift from the bottom floor to the top floor of a hospital in a time of 60 seconds.

Calculate the power of the motor.

2 A car accessories shop sells a vacuum cleaner which works from a car battery. A motorist buys the vacuum cleaner and decides to check its power rating.

a Copy and complete the circuit diagram below to show how this could be done using an ammeter and voltmeter.

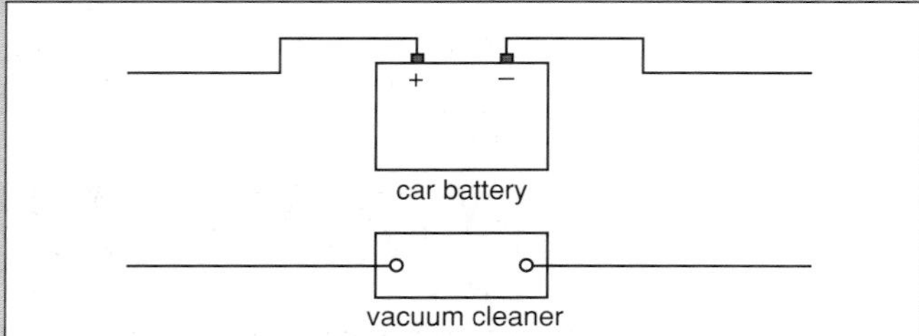

b How would the motorist use the meter readings to find the power rating of the vacuum cleaner?

3a The mains supply and the car battery are two common sources of electricity. The table below lists the voltage, frequency and type of current for one or other of these sources.

Source	Voltage	Frequency	Type of current
mains supply			a.c.
car battery	12 volts	0	

Copy and complete the table, providing the missing details.

b A 12 volt car battery supplies the electrical energy for a car's 60 watt hi-fi system.

i) What is the maximum electrical energy transformed each second in the hi-fi system?

ii) Calculate the current drawn from the battery when the system is operated at full volume.

iii) The interior lamp in the car draws a current of 0.5 ampere when it is switched on.

Calculate the resistance of the lamp.

4 The diagram below shows the connections between a 12 volt car battery and a rear window heater.

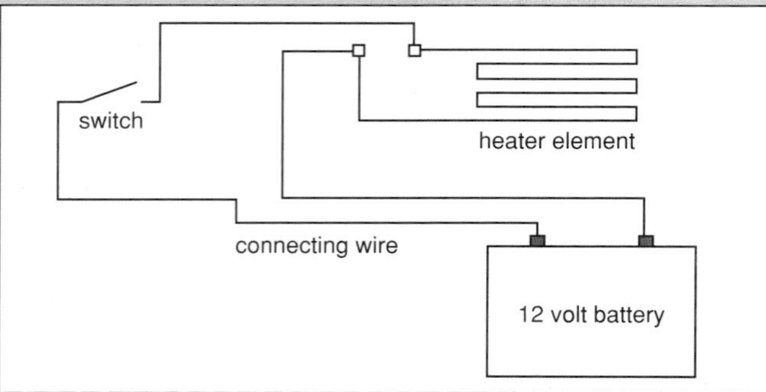

When the switch is closed, there is a current of 10 amperes in the circuit.

a Calculate the power of the heater.

b What is the resistance of the heater?

c The heater element becomes hot but the connecting wires remain cold.

Copy and complete the following statement by putting the phrase *less than* **or** *the same as* **or** *greater than* in the space.

The resistance of the connecting wires is . . . . the resistance of the heater element.

5 A teamaker consists of a lamp, a clock and a kettle. The rating plate for the teamaker is shown below.

230 volts ~ 50 hertz
Lamp 30 watts
Clock 2 watts
Kettle 500 watts
Capacity 0.65 kilogram

a Calculate the current drawn from the mains supply when the lamp, clock and kettle are all switched on.

b Fuses for the plug are available as shown below.

Fuse values in amperes (A)	1A	2A	3A	10A	13A

Select the correct fuse value for the plug of the teamaker.

6 Read the following passage about two types of lamp.

Filament lamps have a very thin coil of wire, with a high resistance. When there is a current in the filament, it heats up to a temperature above 2000 degrees celsius and glows white hot. In a filament lamp, about 3 percent of the electrical energy is converted to light.

A compact fluorescent tube is filled with a low pressure gas which can conduct electricity. When there is a current in the gas, light is produced. Compact fluorescent tubes convert about 40 percent of the electrical energy into light.

The table below shows some information on four metals P, Q, R and S.

Metal	Melting point (degrees celsius)	Resistance
P	420	high
Q	3400	high
R	660	low
S	2500	low

a From the information given in the passage about lamps and the table on metals, select the most suitable metal for the filament of a lamp.

b Explain your choice of metal.

Controlling current

Components which depend on their *resistance* to operate, such as resistors, bulbs and heating elements, are not affected by the direction in which a current flows. It does not matter which terminals of a battery are connected to a bulb, nor does it matter if the current is a.c. or d.c. Some components, however, do produce a different effect on the current depending on which way they are connected.

A **diode** only allows a current to flow in one direction – it is like a one way 'valve'. If the connections to the battery are reversed, no charge flows.

If a diode and resistor are connected to an a.c. supply as in picture 1, and we connect an oscilloscope across the resistor, we can see from the trace on the screen that a current only flows for half the time. When the voltage tries to push a current 'back' through the diode, nothing happens.

A **capacitor** can store electrical charge. A current will flow until it is 'full', and then the flow stops. This means that, apart from a brief surge when the capacitor is connected, a d.c. current cannot flow through a capacitor. The stored charge can be released if we connect the capacitor to another component, for example a bulb. The bulb will briefly glow as the charge drains through it (picture 2a).

If we apply an a.c. voltage, current moves one way to fill the capacitor, then as the voltage drops to zero, the capacitor discharges. As the voltage reverses, the capacitor starts to fill up from the other direction. This means that an alternating current can flow in a circuit containing a capacitor (picture 2b).

If we use a diode *and* a capacitor in an a.c. circuit (picture 3), the capacitor discharges during the period when no current can flow. This 'tops up' the current, so that it does not fall to zero. When the voltage changes back, the current flows again and the capacitor recharges. This means that we do not have the abrupt 'bumps' of current that were produced when only a diode was in the circuit. We say we have **smoothed** the current. As it now flows only in one direction, we have changed the **a.c.** to **d.c.**, or **rectified** it.

Circuit symbols	
cell	
capacitor	
battery	
microphone	
variable power supply	0 – 12V + dc –
motor	
lamps	
loudspeaker	
resistor	
transformer	
switches	
bell	
LED	
buzzer	
variable resistor	
ammeter	
voltage divider	
voltmeter	

Picture 4 Component symbols.

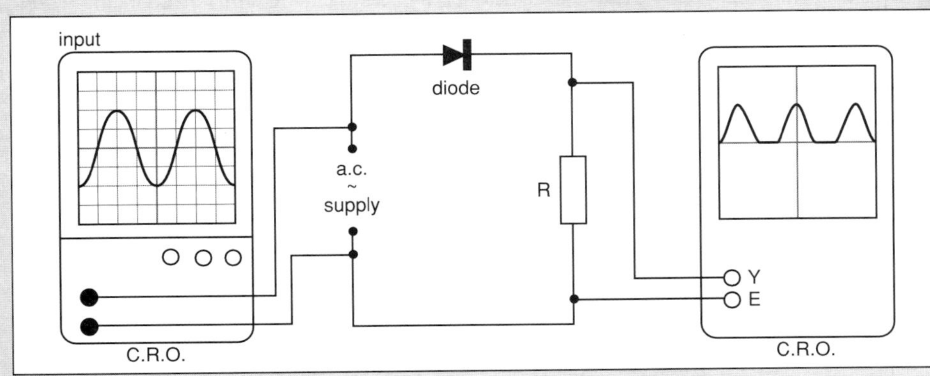

Picture 1

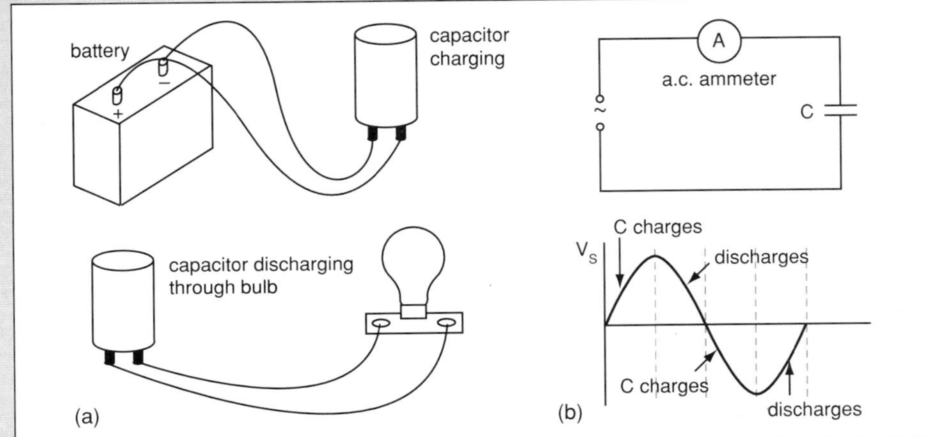

Picture 2

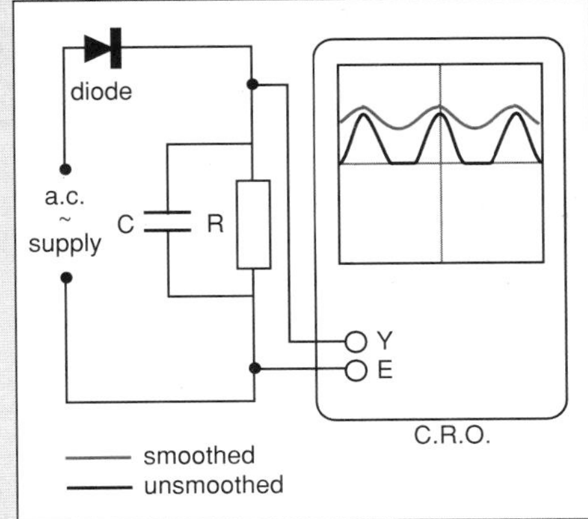

Picture 3

B5 Using circuits

The key to using electricity is the circuit.

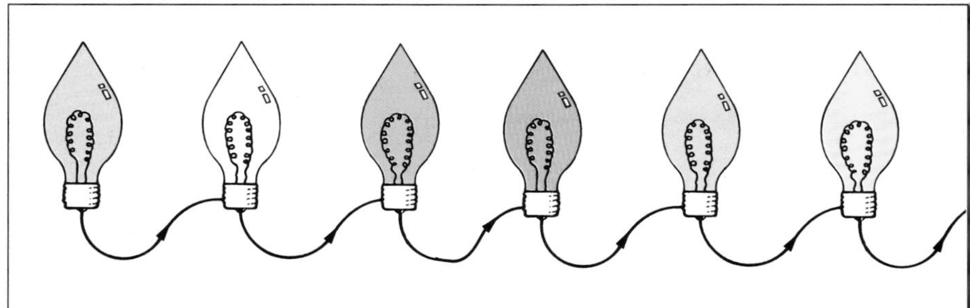

Picture 1 Christmas tree lamps are connected in series. The same current goes through

Picture 2 A Christmas tree. How are the lights controlled?

How do flashing lights work?

In picture 1 we can see how Christmas tree lights are connected together to form a long chain. Sometimes a bulb fails, and all the lights go off. We then have a long and boring job to search through all the bulbs to find the faulty one.

Picture 2 shows a Christmas tree, decorated with coloured lights that can flash on and off. The flashing is controlled by just one bulb that is different from the others. When the filament in the bulb gets hot enough it switches itself off. Then it cools down and switches itself on again (see picture 3). When this control lamp is out all the other lamps go out as well. They only work when the control lamp is on.

Sometimes a lamp in your home stops working and goes out. But this doesn't make all the other lamps go out. Why is this?

Series connections

The Christmas tree lights are connected in a line, one after the other. When a connection is broken in one lamp the charge cannot flow, so all the lamps go out. This way of connecting things in a circuit is called **series** connection.

Switches in series

The control lamp in the Christmas lights is acting as a switch. Most equipment which we plug in to a socket in the home has an on/off switch. This switch is *in series* with the socket switch. For example, a table lamp cannot be switched on unless the socket switch is also on. Having two switches in series is safer, as it makes it less likely that an appliance will be switched on accidentally.

People often leave their car sidelights on. The car lighting circuit in picture 4 has been designed so that the light switches are in series with the ignition switch, so that when the engine is turned off, the lights cannot be left on. This avoids the possibility of the battery being drained.

Emergency master switches, which can cut off the power to a piece of equipment when a dangerous situation arises, are used in many science labs. The switch is in series with all the other electrical sockets in the room, so that your teacher can shut everything off with one movement.

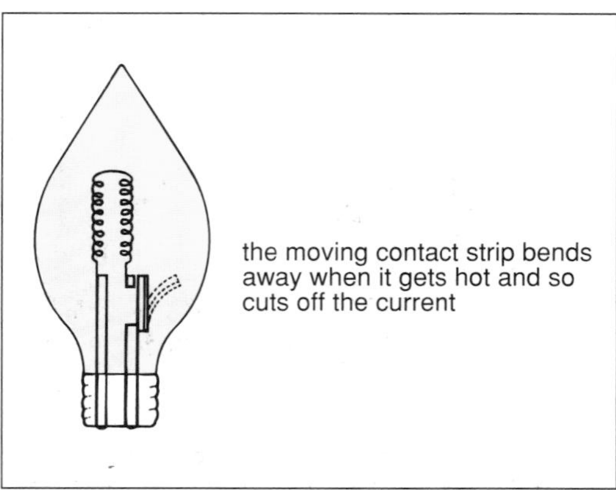

Picture 3 How a flashing lamp works.

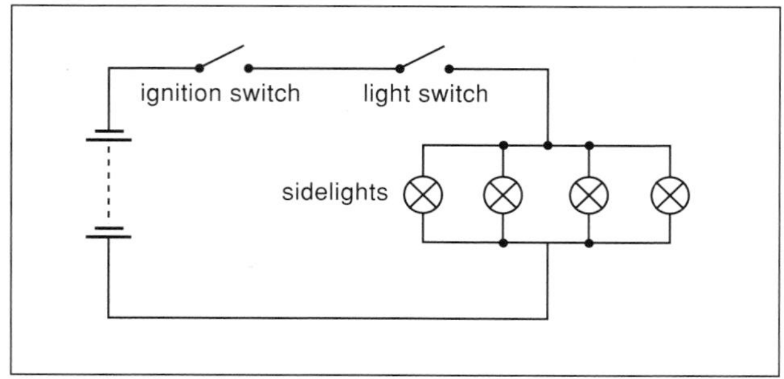

Picture 4 Switches in series prevent the car lights being left on.

Resistors in series

If we connect more lamps into a series circuit, the lamps get dimmer and dimmer, showing that the current in the circuit is getting smaller. The same thing happens with resistors. If we use an ammeter, we can measure the decrease in current each time a new resistor is connected in series.

Pull a length of string through a piece of rubber tubing which is being squeezed firmly by another student (picture 5). The tube feels warmer as the string moves through it. You are supplying energy to move the string, but some of the movement energy is being transferred to the tube, heating it by friction. The string is like an electrical current, and the tubing is acting in the same way as a resistor. Add a second tube, and ask another student to also hold it firmly. The string moves more *slowly*, although you are exerting the same force. The 'current' is *less*, as additional movement energy is being diverted when the string passes through the second 'resistor'. We could say that the 'resistance' has increased. Notice something very important, however, – the *amount* of string that flows through each tube in one second is the *same*.

The current in a series circuit is the *same* at *all* the points in the circuit. If we connect two lamps in series, the current flowing through them is the same. As the lamps are identical, the amount of energy needed to push the current through each lamp will also be the same. The drop in voltage across each lamp will be equal in size. If we have 20 Christmas tree lights connected to a 230 V supply, the voltage across each lamp will be: $\frac{230}{20} = 11$ V.

If one of the tubes in picture 5 is squeezed more tightly than the other, more energy is 'lost' getting the string through that tube than the other. If we connect different sized resistors in series, the same current flows through both, but more energy is transferred moving it through the *bigger* resistor.

Picture 6 shows a 10 Ω, 20 Ω, and a 30 Ω resistor connected in series. The voltage drop across each will be proportional to their sizes. The *total* voltage drop will be equal to the supply voltage, $\boldsymbol{V_S}$.

We can write: $\boldsymbol{V_S = V_1 + V_2 + V_3}$

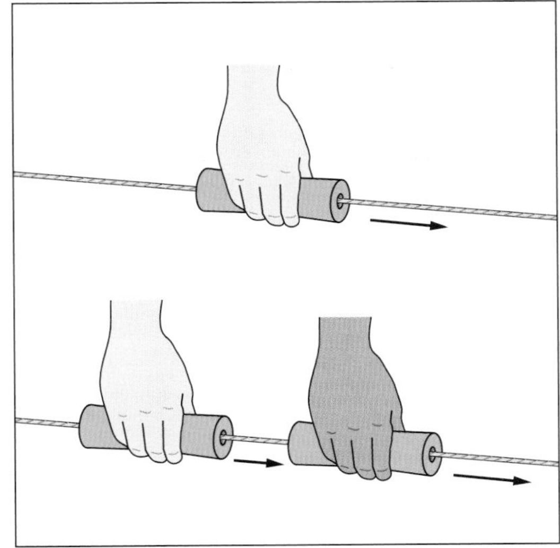

Picture 5 A model of resistors in series.

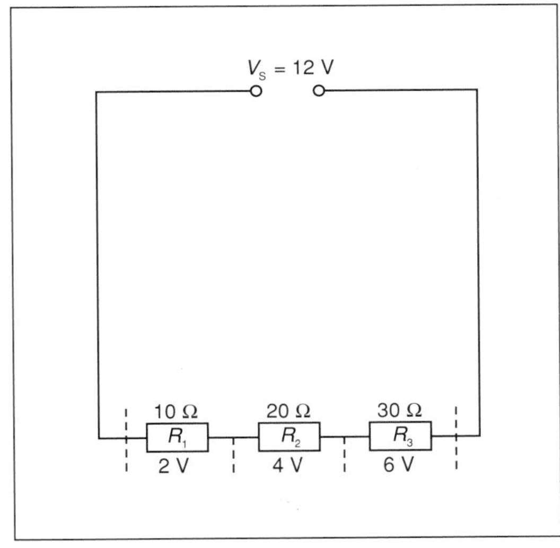

Picture 6 The supply voltage equals the total drop in voltage across the resistors.

Calculating series resistance

If we use an ohmmeter, as in picture 7, and measure the total resistance produced when we connect resistors in series, it appears that we simply add the resistance values together. This seems to be common sense, but in Physics we must be able to show that this is true for all situations. From Ohm's Law, we know that if the total series resistance is R_S, then the supply voltage is given by:

$$\boldsymbol{V_S = IR_S}$$

The voltage across each resistor can be found in the same way:

$$V_1 = IR_1 \qquad V_2 = IR_2 \qquad V_3 = IR_3$$

As $\qquad V_S = V_1 + V_2 + V_3$

we can write: $\qquad IR_S = IR_1 + IR_2 + IR_3$

As the current I is the same through all the resistors,

$$IR_S = I(R_1 + R_2 + R_3)$$

Which gives us: $\boldsymbol{R_S = R_1 + R_2 + R_3}$

The **total** series resistance is equal to the **sum** of all the individual resistances.

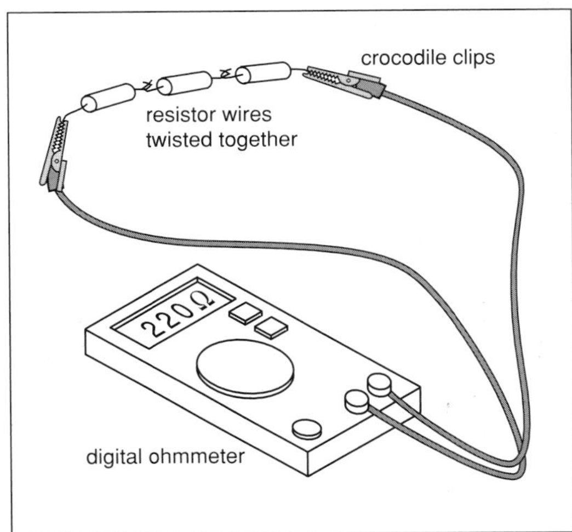

Picture 7 Digital ohmmeter being used to measure several resistors connected in series.

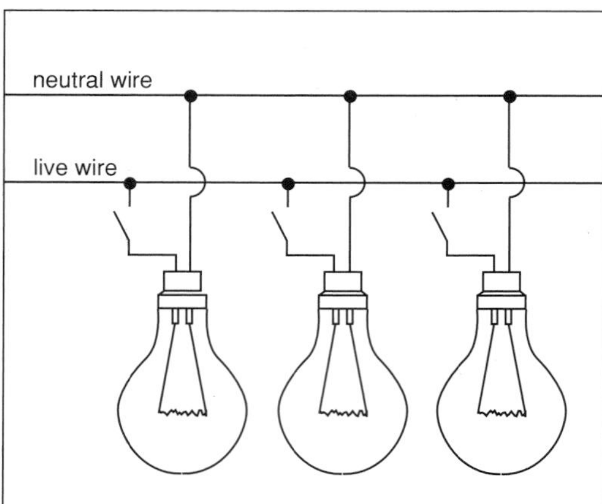

Picture 8 House lights have the lamps connected separately to the mains (i.e. in parallel).

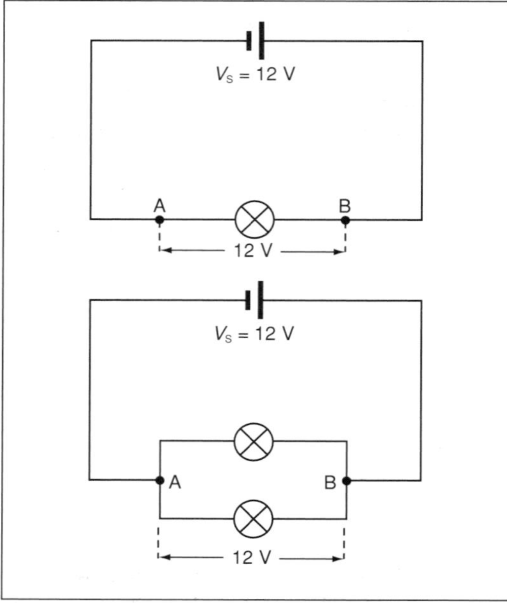

Picture 9 The voltage across components connected in parallel is the same.

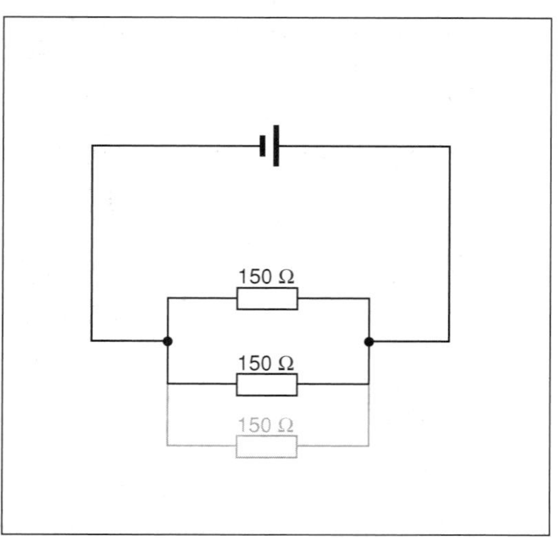

Picture 10 More resistors in parallel – less total resistance.

Parallel connections

It would be very annoying if all the lights in a house behaved like the Christmas lights, and went out because one lamp wasn't working. Although the switch in a table lamp is in series with the socket switch, each *socket* is connected *separately* to the mains supply. The same is true of fixed lighting, such as the ceiling or wall lamps in a room. Each lamp can have its own wall switch, and we can have any lamp lit, or none of them. This is called **parallel** connection (picture 8). The sidelights in a car are connected in parallel with each other, so that if one lamp fails, the others stay on.

Car doors have switches in them. The switches are connected in parallel, so that the inside light of the car comes on when either door opens. A two-bar electric heater will have a switch for each heating element. They are connected in parallel, so that the elements can be switched on individually.

Why do we use parallel circuits in the home?

Like the elements of the heater, electrical devices in the home are connected in parallel because we want to control them independently. Each is connected directly to the mains, so that it gets its proper voltage. Also, we can easily connect other devices into the circuit, without having to 'break in' to the circuit.

Of course, when we connect more devices in the circuit in parallel, we must take more current from the supply in order to make these extra devices work.

We can understand this idea by using a simple circuit that you could try for yourself in the lab (picture 9). The voltage between points **A** and **B** is the supply voltage, 12 V. This means that the supply will provide 12 J of energy to move a coulomb of charge from **A** to **B**, *regardless* of which path it takes.

It doesn't matter how many components we connect in parallel across **AB** – the voltage across *each* is 12 V. This is a general rule for *any* parallel circuit – the *voltage* across parallel components is the *same*.

If we start with just one 12 V lamp, we can calculate the current through it by using the formula

$$I = \frac{V}{R}$$

For one lamp this might be just 1 A. If we add another lamp, it too will have 12 V across it, and the supply will have to deliver 1 A through each bulb. The total current in the circuit will now be 2 A. If we keep adding components, the total current drawn from the supply increases.

In the first case,

$$R = \frac{V}{I}$$

tells us the circuit resistance is 12 Ω. In the second case, with two lamps, the supply delivers 2 A, so the circuit resistance is now 6 Ω – the total resistance has *decreased*.

Parallel resistances

If we take two identical resistors and connect them in parallel, we *halve* the total resistance of a circuit (picture 10). Two 150 Ω resistors would give us a parallel resistance of 75 Ω. Adding another makes the resistance drop to a third of its original value, so we would get 50 Ω.

It seems strange that *adding* resistors make the total resistance *decrease*. However, as we saw with the example of the lamps, the more paths that are available, the larger the total current that will flow.

Compare this with a situation where a wide road crosses a stream by a narrow bridge. Cars are queing to cross and tailing back along the road, and only a few cars per minute can cross the bridge. Regardless of the width of the road, the traffic on it must also flow at this rate. If we build an identical bridge next to the first, it is just as difficult and narrow, but nevertheless the rate of traffic flow across the stream can double.

Combinations of resistors

What happens if we add resistors of different values? Picture 11 shows a 60 Ω resistor. The supply voltage is 12 V, and so the current is:

$$I = \frac{V}{R} = \frac{12}{60} = 0.2 \text{ A}$$

If we add a 120 Ω resistor in parallel, the current through it will be 0.1 A. This gives a total current of 0.3 A at 12 V, so the total resistance must be:

$$R = \frac{V}{I} = \frac{12}{0.3} = 40 \ \Omega$$

Is it really possible that adding a resistor which is much *larger* than the first will still *reduce* the total resistance? Think back to our bridge – we can divert some traffic along a narrow country lane that crosses the stream elsewhere. The lane may be slower and more difficult for cars, but we will still get a larger overall flow of traffic.

In the above examples, we were able to work out the total resistance because we knew the supply voltage and could calculate the total current. What if we need a particular resistance, but all the resistors we have are too large? If we knew a method of calculating parallel resistance, we could connect a combination of resistors to produce our lower resistance.

Picture 11 Combining different values of resistors.

We know that the total current equals the currents in the branches of a circuit.

This gives us: $\boldsymbol{I_T = I_1 + I_2 + I_3}$

From Ohm's Law, $I = \frac{V}{R}$

therefore $\frac{V}{R_T} = \frac{V}{R_1} + \frac{V}{R_2} + \frac{V}{R_3}$

V is the same across all the resistors, so we can remove it to give:

$$\boldsymbol{\frac{1}{R_T} = \frac{1}{R_1} + \frac{1}{R_2} + \frac{1}{R_3}}$$

Questions

1 The heating elements of one make of toaster are connected as shown in figure 1. Figure 2 shows how the heating elements are arranged in a second make of toaster. The resistances of the heating elements are as indicated in the figures.

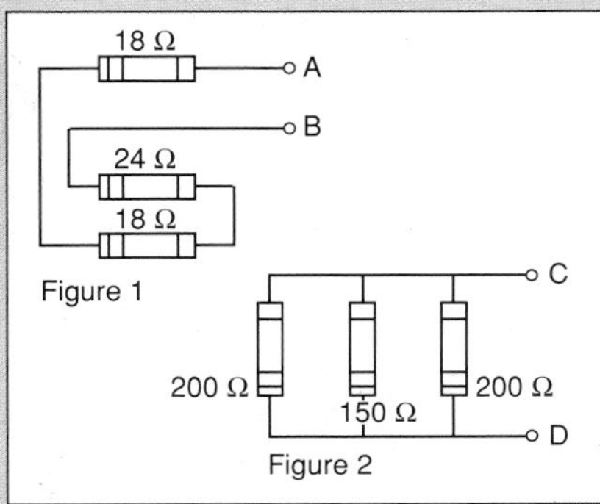

a Calculate the resistance between points A and B in figure 1.

b Calculate the resistance between points C and D in figure 2.

c Calculate the power of the toaster shown in figure 2 when the 230 V mains supply is connected to C and D.

d One of the heating elements shown in **figure 1** burns out and the toaster stops working. This fault cannot be seen.

An electrician tries to identify which heating element is faulty. She disconnects the toaster from the mains supply and uses a multimeter which can be set to measure either **current** or **voltage** or **resistance**.

She connects the multimeter across each element in turn.

i) What quantity should the multimeter be set to measure?

ii) How does the electrician use the multimeter readings to identify the faulty element?

iii) The multimeter will indicate either an open or a short circuit when connected across the faulty element. Which fault will it indicate in this case?

2 A tail and brake lamp on a car has two filaments in the same glass bulb. One filament has a resistance of 7 Ω and the other a resistance of 28 Ω.

a What is the resistance of the two filaments when connected in parallel?

b For safety reasons, the brake light has a higher power than the tail light. Explain which filament acts as the brake light.

B6
Behind the wall

The wiring system in a house can be quite complicated.

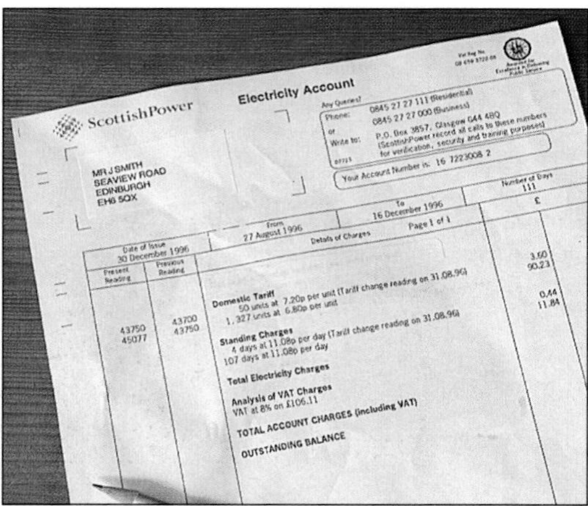

Picture 1 Paying for energy.

An electricity company sends regular bills to your house (picture 1). Actually, yo do not pay for electricity at all – what you pay for is the **energy** that is transferre when the electricity runs machines and heaters in your home. Electricity is no a *source* of energy. Fuels, such as coal and oil, are energy sources. When they ar burned in a power station, the energy they contain is released. We say electricit is an **energy carrier**, because it delivers this energy to your house.

We know that energy is measured in **joules**. How much energy do we bu from the power company when we switch on an electric fire for a few hours? We can use the formula for power, energy, and time:

$$\text{energy} = \text{power} \times \text{time} \quad \text{or} \quad E = Pt$$

A two-bar electric fire usually has a power rating of 2 kW, or 2000 W. If w switch it on for two hours, or 7200 seconds, then:

$$E = Pt = 2000 \times 7200 = 14\,400\,000\text{ J}$$

We can see that using *one* appliance for a short time involves a large amount o joules. Think of all the appliances used every day in an average house, then imagin an electricity bill for three months worth of energy, with the amount detailed i joules – the postman might have difficulty delivering that amount of paper!

Power companies use a larger and more convenient unit when charging us fo energy. The equation *energy* = *power* × *time* is still used, but the power i expressed in **kilowatts**, and time in **hours**. The unit is therefore called th **kilowatt-hour** (kWh).

If we now recalculate our previous example of the electric fire:

$$E = Pt = 2\text{ kW} \times 2\text{ hours} = 4\text{ kWh}$$

The company will now charge us for 4 units of electricity. The cost of energ from electricity is a few pence a unit. This changes as the electricity companie change their prices, but a typical cost might be 7p per unit. Our electric fire ha therefore cost 28p for 2 hours of use. We can calculate the running costs o different appliances by finding their power ratings on the rating plates (page 36).

The mains supply

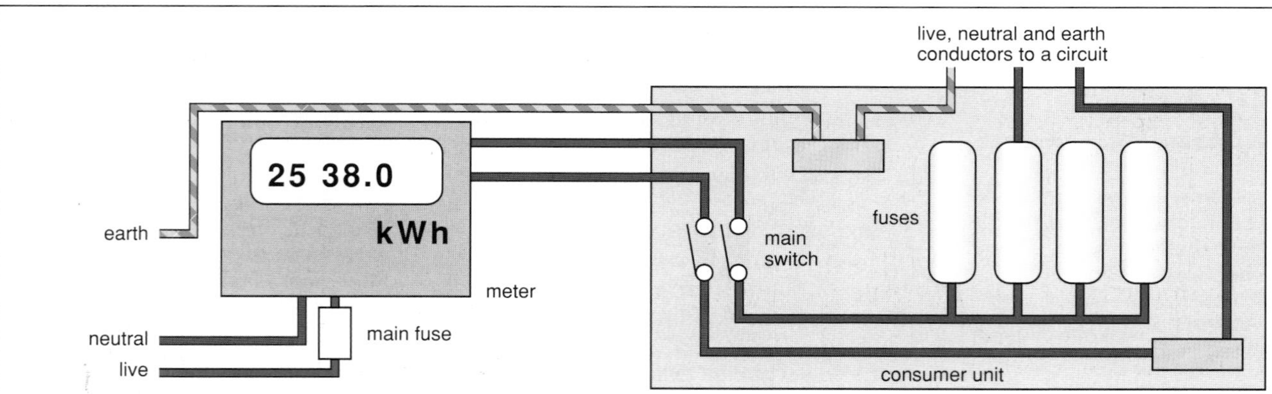

Picture 2 The meter board in a typical house.

To measure the energy used by a house, the electricity meter must be positioned where the mains cable enters the house, at the **meter board** (picture 2). The main supply cable contains two thick wires – the **live** and **neutral** cables. A mains fuse is connected in the live cable. Any current, flowing in any circuit in the house, must be drawn from the mains cable through the meter. Modern meters have a digital readout, while older ones have dials. The current now passes through the **consumer unit**, which contains the **mains switch** and **fuses**. The supply is then split up into various circuits serving the different parts of the house. The lighting, the wall sockets, and the cooker al have their own separate circuits and fuses. The fuses are always fitted in serie with the **live** supply cables.

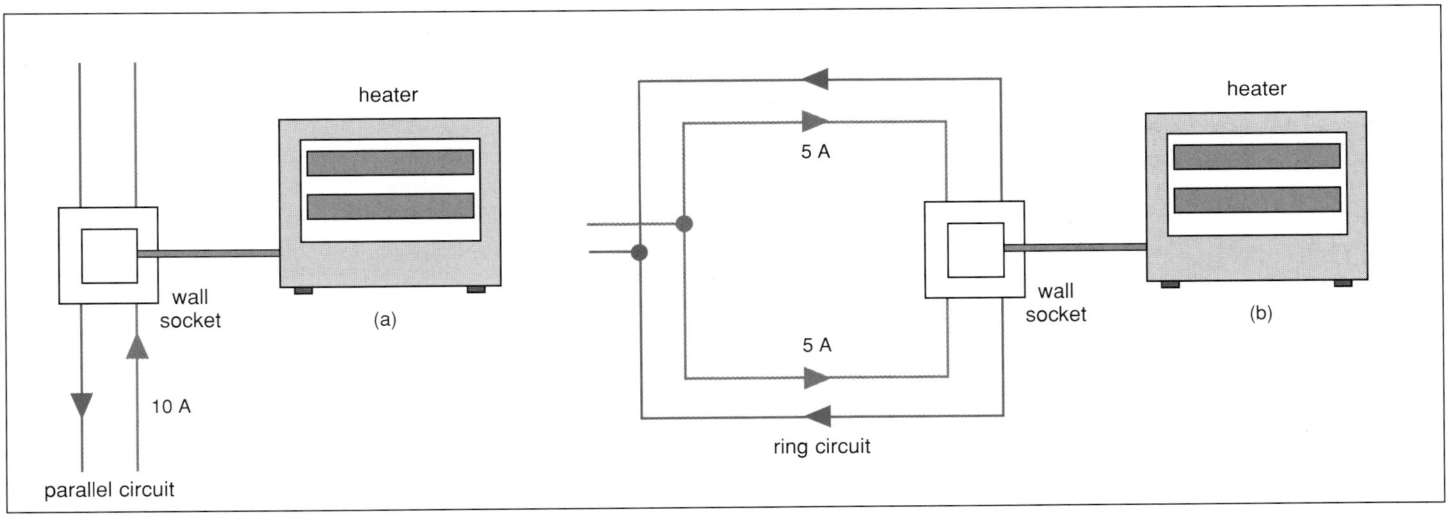

Picture 3 A ring circuit reduces the size of the current in one wire.

Domestic circuits

As mentioned in topic B6, lights and wall sockets are wired in parallel. The sockets are connected in a special arrangement called a **ring circuit**. This means that the live wire is a large 'loop' round a room, with the neutral cable forming a second loop next to it. Sockets can be connected across this loop at any position in the room. The advantage of this arrangement can be seen in picture 3. In part (a), an electric heater is connected in an ordinary parallel circuit. Ten amps of current are flowing through the single wires. In part (b), the room has been rewired with a ring circuit. There are now *two* paths for the current to take, so that the current in any part of the wire is a maximum of 5 A. This reduces the danger of overheating, and also means that thinner wire can be used, lowering the costs. The earth wire forms a third loop, but is not shown in the diagram.

Picture 4 shows the typical fuses that are used in the consumer unit to protect the different circuits. Lighting circuits carry low currents, so they are normally protected with a 5 A fuse. This means that the cables can be much thinner, and do not need a ring circuit.

Powerful electrical appliances, such as immersion heaters and cookers, are wired separately, with their own fuse in the consumer unit.

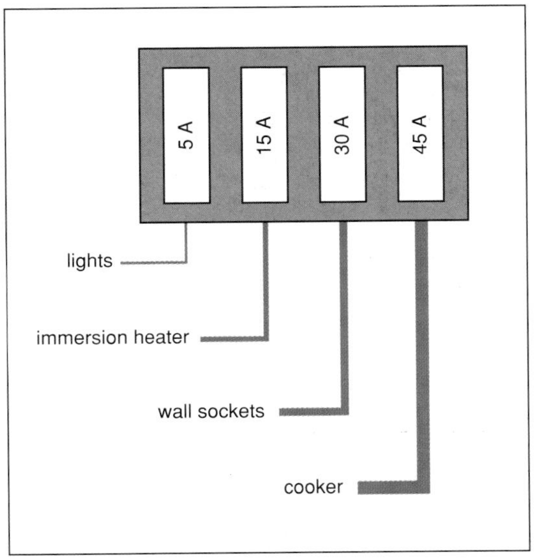

Picture 4

Circuit breakers

Modern houses often have circuit breakers (page 34) fitted instead of fuses. These have several advantages:

- they can cut off a current very quickly,
- they can be reset, so that they are reusable, unlike fuses,
- they cannot be tampered with – people have been known to replace fuses with pieces of wire, which means the circuit could be dangerous if a fault develops.

Picture 5 shows a simplified version of how one type of circuit breaker works. The circuit breaker has two electromagnets, one made from the live wire and one from the neutral wire. Their magnetic effects cancel each other, as long as the same current is flowing in each. If there is a fault, a greater current flows in the live part of the circuit. This makes its electromagnet stronger. It attracts the switch and breaks the current.

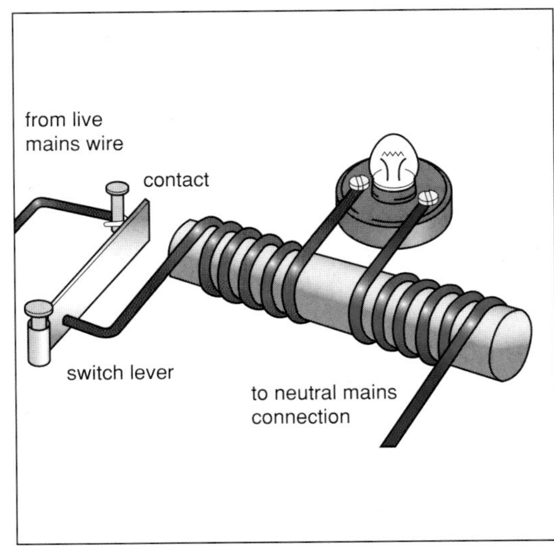

Picture 5

Live, earth, and neutral

What is the difference between the three cables which are used in the electricity supply? Let us examine in detail what each wire does.

The **earth** wire is, as the name suggests, connected to the Earth through the cold water pipes of the house. The copper pipes provide a good conducting path. The earth wiring runs through the house to every socket, and so connects to the earth pin of any plug that is inserted (picture 1). If the plug is properly wired, the metal casing of any appliance is therefore connected to the Earth. All electric charge will make its way to earth, if given the opportunity.

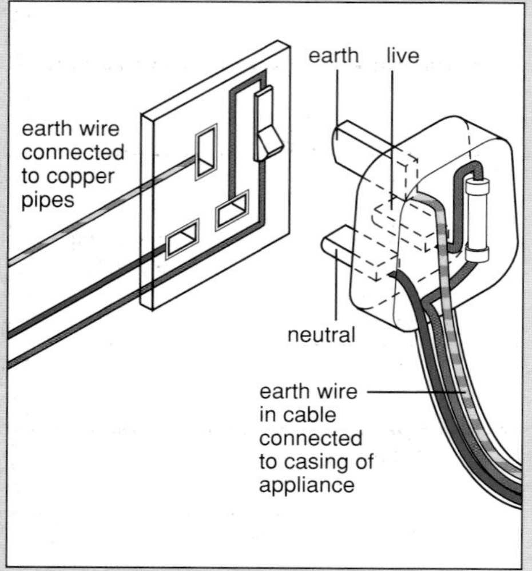

Picture 1 Earth wiring in house.

We know that a complete circuit is required for electric current to flow. If domestic electricity worked by using **d.c.**, we could say that the **live** wire was where the current entered an appliance, and the **neutral** wire provided the return path. We already know, however, that mains electricity is a.c. – the current flows first one way, then the other, 50 times a second. If the current flows from live to neutral, and then from neutral to live, is there any real distinction between the two wires? The answer is *yes* – there is always a *large* voltage difference between the *live* wire and *earth*. If we say that the earth is at *zero* volts, then the live wire changes between *+325* or *−325* V, every fiftieth of a second.

Imagine that you were unlucky enough to touch a bare live cable. At first the a.c. voltage is **positive** with respect to the Earth. This means that electrons flow up *from* the Earth through you. The a.c. voltage then changes and becomes **negative** with respect to the Earth – electrons flow in the other direction through you down *to* the ground. There is hardly *any* voltage difference between the neutral wire and earth (this does not mean it is a good idea to touch the neutral sections of the electricity supply!). Because of this, the neutral wire can be regarded as being at *zero* volts.

In an appliance such as an electric heater, current flows back and forward through the heating element. The electrons are moved back and forward by the voltage difference between the live and neutral wires at either end of the element (picture 2(a)).

If the live wire becomes loose or frayed and touches the metal casing, the current does not have to pass through the high resistance of the element. Instead, it has a much easier path to Earth, through the casing and down the earth wire. An unusually high current flows and the fuse melts, cutting off the supply. Even if the fuse does not work, when the switch is at *off*, the casing is disconnected from the live part of the supply. If anyone touches it, they will not receive a shock.

If the plug is wired wrongly as in picture 2(b), so that the neutral wire is at a *high* voltage, the casing is live, even when the switch is *off*. Anyone touching it could be electrocuted. The fuse and switch must always be connected in the *live* part of the circuit.

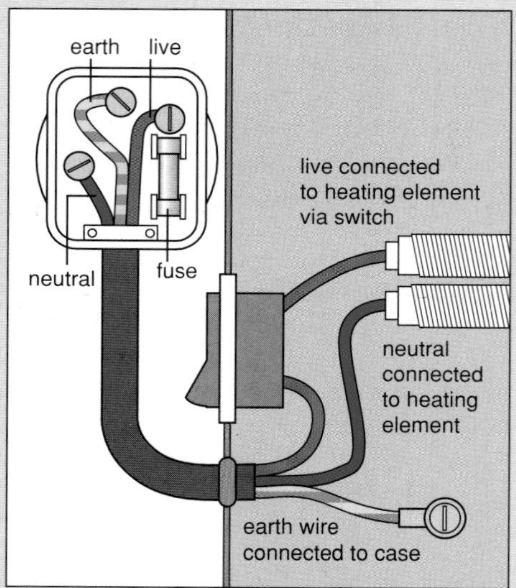

Picture 2(a) Correct wiring.

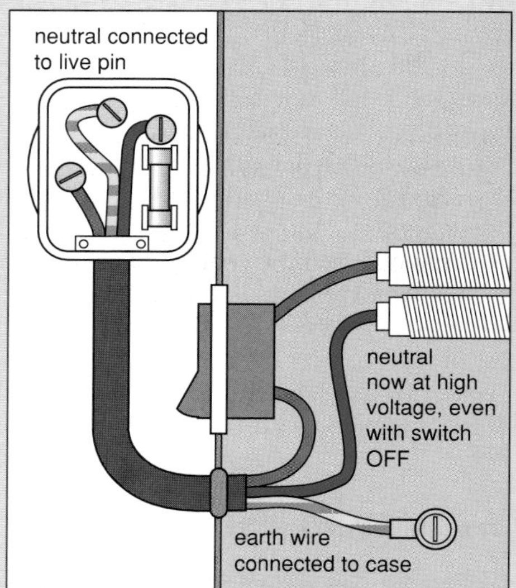

Picture 2(b) Incorrect wiring

Questions

1 The diagram opposite shows one of the lighting circuits and one of the power ring circuits in a home. The earth wire is not shown in the diagram.

a In the lighting circuit, the lamps are connected in parallel.

i) Give **one** advantage of connecting the lamps in parallel rather than in series.

ii) One lamp has a resistance of 900 Ω and each of the other two has a resistance of 600 Ω.

Calculate the resistance of the lighting circuit when all the lamps are switched on.

b State **one** advantage of connecting the power sockets in a ring circuit.

c The mains fuses protect the wiring in each circuit. A circuit breaker can be used instead of fuse.

Give **one** reason why a circuit breaker may be preferred to a fuse.

2 A mains flex is to be connected to a sandwich toaster. The flex and part of the layout of the toaster are shown opposite.

a State clearly which wire in the flex should be connected to terminals X, Y and Z.

b What is the purpose of having the lamp connected as shown in the toaster circuit?

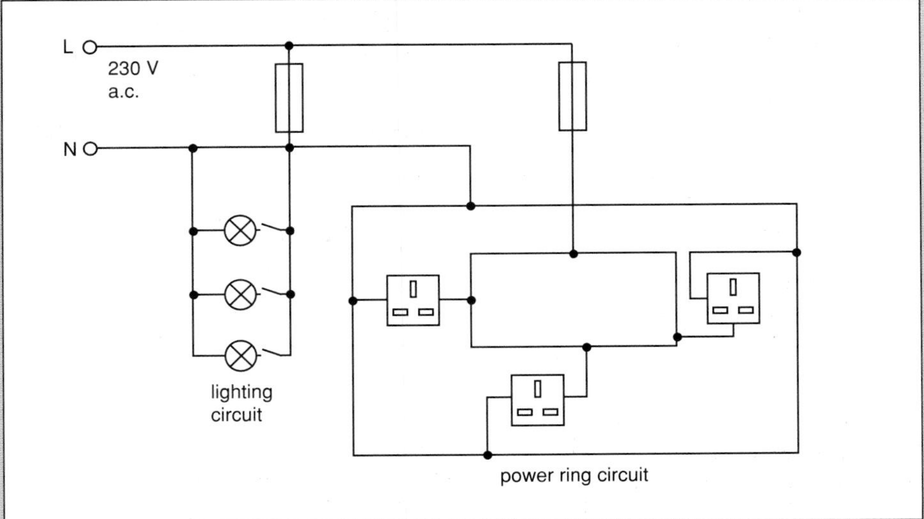

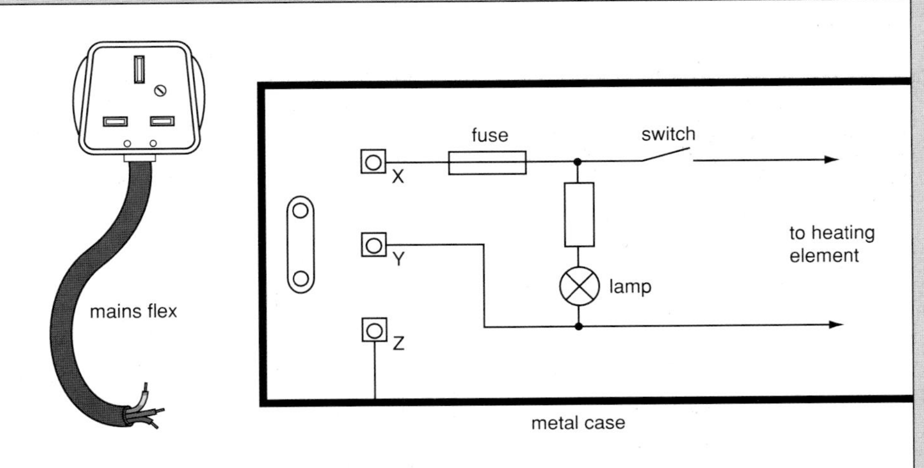

B7 Using electricity: motors and dynamos

Electric currents and magnetism can work together to make things move.

Picture 1 Michael Faraday lecturing to his students.

Poor boy makes good!

Two hundred years ago it wasn't easy for a poor boy to get an education, even if he was a genius. Michael Faraday (born in 1791) was the son of a blacksmith. He learned to read and write and do arithmetic but left school at 13 to work as an errand boy for a bookbinder.

At 14 he was promoted to apprentice bookbinder. Keen to learn, he started to read the books that he bound. He was fascinated by the science books, especially the ones about physics and chemistry. He spent some of his small pay on materials and started experimenting at home. He made lots of smells – and an electrical machine.

Later on, he went to lectures put on for the public at a great research laboratory in London called the Royal Institution. He was very interested by four lectures given by a famous scientist called Sir Humphrey Davy, who was the director of the Institution. He made careful notes of what he heard and wrote them out neatly. He used his skills to bind these notes and sent them off to the great man, with a letter asking for a job as a lab assistant.

He was given the job, and at the age of 21 he was able to give up bookbinding for ever. Twelve years later Michael was made Director of the Institution, and had become one of the most famous scientists in the world. Nearly everything you will learn about in this chapter was first discovered by him.The equipment he used can still be seen at the Royal Institution.

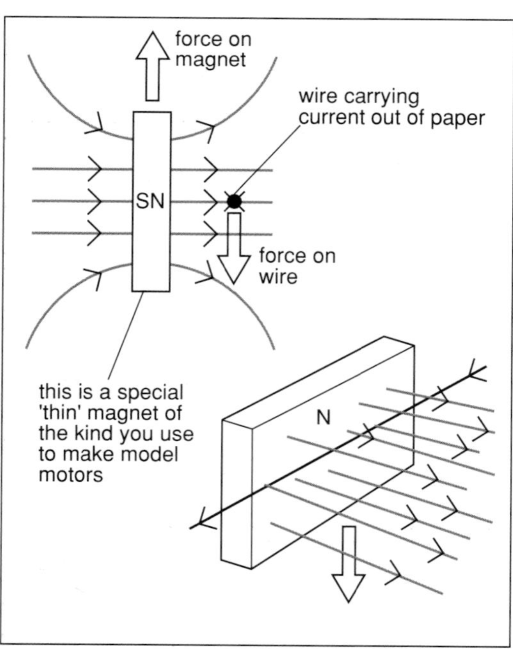

Picture 2 Interaction between a magnet and a wire carrying a current.

Electricity and magnetism working together

An electric current produces a magnetic field. Put a wire in the field of a magnet and pass a current through it. Both wire and magnet will try to move. There is a force between them caused by the interaction of their magnetic fields (picture 2). This is the **motor effect** which is used in all electric motors, from toy cars to large electric locomotives.

Strangely, the force is exerted at right angles to both the current direction and the magnetic field lines. When you change the direction of the current in the wire, the force on it changes to the opposite direction too. Changing the poles around so that the field is now in the opposite direction also changes the direction of the force on the wire.

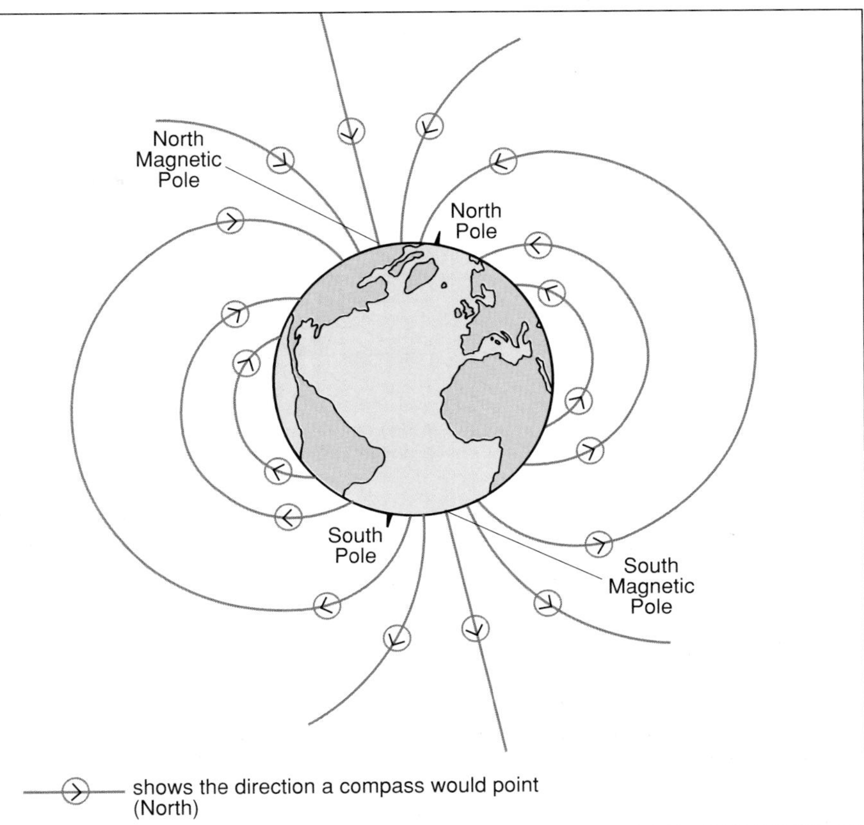

Picture 3 The magnetic field of the Earth.

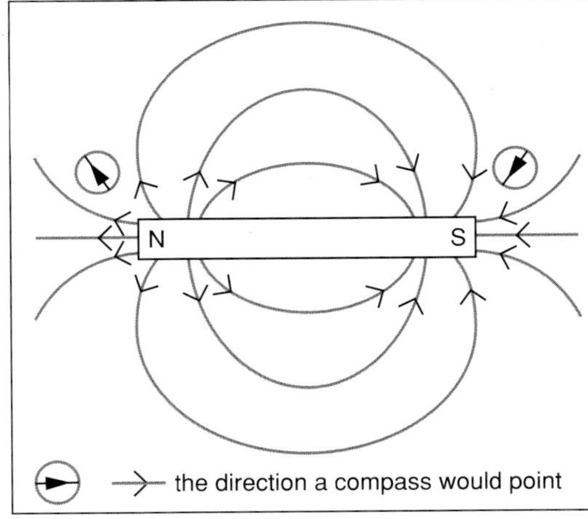

Picture 4 The magnetic field of a bar magnet.

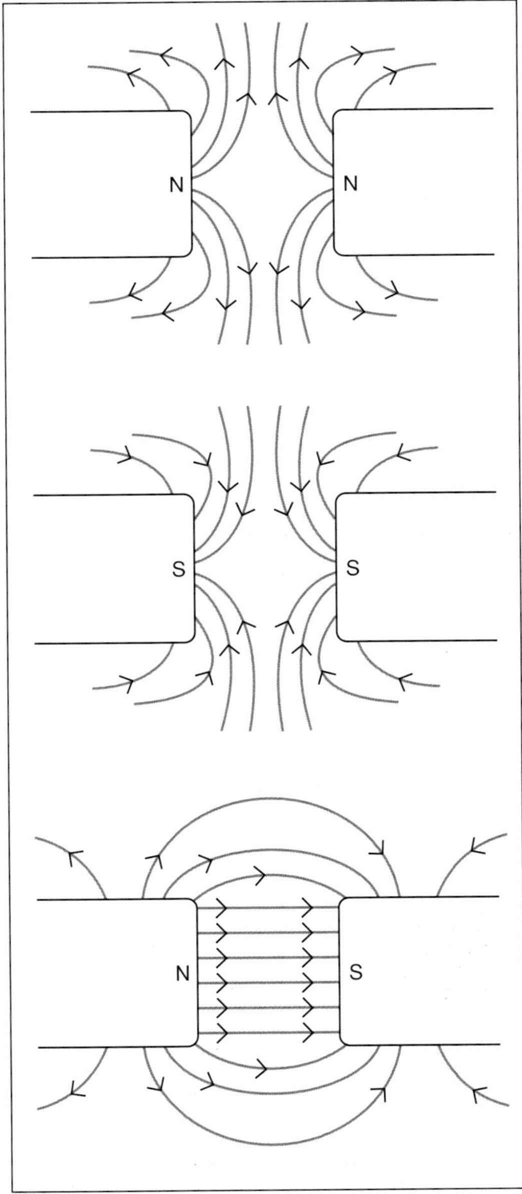

Picture 5 The fields between magnetic poles.

The Earth's magnetic field

The Earth has a magnetic field of its own, but it is quite weak. It is too weak to line iron filings up. But if you set up a thousand compasses all around your school, they would line up to show what the Earth's field is like in your area. It wouldn't look very interesting.

The direction of the field lines is the same as the way a compass would point (to the north). The arrows in picture 4 are in the direction that a small compass needle would point if you put it in the field of a bar magnet.

A suspended bar magnet, or a compass needle, lines up so that one end points north, the other south. The end (or 'pole') that points north is called the north-seeking pole, or N-pole. The other end is the south-seeking or S-pole. They show the direction of the field lines (or lines of force) of the Earth's magnetic field.

Attraction and repulsion

The rule about magnets is quite simple:

like poles repel; unlike poles attract

This means that N-poles attract S-poles, and vice versa. N-poles repel N-poles and S-poles repel S-poles. This seems to be a basic law of nature; much the same applies to electric charges. The field-patterns of like or unlike poles near each other seem to show this (picture 5). The lines go as directly as they can from N-pole to S-pole, but veer away from each other when like poles are placed close to each other.

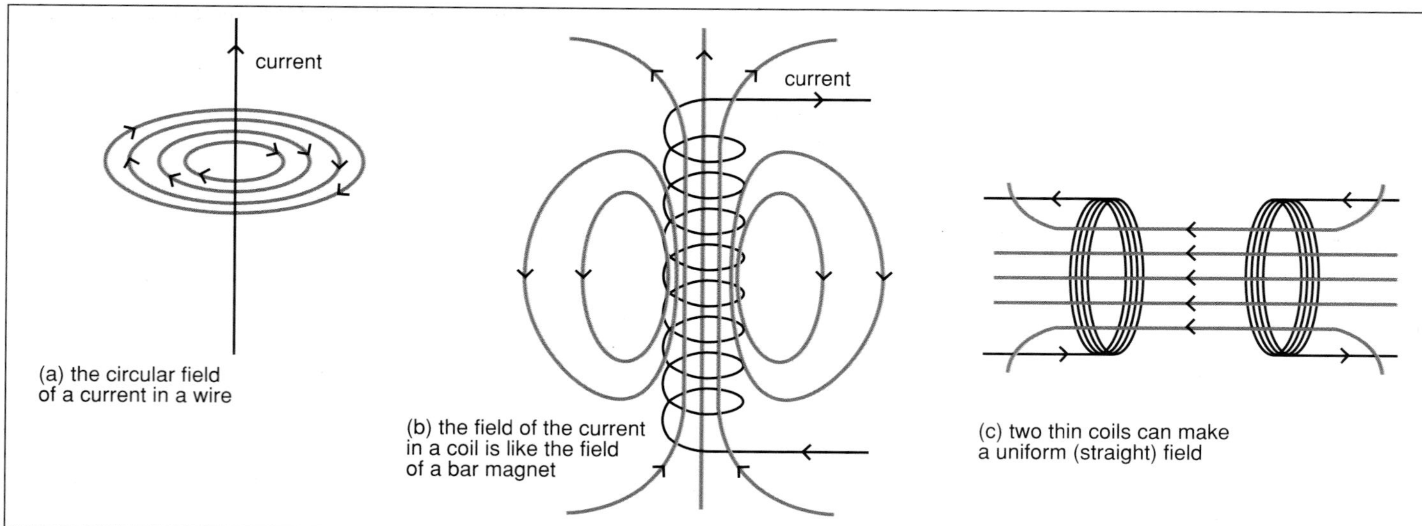

Picture 6 How different magnetic fields can be made.

Electromagnets

Electromagnets are easy to make, and can be very strong. There is a magnetic field around every conductor carrying a current. Picture 6 shows how different kinds of effect can be made by winding the wire in different ways.

An electromagnet can be made to have a field just like the field of a bar magnet. All you have to do is wrap the wire around a pencil to make a coil – see picture 6(b).

The field can be made a lot stronger if the coil is wrapped around a piece of iron. This is because the iron is turned into a magnet, and adds its strength to the field of the coil itself (picture 7).

You can use a small compass or iron filings to investigate the direction of the field near electromagnets.

Why electromagnets are useful

Electromagnets can be switched on and off, so that you can have a magnet only when you want it. Also, by making the current larger or smaller you can make the force field stronger or weaker. Electromagnets are more controllable than permanent magnets. Permanent magnets and electromagnets are used in many everyday devices.

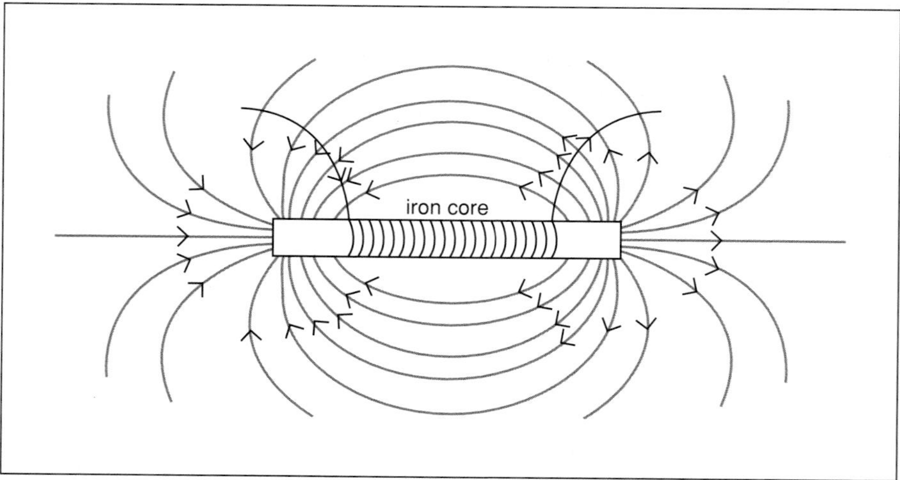

Picture 7 The field of an electromagnet.

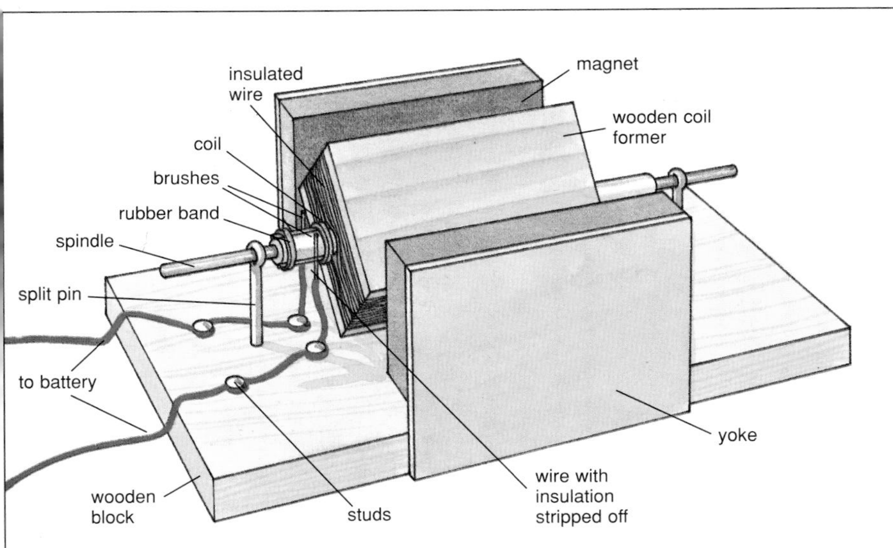

Picture 8 A model electric motor you could make.

Electric motors

Simple electric motors are scaled up versions of ones you can build yourself, from a length of wire and two magnets (picture 8). A model motor uses a special pair of slab magnets that give a straight field between them. The force makes a turning effect that is greatest when the spinning coil is at points **A** and **B** (picture 9).

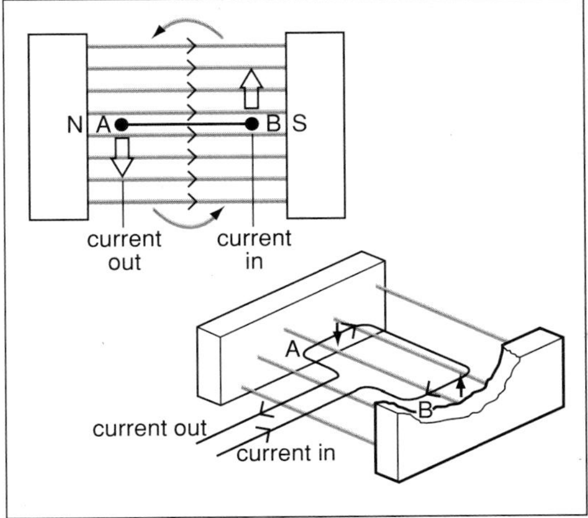

Picture 9 The forces on a coil in a magnetic field make it spin.

Small working motors

Picture 10 shows the inside of a small electric motor. A motor like this is used in electric drills or vacuum cleaners. It has several **rotating coils**, which are wrapped round some soft iron to strengthen their magnetic fields. Each coil has its own set of contacts. These contacts form the segments of the **commutator**, through which the current flows into each coil. The current is supplied through carbon (graphite) contacts called **brushes**. These are good conductors and slide over the commutator as it spins. The carbon is soft enough to wear away slowly without damaging the commutator. They are held in contact by springs. If the wear on the brushes becomes severe, they can be removed and replaced.

As the motor spins, one coil after the other is brought into action, so that the force is almost continuous. This make the rotation much smoother.

In a real motor, the magnets *producing* the field are electromagnets, not permanent ones. These fixed coils are usually called **field coils**, and are much lighter and cheaper than permanent magnets.

Many motors used in household appliances operate on a.c., which makes their design slightly different. The currents in the field coils and the rotating coils will change direction together, so that their magnetic effects reverse at the same time.

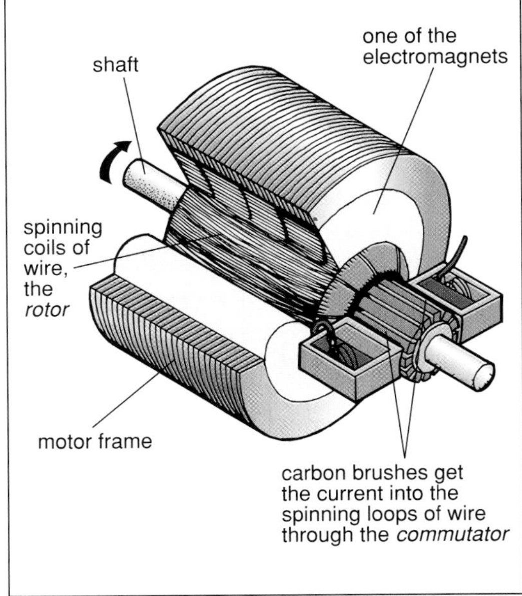

Picture 10 A large electric motor that has been cut open.

Predicting magnetic effects

We can work out the direction of the circular magnetic field produced by a current in a wire. Imagine you are looking at a 'slice' through the wire (its cross section), as in picture 1. The direction of the **electron** current (negative to positive) will either be towards or away from you. Picture a dart being thrown *away* from you – you will see the crossed feathers of the flight.

If the dart is moving straight *towards* you, you see the point. We use these symbols to represent the direction in which the electrons are moving. It is therefore very easy to remember the direction of the magnetic field:

- if the current is ***C***oming towards you – the field is ***C***lockwise
- if the current is ***A***way from you – the field is ***A***nti-clockwise

We can also use our **left** hands to visualise this. Hold your left hand with the thumb pointing towards your nose. If your thumb is pointing in the direction of electron flow, your fingers curl round naturally in a clockwise manner.

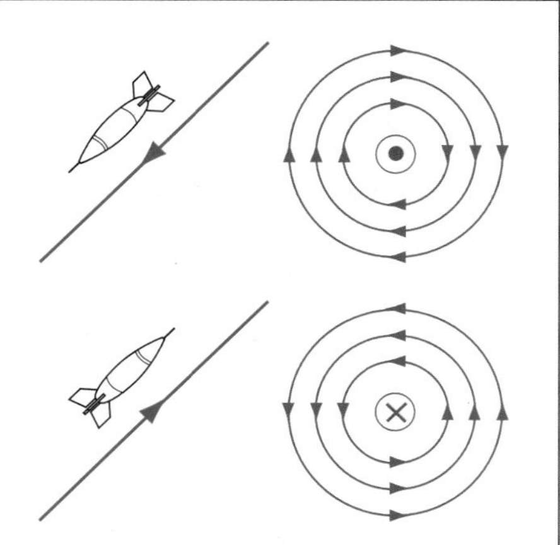

Picture 1

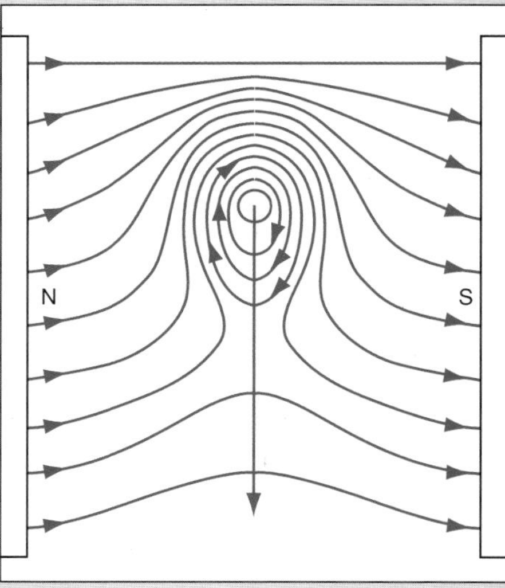

Picture 2

Motor effect

Imagine your piece of wire is now placed between the poles of a magnet. We can see how the circular and straight lines of force will either cancel or combine to change the strength and direction of the field at different points. This produces the upwards or downwards force (picture 2).

Use the fingers of your **right** hand (picture 3) to predict which way the wire will move:

- the ***F***irst finger points in the direction of the ***F***ield,
- the se***C***ond finger points in the direction of the ***C***urrent,
- the ***TH***umb will point in the direction of ***TH***rust.

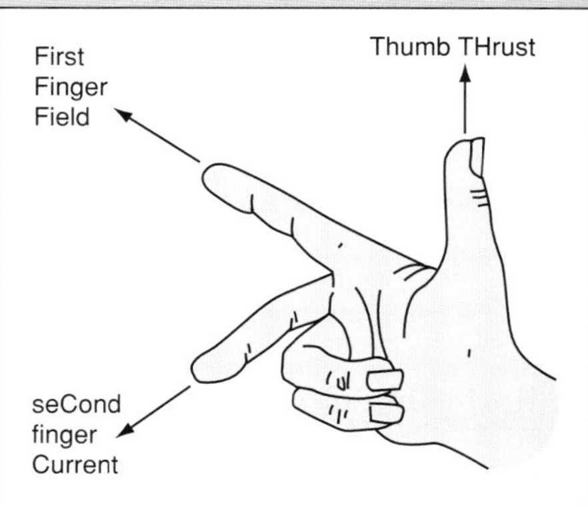

Picture 3

How does it work? An electric bell

The diagram below shows the main parts of an electric bell. Your task is to describe how it works. You can use some clues, which are given here.

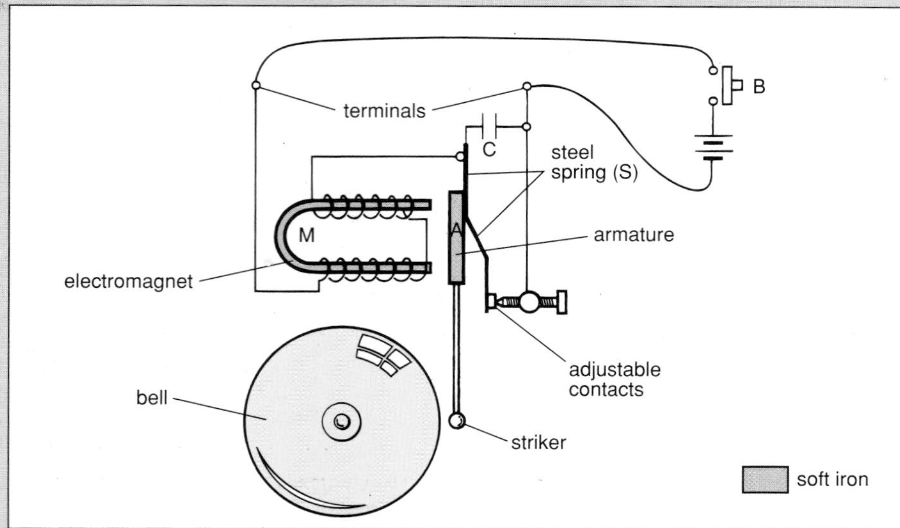

Facts

1. When you press the bell-push (a switch, **B**), current flows through the circuit that includes the electromagnet.
2. The core of the electromagnet (**M**) is made of an alloy (e.g. 'soft iron') which is easily magnetised in a magnetic field, but loses its magnetism very quickly when the field disappears.
3. The bell hammer is connected to a piece of springy steel (**S**), which has another piece of soft iron attached to it (**A**).

Clues

What happens to the circuit when the electromagnet pulls **A** towards it?

Then what happens to the electromagnet?

Task

Now describe as clearly and logically as you can how the bell keeps on ringing as long as you keep your finger on the bell-push.

Questions

1 a A current carrying wire is placed between the poles of a magnet. The direction of the electron current in the wire is as indicated in figure 1. The conductor experiences an upward force as shown below.

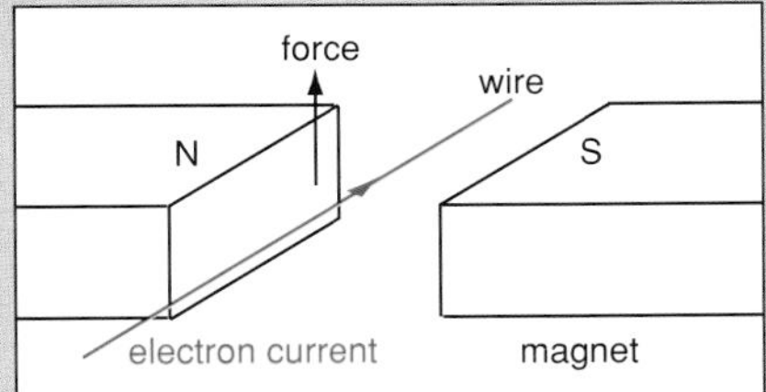

Figure 1

Figures 2 and 3 show other current carrying wires placed between the poles of magnets.

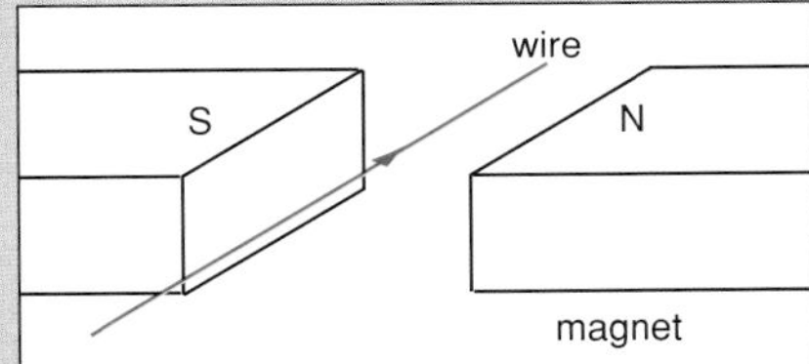

Figure 2

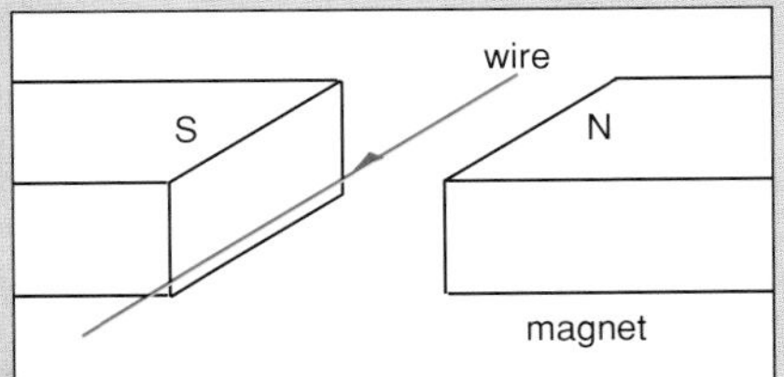

Figure 3

In each case, state the direction of the force on the wire.

b Figure 4 shows a simple electric motor with a coil WXYZ free to spin about a shaft PQ.

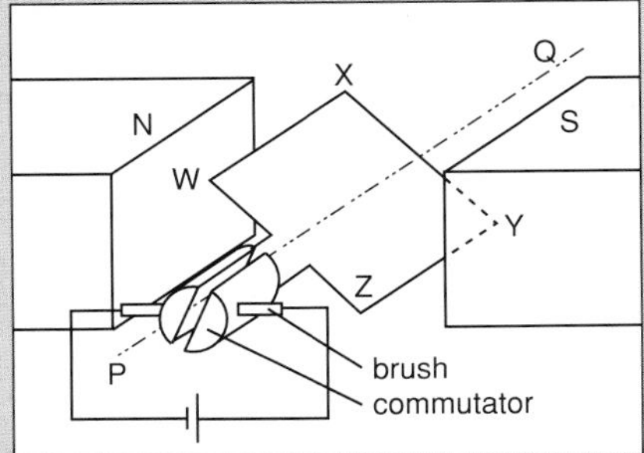

Figure 4

i) By looking at the diagram and using the conclusions you reached in part a state:

(A) the direction of the electron current in the coil,

(B) the directions of the forces on the coil,

(C) the direction of rotation of the coil.

ii) Describe how the brushes and the commutator allow the coil to keep spinning.

c In commercial motors, explain why:

i) more then one rotating coil is used;

ii) field coils rather than permanent magnets are used.

2 The diagram below shows the main parts of an electric motor.

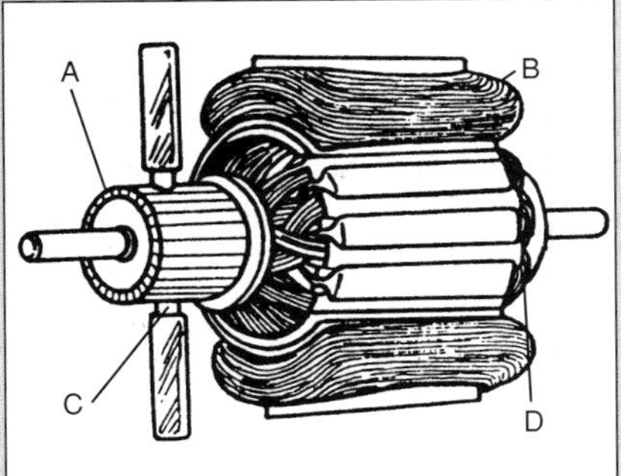

The parts of the motor are listed below.

Rotating coil *Field coil (magnet)*
Brushes *Commutator*

Use the list of parts to name the parts A, B, C and D on the diagram.

3 The diagram below shows a circuit, designed by a pupil, to be used as a burglar alarm in a house.

The iron rod can turn about the pivot.

Explain how this alarm works.

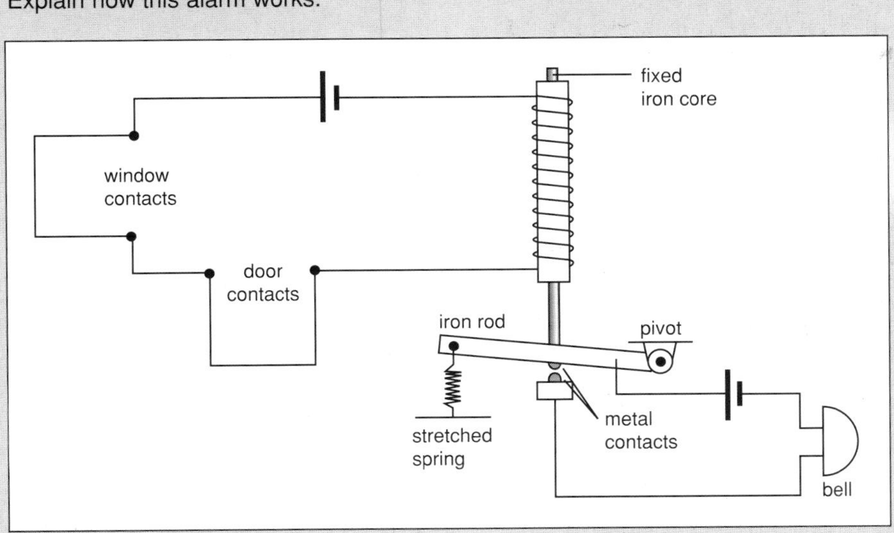

4 Which of the following objects or materials would be attracted by a magnet?

a a coin,
b glass,
c copper wire,
d wood,
e iron,
f carbon,
g a knife blade.

Give two differences between permanent magnets and electromagnets.

C1 Thermometers

How can we measure a person's temperature?

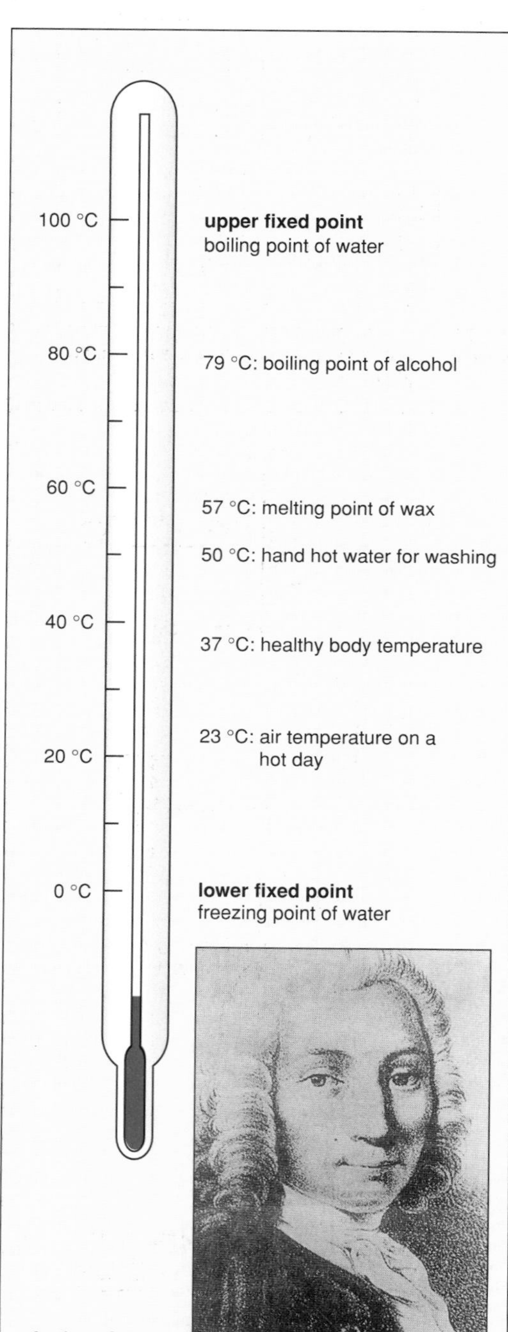

Picture 1 The Celsius scale.

Diagnosis and treatment

When doctors decide what is wrong with a patient, we say they make a *diagnosis*. They can do this correctly only if they have as much information about the patient as possible. They must then use a treatment which has the best chance of restoring the patient to health. Knowledge of Physics can provide instruments and techniques for diagnosis and treatment, and sometimes both.

For example, X-ray photography (page 85) can be used to find out what is wrong with a patient. Beams of X-rays can be used to destroy unhealthy tissue. In this section, we will look at the Physics behind methods of diagnosis and treatment. One of the oldest diagnostic techniques is to take the patient's temperature.

Heat and temperature

Which is at the higher temperature – a thimble full of boiling water, or a lukewarm bath? Most of you will immediately reply with the correct answer – the water in the thimble. Now think carefully – which contains more *heat* energy? After a moment, it is obvious that a large quantity of energy is needed to warm a bath full of water. Adding a very small amount of energy can boil the water in the thimble. Heat and temperature are *not* the same, although they are linked. Temperature is proportional to the *average* amount of energy that the particles of a substance have. On average, each water molecule in the thimble has more energy than those in the bath. The thimble contains far fewer molecules, so the *total* heat supplied is less.

We measure temperature using the **Celsius** scale (see picture 1). When we *add* energy to a substance, its temperature *increases*. A device which measures temperature is a **thermometer**. All thermometers use some property of a substance that changes with temperature, and measure that property. Picture 2 shows examples of temperature measurement using different properties of materials.

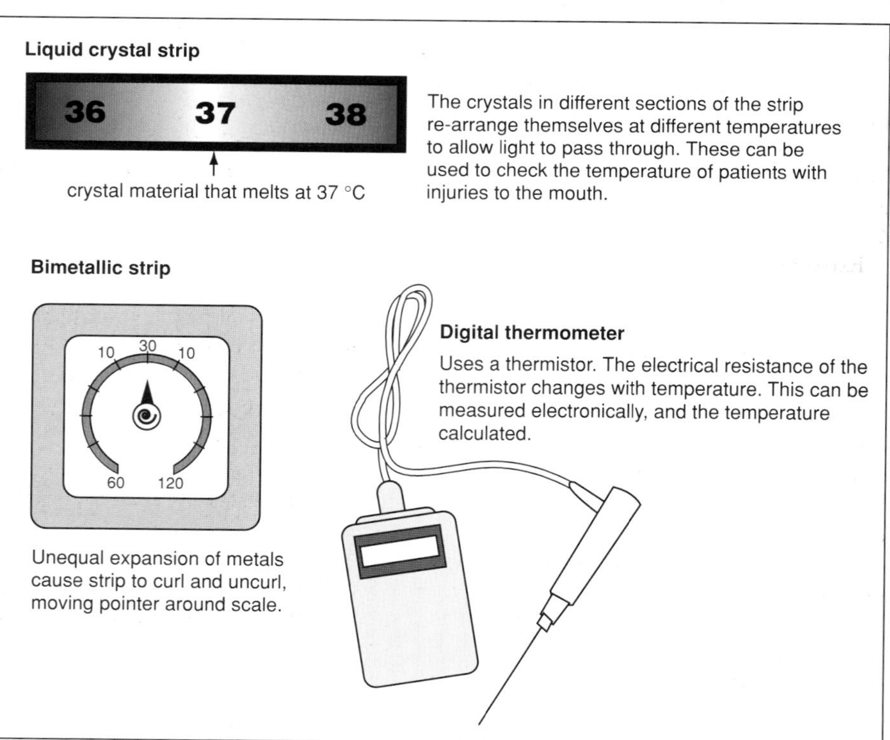

Picture 2

The mercury thermometer

We know that substances expand when heated. The earliest methods of temperature measurement used this change. Some thermometers used the expansion of air. Others used liquids which rose up a thin glass tube as they expanded. **Liquid-in-glass** thermometers are commonly used today. In some the liquid is alcohol, but you are probably most familiar with the type which uses a liquid metal – mercury. The thermometer in picture 1 is a mercury thermometer. In a science laboratory, the thermometers usually measure temperatures between 110 °C and –10 °C. If your body temperature was near these extremes, it would be far too late to help you! Normal body temperature is 37 °C, but this refers to the inside of your body – your **core** temperature. Your skin surface is usually a few degrees lower. If your body temperature rises or falls by a few degrees, then you have a problem. Because of this, thermometers used in medicine measure a much narrower range of temperatures than a laboratory thermometer.

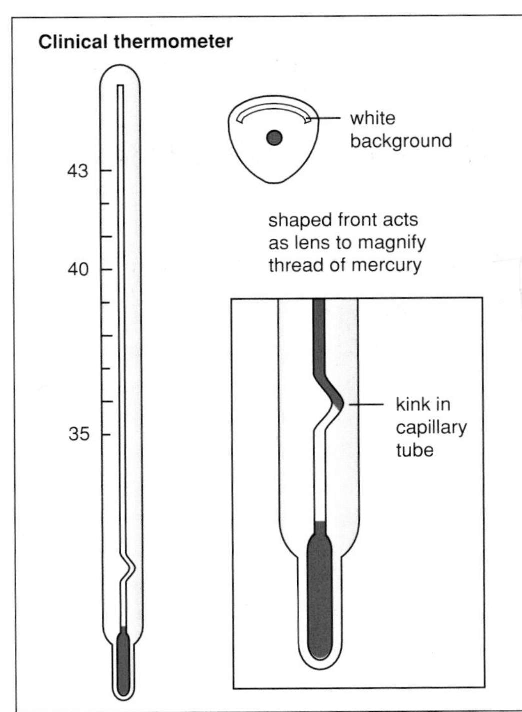

Picture 3 A clinical thermometer maintains its reading.

The clinical thermometer

A typical clinical thermometer (picture 3) has a range of 35–43 °C. It has a lens shape which magnifies the mercury 'thread', and makes taking a reading easier. If a nurse took an ordinary laboratory thermometer out of your mouth, and paused to read it, the mercury would move down as it cooled. Clinical thermometers have a kink in the tube, which prevents the mercury above the kink moving downwards. The thermometer continues to show the original temperature reading, until the nurse shakes it and moves the mercury back down into the bulb. **Digital** clinical thermometers use an electronic circuit to store the highest recorded temperature. They are reset by a small switch.

Reading the signs

Many microbes can only survive in a narrow range of temperatures. Your body reacts to infection by heating up, so that conditions for the microbes are more difficult. This is called a 'fever'. A rise in body temperature is a sign to the doctor that you are ill.

High external temperatures are also dangerous to humans. On a hot day we produce sweat. The moisture takes energy from our skin and evaporates, carrying it away so that there is a cooling effect. If we still cannot reduce our body temperature, our heart rate rises, blood vessels widen, and the brain is affected. At 41 °C we experience convulsions, and death will occur between 43 °C and 45 °C.

Extremely cold weather conditions cause a person to lose body heat. If they are also wet, the loss is increased, just as in sweating. The body reacts to prevent heat loss. Blood vessels near the surface of the skin close up, and muscles vibrate to generate more heat – we shiver. If heat continues to be lost, then the core temperature of the body starts to drop to dangerous levels. This is a condition called **hypothermia**. If the person's temperature falls below 28 °C, unconsciousness and death will follow. Mountaineers and hillwalkers should always carry a change of warm dry clothing. Divers working in low temperatures have special heated suits, as the surrounding water carries body heat away very effectively.

Old people are less active, so they generate less body heat than the average person. In winter, they may not be able to afford high heating bills, and so the house temperature may be low. They may lose heat more gradually than a diver or mountaineer, but eventually hypothermia can set in. In cold weather, always be aware that elderly neighbours are at risk.

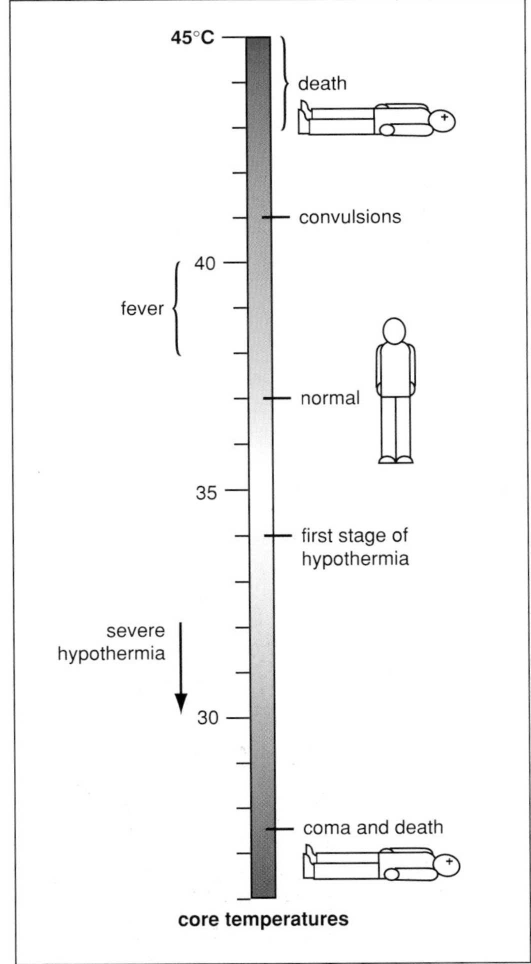

Picture 4 Effects of changes in body temperature.

C2 Using sounds

Sound can damage our bodies or help us understand them.

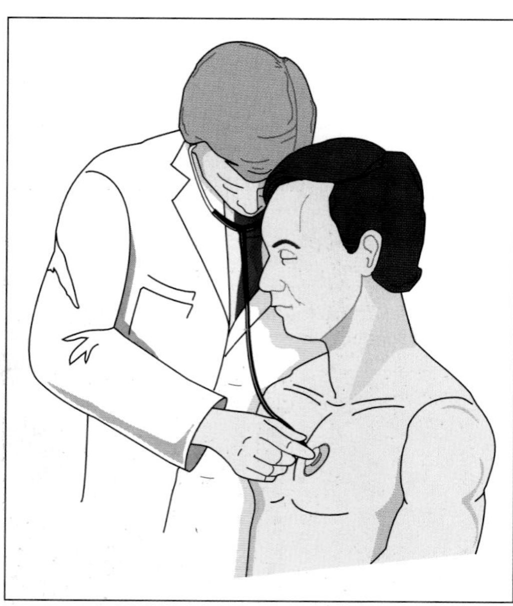

Picture 1 Using a stethoscope.

Say 'Ahhh...'

When a machine such as a car engine is faulty or badly maintained, an exper mechanic can often diagnose the problem by listening to the engine noise Different systems in our body produce sounds as they operate. For example, the heart produces a regular beating sound as it pumps blood round the body Doctors are trained to recognise normal sounds and also those produced by medical problems. On a house visit, or in the surgery, a doctor uses a simple bu very effective tool – the **stethoscope**.

The stethoscope is used to listen to the heart or lungs. These produce different types of sounds, so the end of the stethoscope has two different bell shaped parts. The **open bell** is used to listen to deep rhythmic heart sounds The **closed bell** has a sheet of material, or 'diaphragm', across its opening. It detects higher frequency sounds, such as the movement of air through the lung passages.

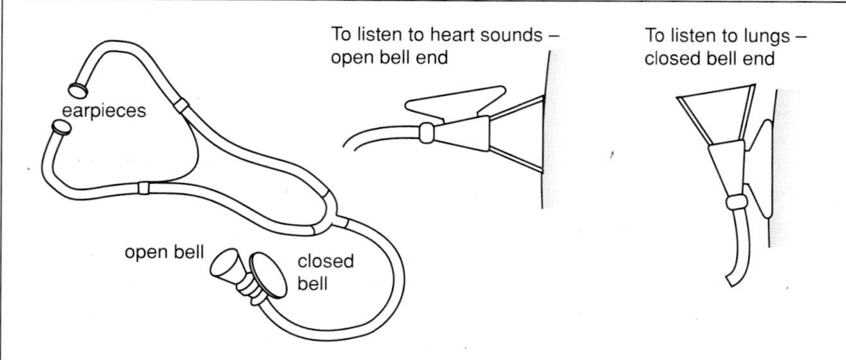

The sounds from a patient's chest travel into the bells and are funnelled into the flexible **tubes**. The sound waves travel through the air in the tubes, until they reach the **earpieces**. The earpieces must fit firmly in the doctor's ears, to prevent outside noises interfering with the sounds from the patient.

Seeing with sound

Bats seem to fly round obstacles, and catch insects, in total darkness and silence. In fact they are very noisy animals, but our ears cannot detect their sounds because they have too high a *frequency* (see topic A2).

Ordinary sound, which we can hear, has frequencies in the range of 20 Hz to 20 000 Hz. Sounds *above* this frequency range are called **ultrasound**. Bats use ultrasound at around 50 kHz (50 000 Hz). The bursts of high frequency sound reflect back from objects. A bat can detect these echoes, and accurately judge the position of a tree branch or insect prey. Dolphins use the same technique in water, and humans use sonar (see page I4) to measure the depth of the seabed or to detect submarines.

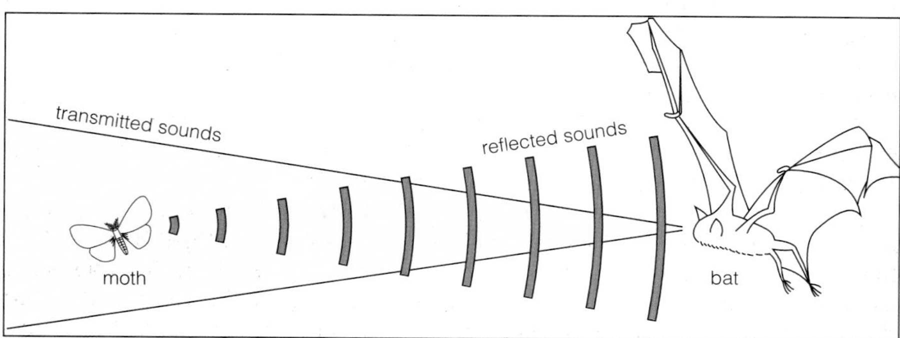

Picture 2 Bats use ultrasound for navigation and hunting.

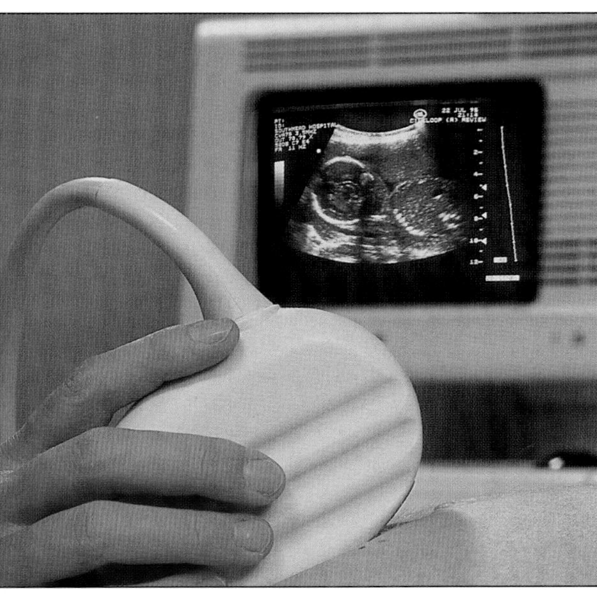

Picture 3 Ultrasound can be used to monitor a baby's development.

Ultrasound can have frequencies up to 15 *million* hertz. This is higher than any animal ear can sense.

One of the most useful body probes is the **ultrasound scanner**. Pulses of ultrasound are sent into the human body. This produces pictures like the one shown in picture 3, which shows a scan of an unborn baby.

At high frequency, the sound can travel through most materials. But some of it is always reflected back when it goes from one type of material into another. How much of it is sent back depends on the material in the way. Some of the ultrasound reflects back when it reaches a boundary between different tissues, such as muscle and bone (see picture 4). The reflections are detected by the scanner probe, and converted into a picture on a screen.

Also, the speed at which the ultrasound travels depends on the material it is travelling in. To make sure that the ultrasound is not reflected back at the boundary between the air and the patient's skin, a special jelly is smeared between the scanner and the body. This removes any air gaps. The speed of sound in the jelly is close to that in the patient's body, so that most of the sound energy travels through the skin.

The advantage of using sound is that it doesn't harm the living cells, as X-rays may do. But if they are to see fine detail, the sound waves must have very small *wavelengths* (see page 10 of topic A2). The wavelengths have to be slightly smaller than the small parts (e.g. blood vessels) of the object being looked at (see picture 5). If they are greater than the size of the object, they do not reflect.

This is the reason for using such very high frequencies. The higher the frequency, the smaller the wavelength. This is because of the wave formula:

$$\textbf{wavelength} = \frac{\textbf{speed}}{\textbf{frequency}}$$

The speed of sound in the human body is about the same as it is in salt water, about 1500 metres per second. To see detail to about 1 mm (0.001 m), the wavelength has to be no more than this length. This means a frequency of at least 1.5 million hertz (1.5 MHz). In hospitals, ultrasound scanners use frequencies between 1 MHz and 15 MHz.

The pulses of ultrasound are transmitted at a rate of roughly 1000 every second, or 1 kHz. It is important not to confuse the frequency of the *pulses* with the frequency of the ultrasound *waves* in those pulses.

Ultrasound can also be used in treatment. Bursts of ultrasound are used to break up painful 'stones' which develop in the kidneys and gall bladder. The high frequency sound causes the stones to vibrate and shatter. The fragments can then pass out of the body normally. The advantage of this treatment is that the patient does not have to be cut open in an operation to remove the stones.

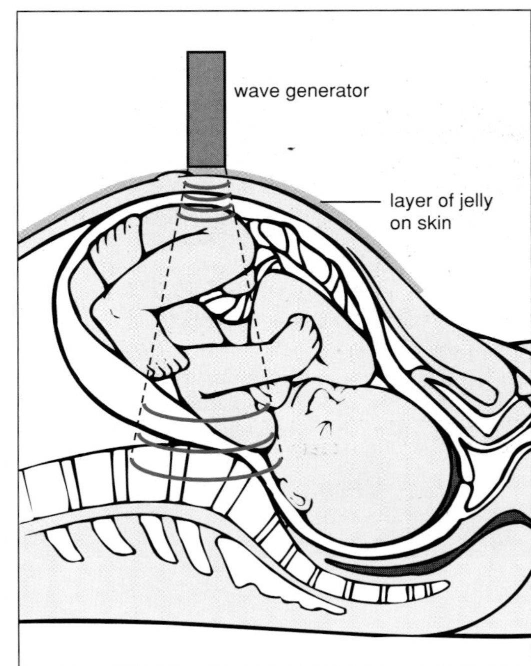

Picture 4 How ultrasound reflects from different layers in the body.

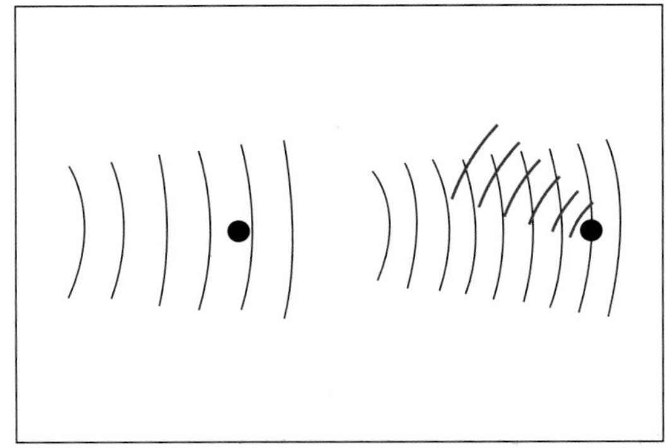

Picture 5 Long waves miss the fine detail.

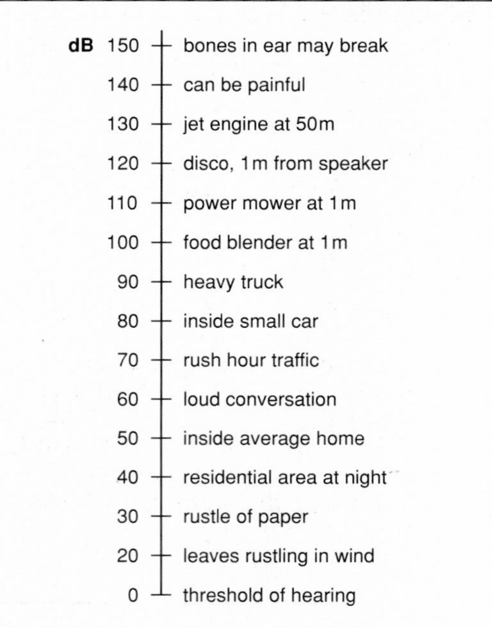

Picture 6 The range of sound intensity.

Sound levels

The 'loudness' of a sound, as we hear it, depends on the way our ears and brain process the sound signal. Just as our eyes adapt to light, our hearing system adapts to different noise levels. To measure accurately the loudness or **intensity** of a sound, we must use a measuring instrument – the **decibel meter**.

The intensity of a sound is measured in **decibels** (dB). The quietest sound that the human ear can detect is called the **threshold of hearing** and is given a value of zero decibels. The loudest sound that we can tolerate is thousands of millions of times more intense than the faint rustle of fallen leaves. The decibel scale is therefore quite an unusual type of scale. Every time the sound level increases by 10 decibels, the intensity of the sound is *multiplied* by 10 (i.e. 10×10 for a 20 dB difference). A 30 dB sound is not *three* times as intense as a 10 dB sound, but *one hundred* times.

Picture 6 shows the range of intensities from the threshold of hearing to the loudest sounds that the human ear can bear. A sound of 120 dB is on the **threshold of pain**. Sounds louder than this can actually hurt your ears and give you a headache. Prolonged noise above 150 dB can cause permanent deafness.

Because of its harmful effects, it is important for noise in the environment to be controlled. Sound levels above 90 dB are not normally allowed in factories but many of the noises which we hear in our everyday lives are much louder than this. People who work close to noisy machinery must wear ear protectors as shown in picture 7.

Picture 7 Loud noises can damage the ears.

What causes deafness?

There are several types of deafness, depending on which part of the ear is affected. Lots of people become slightly deaf from time to time because the outer ear channel gets blocked with hard wax. This is easily removed by the doctor syringing out the ears with warm water.

An explosion, or a blow on the side of the head, may rupture the ear drum causing partial or complete deafness. However, the ear drum usually heals quite quickly and then hearing returns.

More serious deafness is caused by bone tissue growing round the bones in the middle ear chamber. This can prevent them moving, in much the same way as a piston may seize up with rust. If nothing is done about it, this can lead to permanent deafness. However, the person's hearing may be improved by wearing a hearing aid which amplifies the sound waves. In severe cases the bones of the ear may be replaced by artificial ones made of plastic. This type of deafness runs in families, and it can begin when a person is quite young.

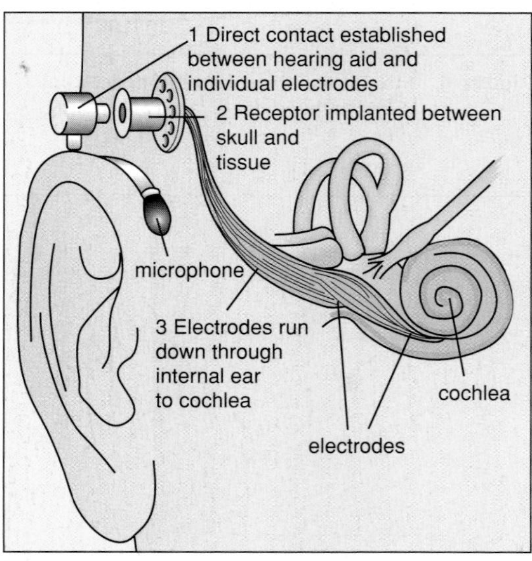

Picture 8

Picture 8 shows a technique used on a man who became deaf after a diving accident. The hearing aid sends a signal down some platinum electrodes implanted in the head. The electrodes bypass the middle ear, and carry the signal to the **cochlea**. This part of the ear contains nerve cells which send a signal to the brain along the **auditory nerve**.

Sometimes deafness is caused if you listen to a very loud sound of a particular pitch for a long time. Eventually the cells in your ear which detect that particular frequency get damaged. The result is that you become deaf to that particular note. Some pop singers have become deaf to certain notes because of this; so have young people who listen to very loud music through headphones. There is no cure for this kind of deafness.

People often get deaf as they grow old. This is usually caused by the auditory nerve failing to carry impulses to the brain in the usual way.

Questions

Frequency of sound in hertz	100	250	500	1000	2000	4000	8000
Hearing loss in decibels	20	20	20	25	70	70	70

1 Why can't we hear ultrasound?

2 Doctors prefer to use ultrasound for looking at babies in the mother's womb, even if the images produced aren't quite as clear as they could get using X-rays. Why is ultrasound preferred to X-rays?

3 Use the formula given on page 69 to calculate the size of the smallest object you could 'see' using ultrasound at 15 MHz.

4 Bats find their way around at night, and detect their insect prey, using ultrasound at about 50 kHz (50 000 Hz). Suggest why they don't need to use frequencies a lot higher than this, as in ultrasound scanners.

5 The diagrams below show three types of liquid-in-glass thermometers.

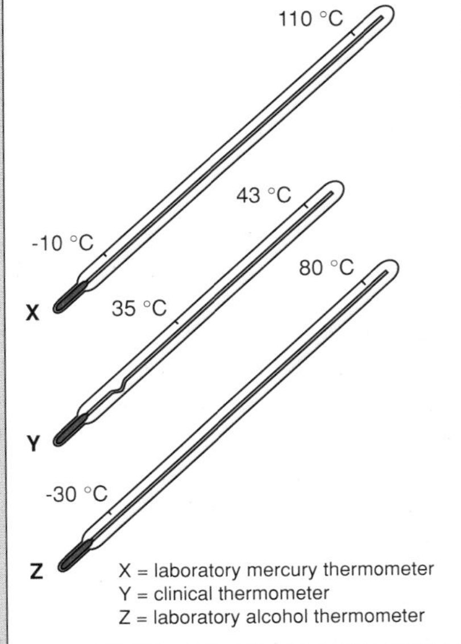

a Which of the thermometers should be used to:

i) measure the temperature of boiling water;

ii) check that a freezer is at its correct temperature of –18 degrees celsius?

b Give a reason why the clinical thermometer scale ranges only from 35 degrees celsius to 42 degrees celsius.

c Nowadays, doctors often use electronic digital thermometers rather than liquid-in-glass thermometers.

Suggest a temperature sensor which could be used in electronic digital thermometers.

6a The result of a man's hearing test are shown in the table above.

In which range of frequencies does most of the hearing loss occur?

b What name is given to frequencies of sound beyond the range of human hearing?

c Pneumatic drill operators wear ear protectors. Explain why the ear protectors are needed.

7 Images which have been produced by ultrasound are sometimes used by doctors.

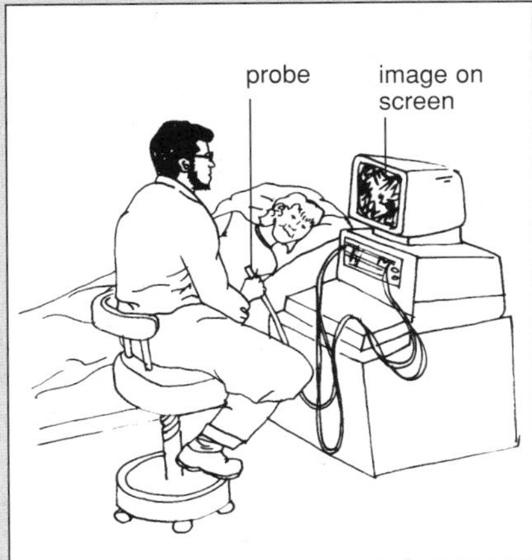

a Read the following passage.

The limit of human hearing is 20 kHz but other animals, such as bats and dolphins, make use of sound in 30–100 kHz range. Sound above the range of human hearing is called ultrasound. Ultrasound behaves in a similar manner to audible sound, having a speed of 340 m/s in air, a speed of 1500 m/s in soft tissue and a speed of 4100 m/s in bone. Ultrasound is used not only to diagnose the cause of an injury but also to help in the healing of injuries. When used in the healing process absorption of the ultrasound takes place.

i) State the lowest frequency of ultrasound.

ii) What is the speed of ultrasound in soft tissue?

iii) State whether energy is absorbed or reflected when ultrasound is used to help the healing process.

b Give **one** example of the use of ultrasound in medicine.

c Why is ultrasound safer in X-rays for some medical investigations?

d The ultrasound is transmitted through the patient's skin from a probe as shown.

i) The ultrasonic waves have a frequency of 8.0 MHz.

Calculate the wavelength of the ultrasound in muscle.

ii) A range of probes with different ultrasonic frequencies may be used. Shorter wavelengths of ultrasound allow sharper images to be produced.

Why does a probe of 8.0 MHz frequency give a sharper images than one of 2.25 MHz?

C3 Using light

This topic explains how light is used and controlled in some everyday devices.

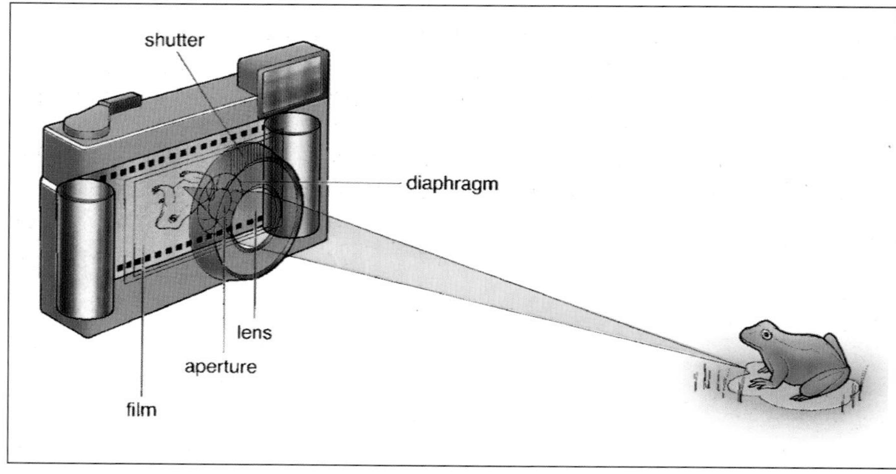

Picture 1 How a camera works.

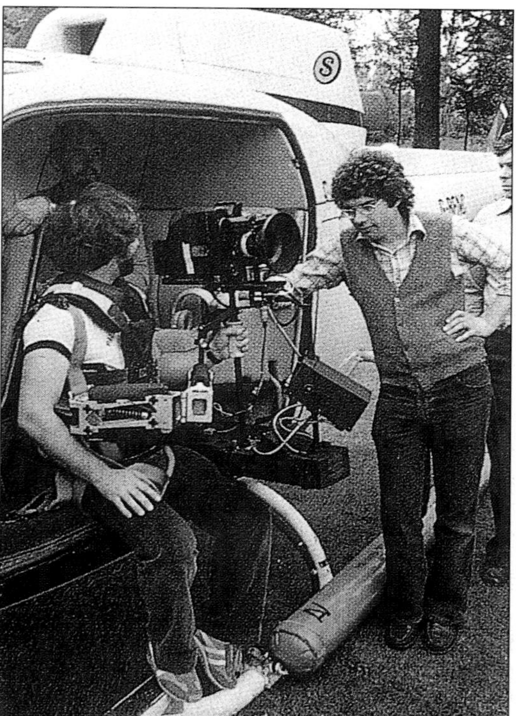

Picture 2 The screen of a TV camera senses light.

Cameras

Cameras use lenses to make a clear **image** on a light-sensitive screen. Picture 1 shows how this is done in a simple camera. A single lens of the kind that you might work with in school doesn't make clear enough pictures. In real cameras more complicated lenses have to be used.

In an ordinary camera the screen is a piece of thin plastic – the **film**. The light produces a chemical change in light-sensitive chemicals held on this film. In a **TV camera** the screen is made up of very small light-sensitive electronic devices (see picture 2). When light reaches these they produce an electronic signal.

Predicting the position and size of images

Optical instruments are amongst the most precise measuring devices that are used. Even in comparatively simple devices like cameras, it is vital that the image is focused clearly on the film. This means that the camera designer must be able to predict as exactly as possible where the image of an object will appear. For a simple lens this may be done by **ray-drawing**.

Picture 3 shows a beam of parallel rays of light entering a lens. A lens with this shape is called a **convex** lens. The beam is brought to a focus at a point (shown as F). This point is called the **principal focus** of the lens. The distance of the principal focus from the centre of the lens is called the **focal length** of the lens. Light travelling in the opposite direction will behave in exactly the same way. Thus a lens has two principal foci, one on each side of the lens (F and F[1] in picture 3). A line through F and F[1] passes through the exact centre of the lens, and is called the **principal axis**.

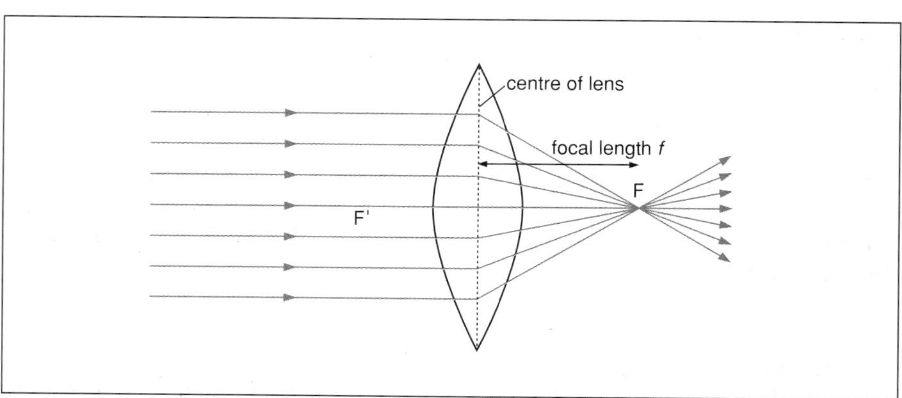

Picture 3 The main defining feature of a lens.

Ray drawing

Picture 4 shows an object labelled OT in front of a convex lens L. We normally draw an object as an upright arrow. Light leaves the object in all directions, and some of it enters the lens. Using a simple set of rules, we can predict where the lens will focus the light to produce an image. We consider just three rays whose behaviour we can predict by drawing. The rays are drawn showing them changing direction at the centre of the lens, shown by the line CC^1.

- **Ray 1** leaves the top of the object T in a direction parallel to the principal axis. All such rays bend so that they pass through a principal focus. This ray must pass through F.

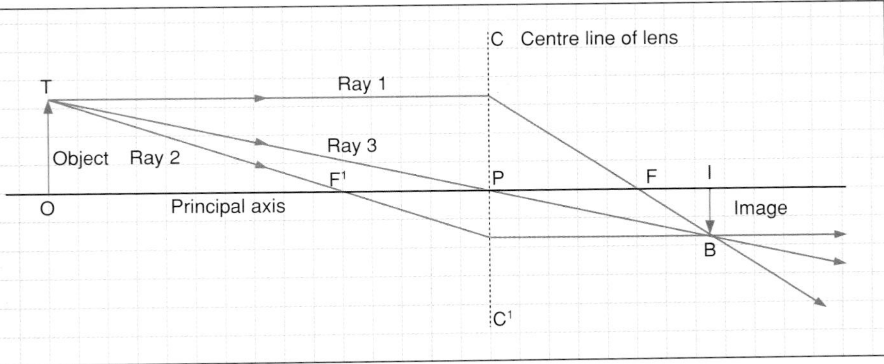

Picture 4 Finding an image by ray drawing.

- **Ray 2** is chosen to pass through the other principal focus of the lens – F^1. Ray 2 changes direction and emerges parallel to the principal axis. Why? If we imagine this ray travelling in the opposite direction we can see that it behaves exactly as Ray 1 does – it would bend to pass through F^1.

  The point B, where Ray 1 and Ray 2 meet, shows where the arrowhead of the image will be produced. All other rays that leave T and pass through the lens also arrive at B. If you imagine drawing similar pairs of rays from any point on the object between O and T, you could build up the rest of the image.
- **Ray 3** is used as a check – a ray does not bend when it passes through the centre of a lens, so it passes through in a straight line. If it it reaches B, then you know that you have drawn the first two rays correctly.

Picture 4 shows the formation of an image such as that produced in a camera. Notice that the image is upside down, or **inverted**. It is also **smaller** than the original object.

If we placed a sheet of film or a screen at I, the light focused by the lens would produce a real picture of the object. By moving a lens back and forward, until the picture is sharply focused, you can find the focal length of the lens. Picture 5 shows a simple version of this method.

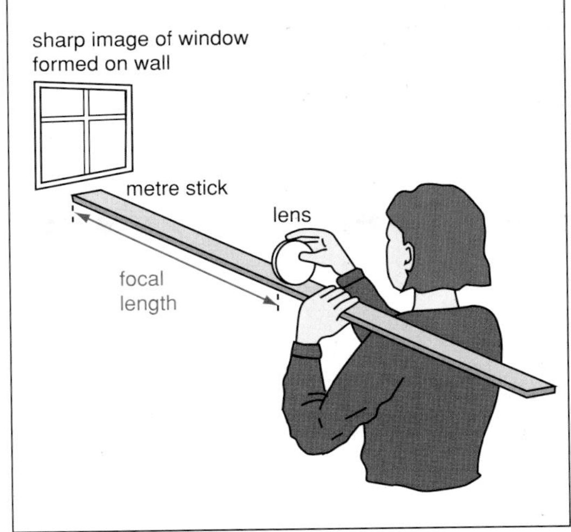

Picture 5 Measuring focal length.

Using a wall as the screen, and with a window behind you, move the lens along a metre stick until the image on the wall is sharp and clear. The distance between the lens and the wall can be read from the metre stick. This is the focal length.

To understand how lenses work, we must study the way light behaves when it moves through different materials.

When light passes at an angle from one transparent material into another it changes direction. This is called **refraction**, and is caused by the fact that light travels at different speeds in the different materials. This effect is used in lenses and optical fibres.

Refraction

Picture 6 shows what happens to a ray of light as it goes from air into glass, and from glass back into air. As it goes into the denser material, it changes direction.

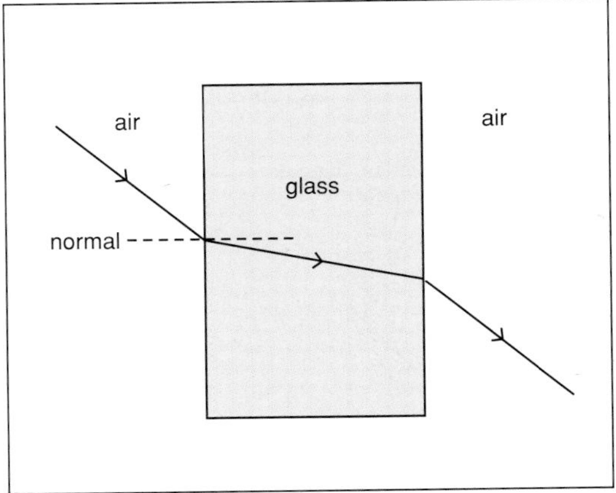

Picture 6 Refraction in a glass block.

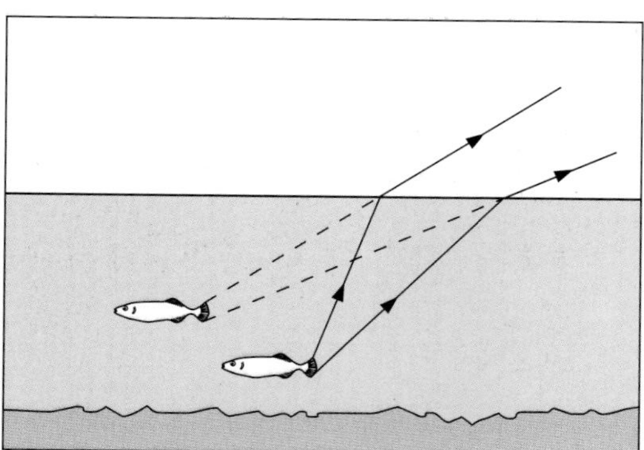

Picture 7 Why pools look shallower then they really are.

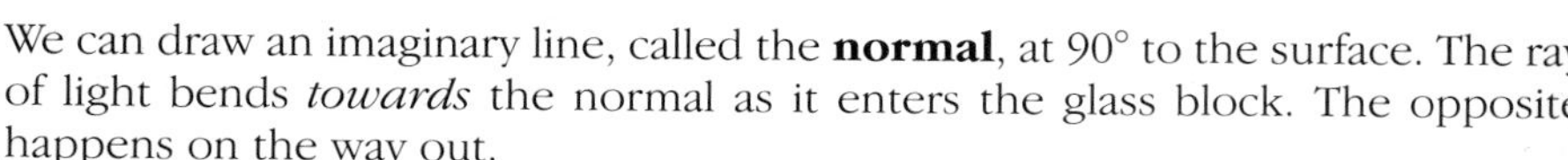

We can draw an imaginary line, called the **normal**, at 90° to the surface. The ray of light bends *towards* the normal as it enters the glass block. The opposite happens on the way out.

Refraction can cause some optical illusions. For example, a pond or swimming pool always looks a lot shallower than it really is. Picture 7 shows why. The light from a fish near the bottom is refracted, and the light *appears* to come from somewhere else, nearer the surface. This is why a straight stick looks bent when you put it in water (picture 8).

A **prism** is a block of glass or plastic with straight sides. It is usually triangular in shape. Light that enters the prism at right angles to a surface carries on unchanged. But if it goes in at an angle it changes direction due to refraction (picture 9).

But prisms are not used to change the direction of light by refraction. The reason is that white light would come out coloured. Prisms produce a **spectrum** of the light.

Picture 8 A straight stick looks bent in water. Why?

Trapped light – total internal reflection

Picture 10 shows light travelling out of water. See what happens as the angle the light makes with the surface is reduced.

At a certain angle the light doesn't get out at all. It is trapped inside, or **totally internally reflected**. The same thing can happen with glass (see page 31).

This effect is used, in prisms, to make very good mirrors. It is also used to send light down long thin fibres of glass – **optical fibres**. Picture 11 shows total internal reflection in action in a prism and a glass fibre.

Lenses are *curved* pieces of very clear glass. When a ray of light reaches a lens, it is bent inwards by refraction. When it leaves the lens, the curve is now reversed, so it bends further toward the centre of the lens (picture 12).

The light reaches the glass surfaces at an angle. The further out from the centre of the lens the bigger the angle is. So the outer rays are bent inwards more than the inner parts. The rays come to a point (converge) before spreading out again. The rays of light have been focused.

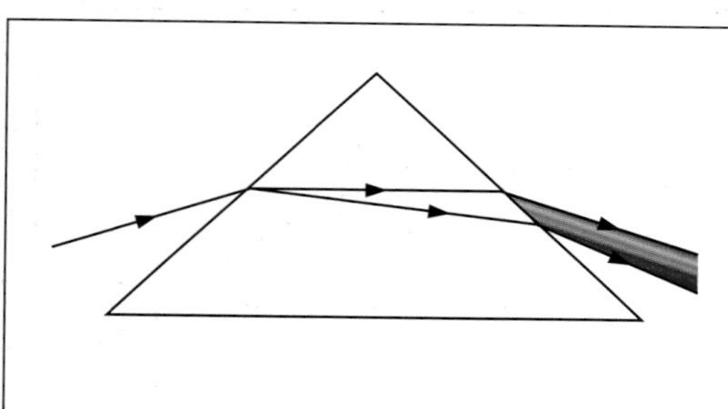

Picture 9 Light passing through a prism.

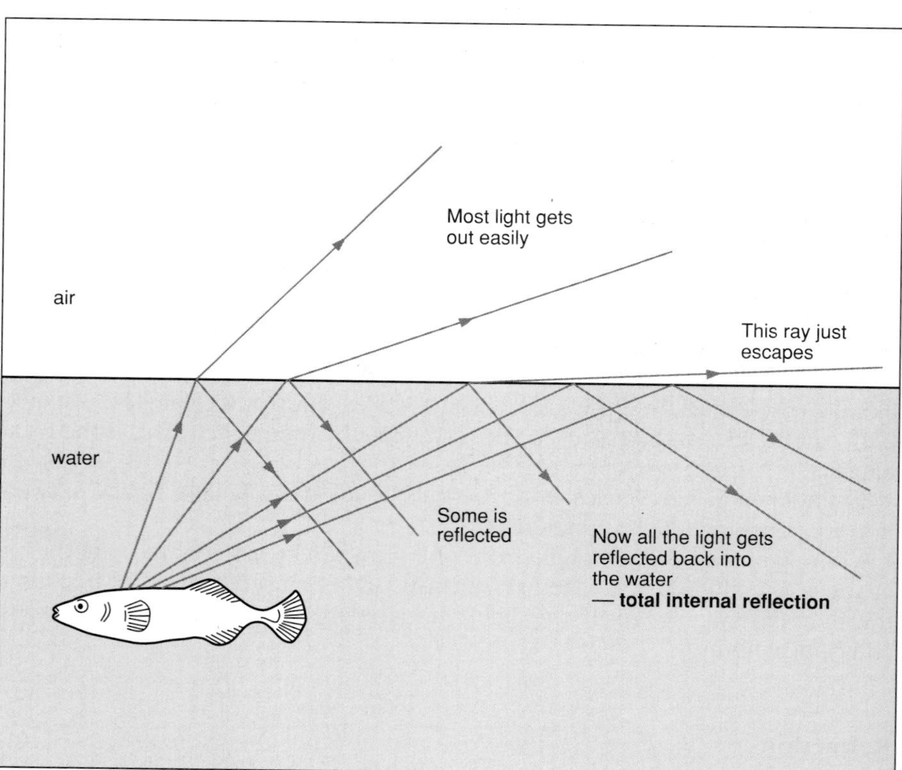

Picture 10 How total internal reflection happens.

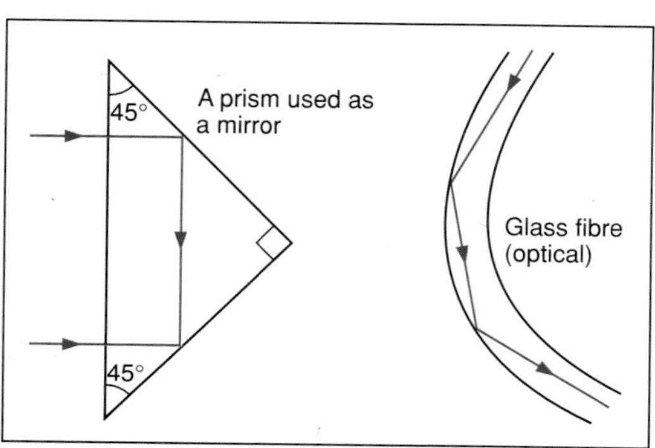

Picture 11 Total internal reflection in action

The lens in picture 12 is a **convex** or **converging** lens. A lens shaped 'the other way', as in picture 13, makes the light beam spread out (diverge). It is a **concave** or **diverging** lens.

The thicker the lens is at the centre, the more curved the lens surfaces are, the more powerful is the lens. Picture 14 shows this. The lens of the eye changes shape to allow us to focus on objects at different distances. How it does this is described in the next section.

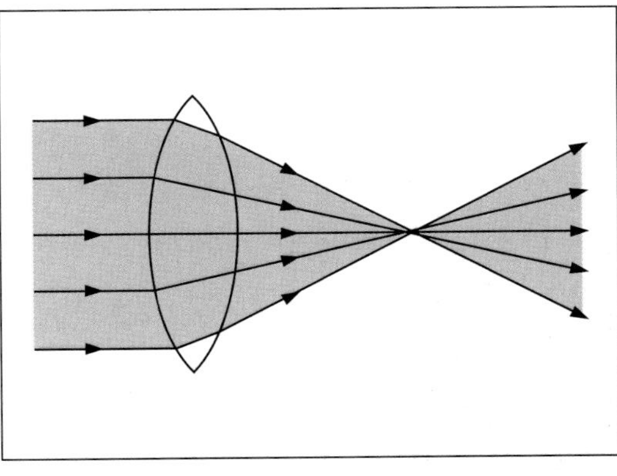

Picture 12 What a positive lens does to light.

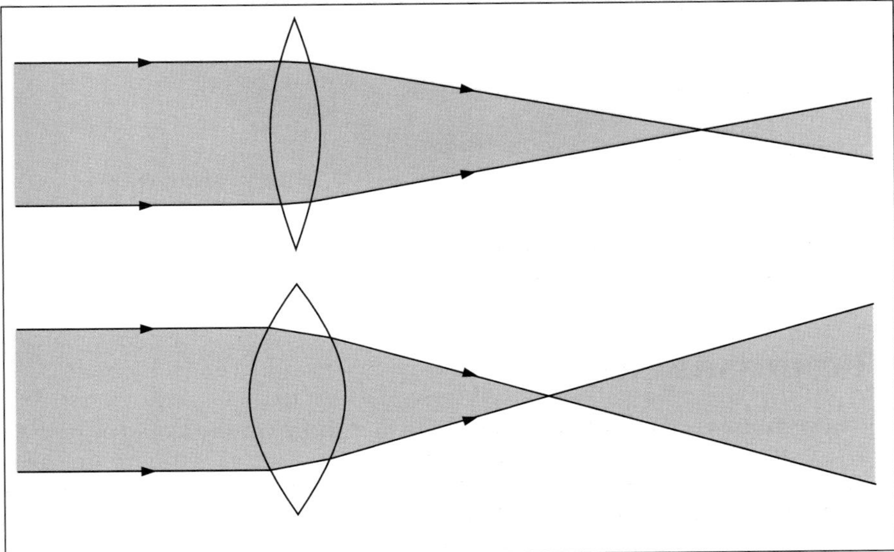

Picture 14 The more curved the lens the more powerful it is.

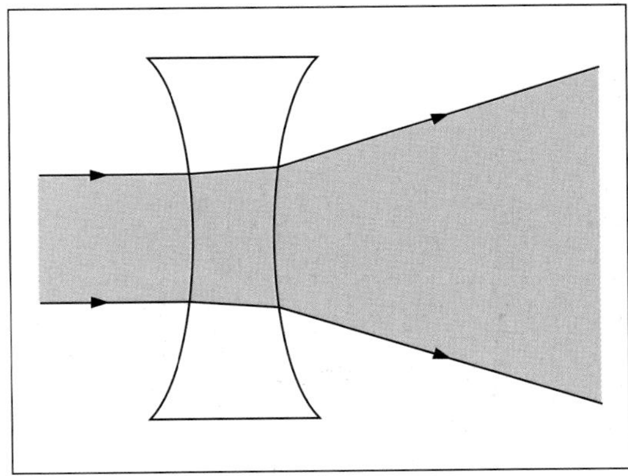

Picture 13 A negative lens makes the light spread out – or diverge.

Lens power

The more powerful a lens, the more it bends light. This means that its principal focus is nearer to the lens, and so the focal length is shorter. We can express the power of a lens using the formula:

$$\text{power} = \frac{1}{\text{focal length}}$$

where the focal length is measured in metres

The unit of power is the **dioptre** (D). The lens shown has a focal length of 25 cm (0.25 m).

$$\text{Power} = \frac{1}{\text{focal length}} = \frac{1}{0.25} = +4\text{ D}$$

A convex lens has a **positive** value for power. Concave lenses spread out (diverge) the light, and so they have a **negative** value.

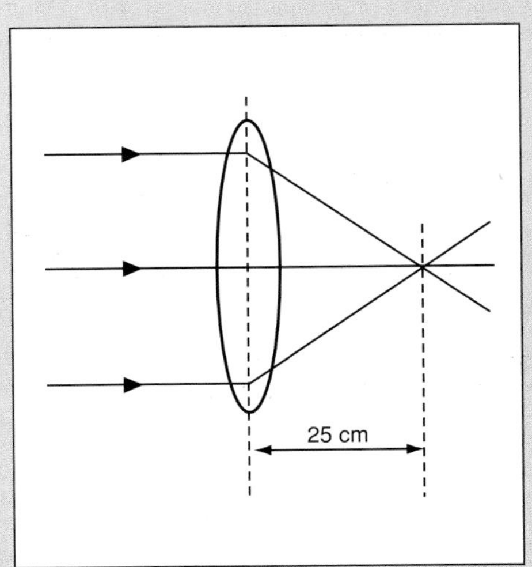

C4
The eye

Close your eyes and imagine what it must be like to live in darkness. Our eyes are amongst our most important organs.

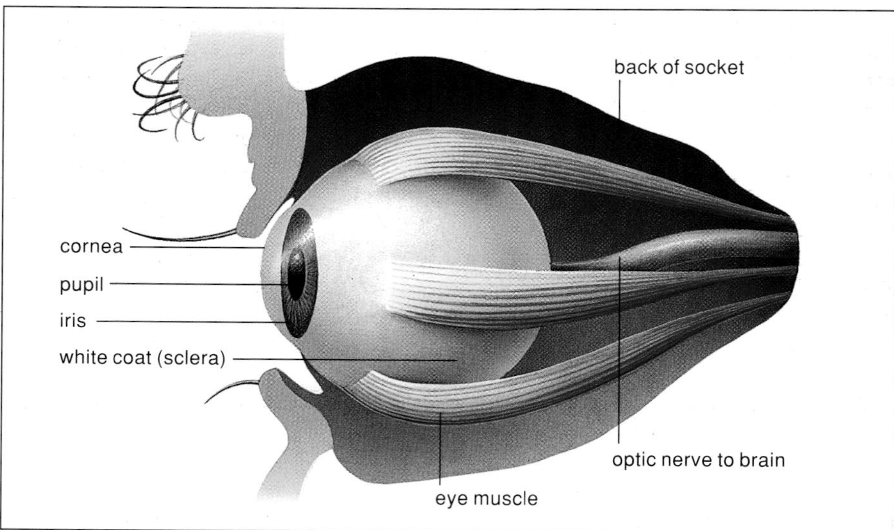

Picture 1 The eyeball in its socket. There are six eye muscles altogether, of which only three are shown here.

The outside of the eye

Each eye consists of an eyeball which rests in a socket in the skull (picture 1). The sides and back of the eyeball are thick and tough – this is the 'white of the eye'. The front is transparent and is called the **cornea**. The cornea is covered by a thin and delicate membrane called the **conjunctiva**. The conjunctiva is kept moist by a lubricating fluid produced by a **tear gland** under the eyelid.

In the centre of the eye is the **pupil**. This is surrounded by the **iris**, the coloured part of the eye.

The eyeball is held in place by muscles which can move it up and down and from side to side. A large **optic nerve** runs from the back of the eye to the brain. When you look at an apple, millions of impulses are sent off in this nerve and when they reach the correct part of the brain you see the apple.

The inside of the eye

Picture 2 shows the inside of the eye. For seeing things, the two most important parts are the **lens** and the **retina**.

Picture 2 The internal structure of the human eye. You must imagine that the eye has been sliced across the middle and that you are looking inside.

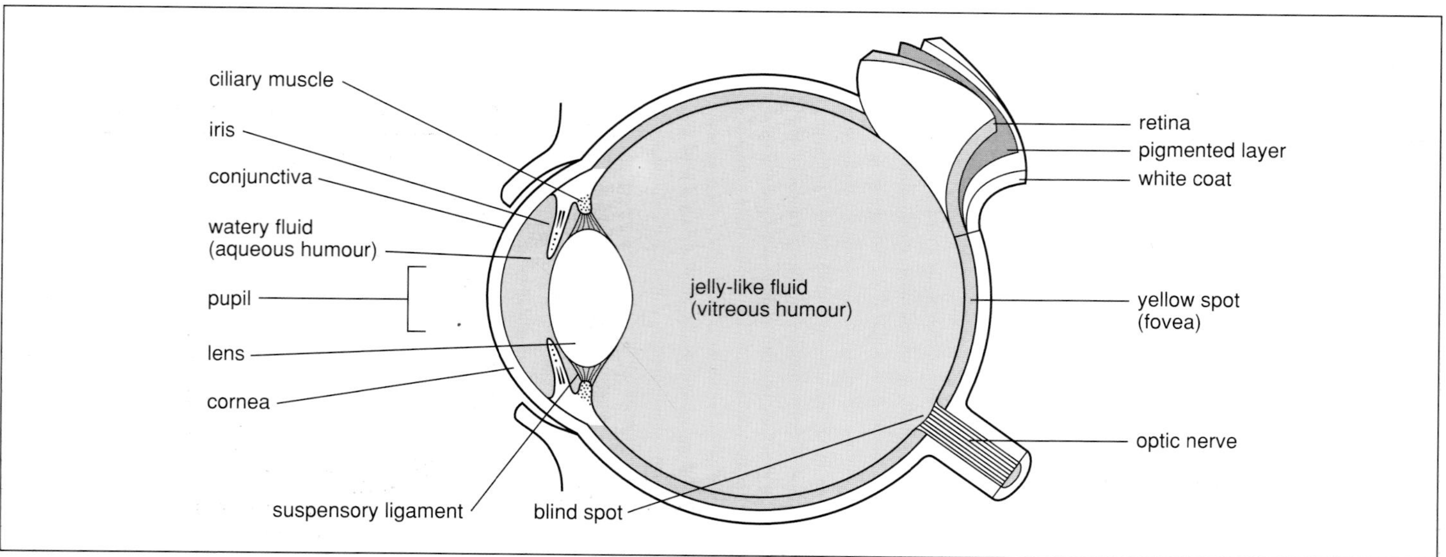

The lens is soft and transparent – rather like a polythene bag full of water – and its shape can change. It is encircled by a ring of muscle called the **ciliary muscle**. The lens is held in position by fine threads which run from it to the surrounding ciliary muscle.

The retina lines the inside of the eyeball. It contains millions of receptor cells. These cells are sensitive to light which has entered the eye through the pupil – this is how the eye sees things. The part of the retina responsible for seeing things most clearly is the **yellow spot** right in the middle.

Beneath the retina is a layer of tissue containing a dark pigment. The pigment absorbs light and prevents it being reflected within the eye. Why would it be a bad thing if this happened?

The pigmented layer also contains lots of blood vessels. They supply the retina with oxygen and food substances.

The point where the optic nerve is attached to the eye is called the **blind spot**. The blind spot has no receptor cells, so it's unable to see things.

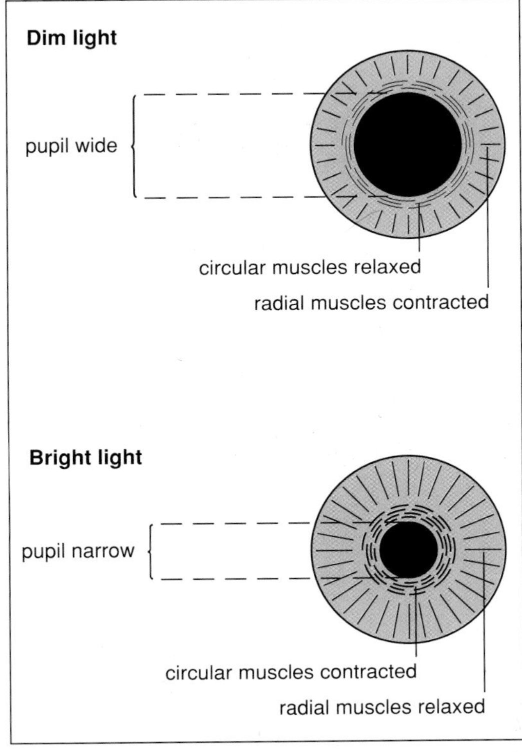

Picture 3 What happens to the pupil when the light intensity changes. These changes are brought about by the iris. Inside the iris there are muscles which can make it either constrict or open up.

Controlling the amount of light that enters the eye

If you look at a bright light, a reflex action occurs: the pupil gets smaller and this stops too much light getting into the eye. The opposite happens in the dark: the pupil gets larger, so more light can enter the eye.

The widening and narrowing of the pupil is brought about by the iris. Picture 3 shows how it works.

How does the eye see things?

When you take pictures with a television camera, light enters the camera and is focused by a lens onto a light-sensitive film at the back. The eye works in the same kind of way.

Suppose you're looking at a dot on the wall. Light rays, reflected from the dot, enter your eye as shown in picture 4. As the light rays pass through the cornea and lens, they are bent inwards so that they meet on the retina. Here they produce an image of the dot.

For the image to be clear and sharp, i.e. in focus, the light rays must meet exactly on the retina. This is achieved by the lens which makes sure that the light rays are always bent to just the right extent. We'll come back to this in a moment.

The bending of the light rays is called **refraction**, and it plays an essential part in giving us good eyesight. Refraction is dealt with in more detail on pages 73 and 74.

Picture 4 How the eye focuses on a dot.

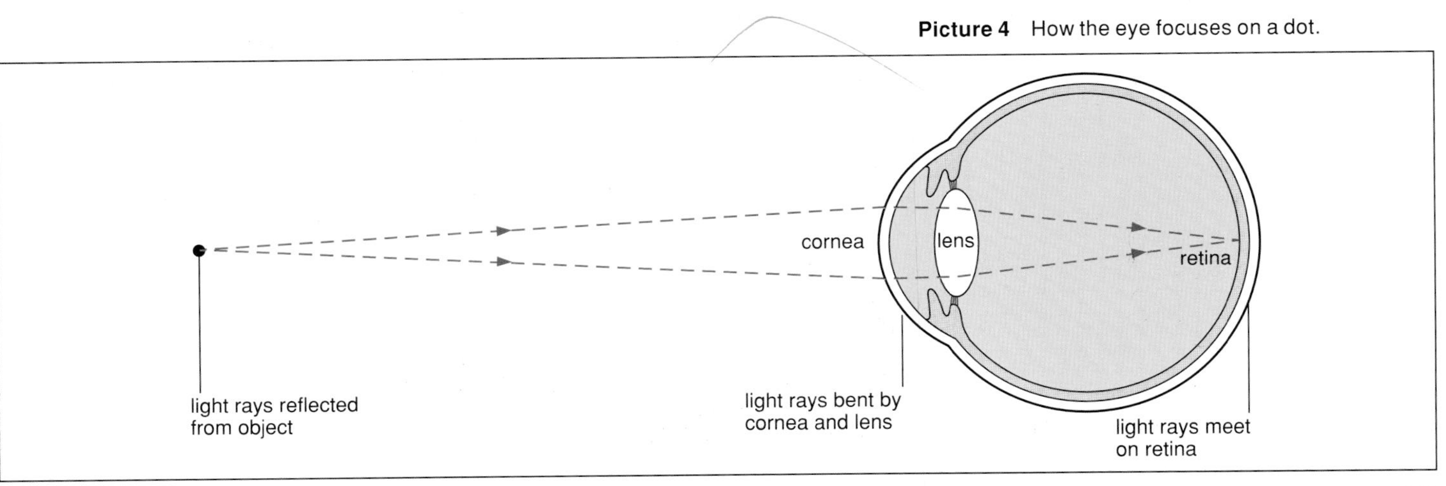

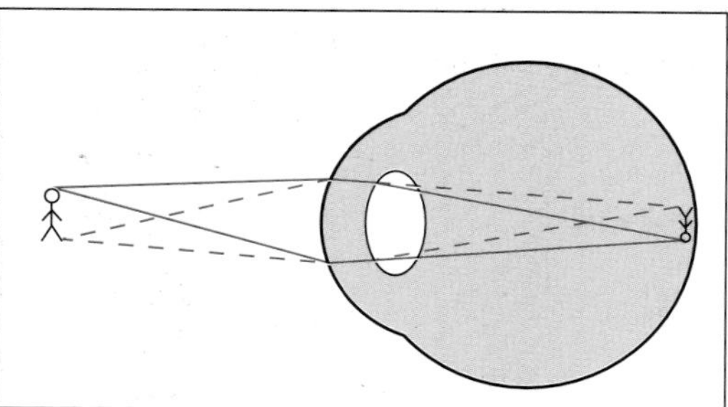

Picture 5 This diagram shows how an image is turned upside down by the lens in the eye. The same thing is done by the lens in a camera.

Seeing things the right way up

Suppose you're looking at a person. Picture 5 shows how the light rays, reflected from the person, pass into your eye. The reason why the light rays behave in this way is explained on pages 72 and 73. The result is that the image is upside down on the retina.

Why then don't we see everything upside down? The answer is that the brain comes to the rescue and turns the picture the right way up for us. Some years ago an experiment was done in which a man was given special glasses that made him see everything upside down. After a while his brain made the necessary correction and he began to see things the right way up again, even though he went on wearing the glasses. What do you think happened when he took the glasses off?

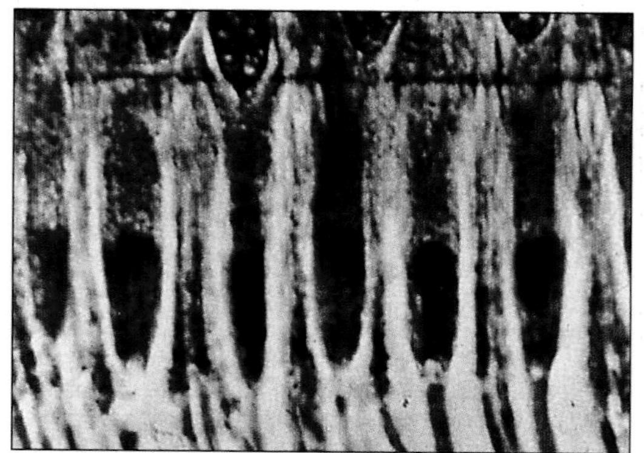

Picture 6 This is a thin section of the retina seen under the microscope. It shows the cone cells and rod cells.

How does the retina work?

If you look straight at an object, and then look at it out of the corner of your eye, its appearance changes. From being clear and sharp, it becomes fuzzy and indistinct. Also it's hard to tell what colour it is.

How can we explain this? Well, it's because there are two types of receptor cells in the retina. They are called **cone cells** and **rod cells** (picture 6). When you look straight at something, you are using the central part of the retina – the yellow spot. This part of the retina contains mainly cone cells, which detect things clearly and in colour. But when you look at something out of the corner of your eye, you are using the part of the retina further out. This contains mainly rod cells. They detect things less clearly, and in black and white.

Seeing in the dark

From what we've just said, you might have got the idea that the outer part of the retina isn't much use. However, it's good at seeing things in dim light. You can prove this for yourself by looking at a faint star on a dark night. It's much easier to see it out of the corner of your eye than by looking straight at it.

The reason for this is that the rod cells are stimulated by even very small amounts of light, so they work in gloomy conditions. The cone cells, on the other hand, are far less sensitive so they will only work in reasonably bright conditions.

Have you noticed that when you go into a gloomy room from bright sunlight, you can't see anything at first but gradually things become visible? The reason is that the bright light causes your rod cells to lose their sensitivity. So when you go into the gloomy room, the rod cells don't work. They need time to become sensitive again. As their sensitivity returns, you begin to see things.

Picture 7 How the eye keeps a ball in focus as it gets closer.

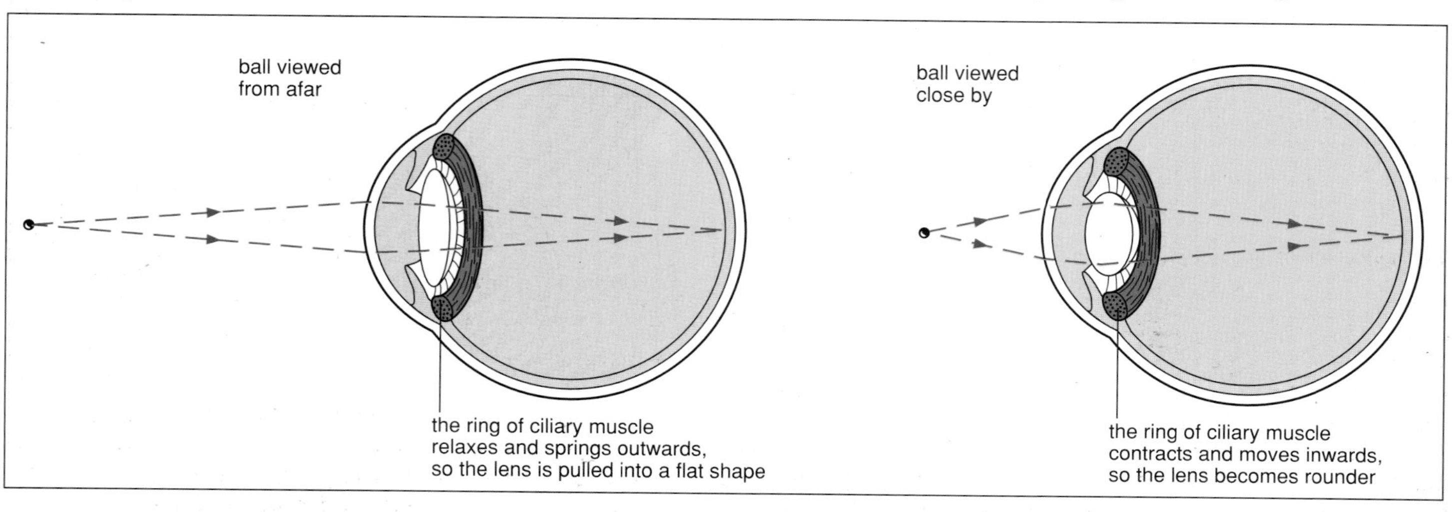

Colour vision

If you've ever been involved with stage-lighting, you will know that almost any colour can be obtained by mixing red, green and blue lights in the right proportions. These are the **primary colours** (see topic A6).

The same principle applies to the way we see colours. Scientists have shown that we have three different kinds of cone cells, each sensitive to one of the primary colours. The colour which we actually see depends on how many cones of each kind are stimulated.

Some people can't see certain colours – they are **colour blind**. In rare cases colours can't be seen at all, so everything looks black, white or grey. A more common condition is where people can't tell the difference between red and green. Red–green colour blindness is inherited.

Keeping things in focus

Suppose you're watching a ball hurtling towards you. If the eye did not adjust, the light rays would stop meeting on the retina as the ball got close to you – so the ball would become out of focus. However, the eye does adjust. The lens becomes rounder and bends the light rays more. So the light rays continue to meet on the retina, and the ball stays in focus.

The eye is able to keep things in focus because the lens is soft and can change its shape. The shape of the lens is changed by the ciliary muscle. This makes the lens flat or more rounded, depending on whether you're looking at something in the distance or close to (picture 7).

Despite this wonderful adjustment mechanism, many people can't focus properly. Such people may be either **short-sighted** or **long-sighted**.

Short-sighted people

A short-sighted person can focus on things close by, but not a long way off. This is due to the lens bending the light rays too much, or to the eyeball being too long. The result is that the light rays meet in front of the retina.

Short-sightedness is corrected by wearing glasses which bend the light rays outwards before they reach the eye (picture 8).

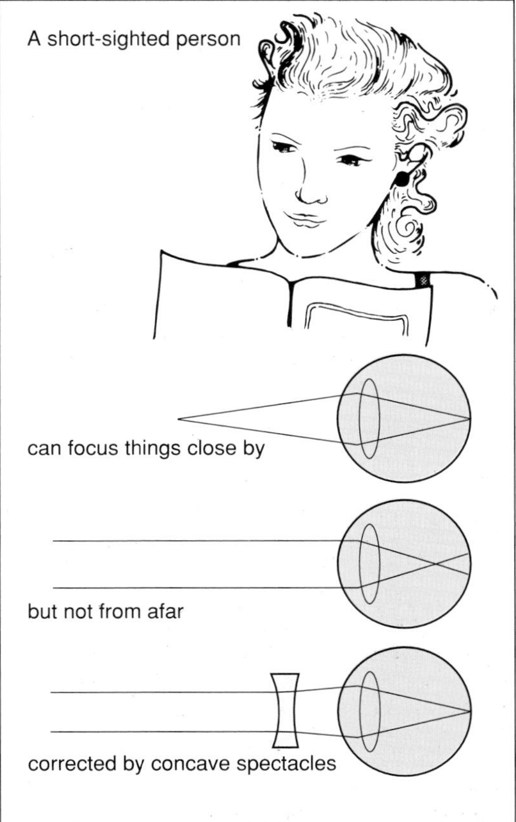

Picture 8 Short-sightedness and how it can be corrected by wearing glasses.

Long-sighted people

A long-sighted person can focus on things a long way off, but not close by. This is due to the lens not bending the light rays enough, or to the eyeball being too short. The result is that the light rays are directed to a point behind the retina.

Long-sightedness is corrected by wearing glasses which bend the light rays inwards before they reach the eye (picture 9).

Long-sightedness is also caused by the lens becoming hard, so it no longer changes its shape in the usual way. This tends to happen in old people, and is one of the main reasons why they often need glasses.

A more serious problem is that the lens may become cloudy and stops letting light through. This is called a **cataract**. The only remedy is to take the lens out in an operation and give the person very strong glasses or contact lenses. In the latest operations, the person's own lens is replaced with an artificial acrylic lens.

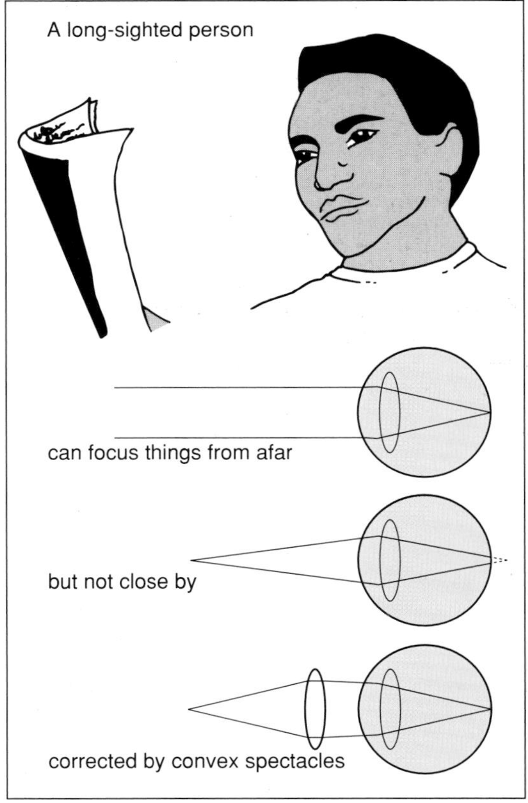

Picture 9 Long-sightedness and how it can be corrected by wearing glasses.

Three-dimensional vision

If you look at a chair, it appears to have depth. In other words you see it in three dimensions. You need two eyes for this. What happens is that each eye sees a slightly different aspect of the chair. In the brain the two images are combined to give a single three-dimensional view of the chair. Seeing with two eyes is called **binocular vision**.

Binocular vision gives us a more complete view of our environment, and it helps us to judge distances. For example, if you're cycling along the road and there's a car in front of you, you know roughly how far away it is.

The endoscope

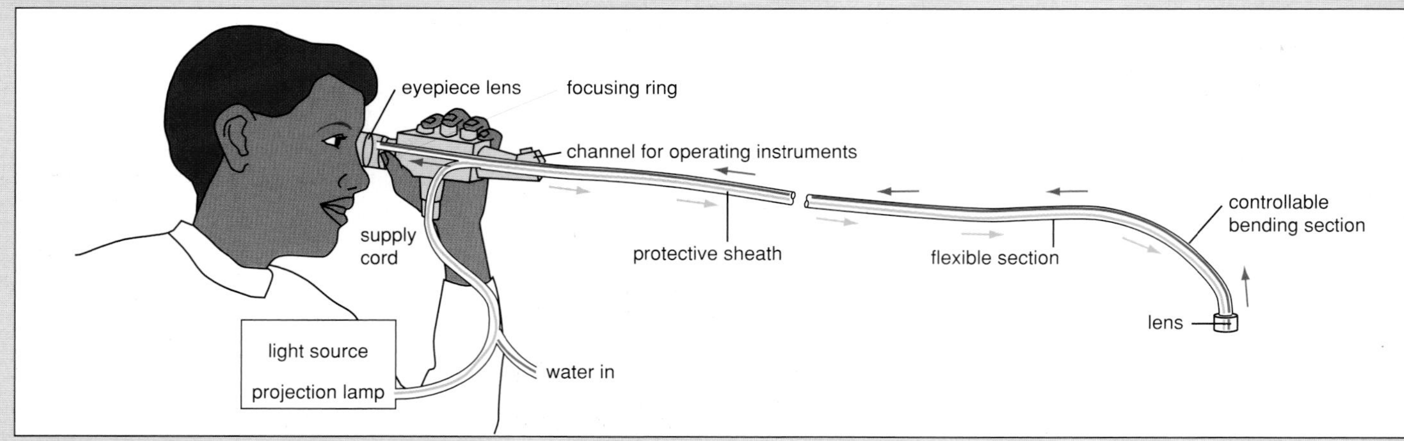

Picture 1 The workings of the endoscope.

We have seen how light can be channelled down thin glass fibres by **total internal reflection** (page 74 of this unit, and topic A7). Doctors can use this principle in a device called the **fibrescope** or **endoscope**. It consists of two separate bundles of thin glass fibres. These are flexible, and can be guided inside the patient, for example to examine the stomach. Light passes down one bundle, illuminating the area inside the patient. The heat from the lamp cannot pass down the fibres. The other bundle has a lens system, and the light passes back up to an eyepiece, enabling the doctor to view the inside of the patient. The doctor can diagnose a medical problem without having to open the patient up, as would have been necessary in the past. The picture may also be fed to a small TV camera, so that other medical staff can watch (picture 2).

Tools can also be fitted to the tip of the endoscope, and controlled by the doctor. This means that small samples of tissue can be snipped off, or damaged tissue can be sewn up. A third set of fibres can carry **laser light**. Topic C5 (next) shows how the lasers and endoscope can be used to perform internal surgery.

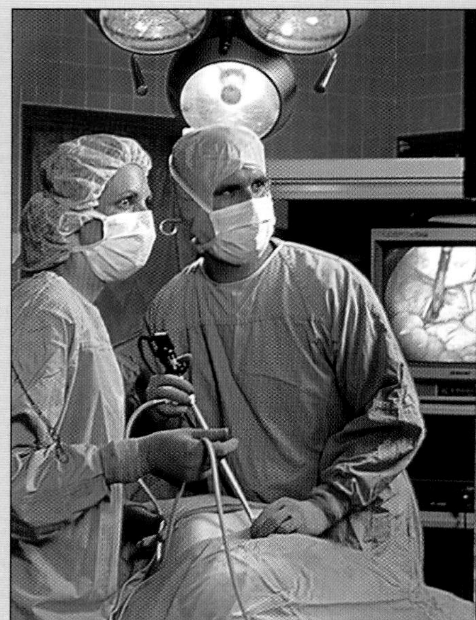

Picture 2

Questions

1 Naheeda draws the diagram on the right to show how an image can be formed using a convex lens.

Copy and complete the diagram to show how an enlarged image is formed by the lens.

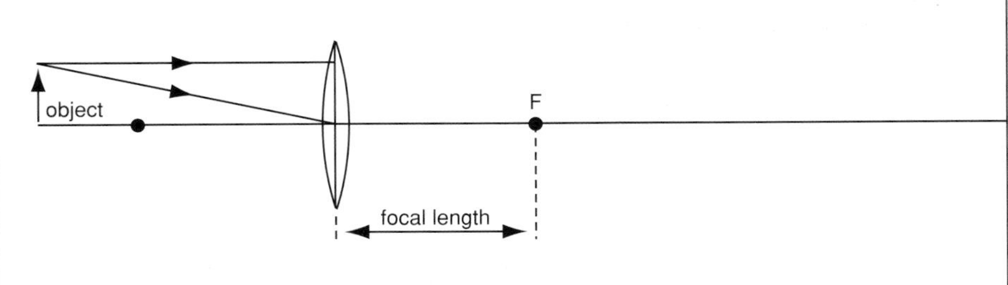

2 Two students, A and B, are looking at the same distant object. Student A is able to see the object clearly. Student B has a sight defect and is unable to see the object clearly.

The diagram below shows the path of rays of light, from the distant object, entering student A's eye.

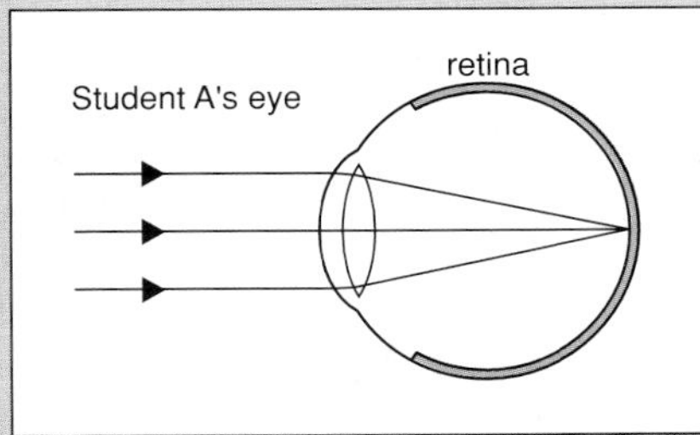

a Copy and complete the following diagram to show what happens to the light rays in student B's eye.

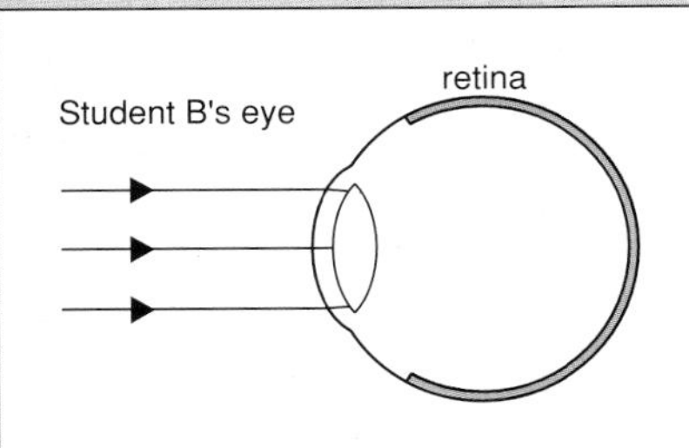

b By referring to your diagram, explain why the image on the retina of student B's eye is blurred.

c Name this sight defect.

d In a normal eye, the image on the retina is smaller than the object being viewed.

State **one** other difference in the image compared to the object viewed.

3 Karen is tidying the reading spectacles on display in a store. The spectacles on the display are labelled 4.0 D, 3.25 D, 2.75 D and 2.5 D. She notices that the label is missing from one pair.

Karen is asked to label correctly this pair of spectacles. She uses one of the spectacle lenses to focus a sharp image of a far-away window on to a piece of paper as shown on the right. The distance between the lens and the paper is 40 cm.

Which label should Karen attach to the spectacles? You **must** show clearly you working which leads you to your answer.

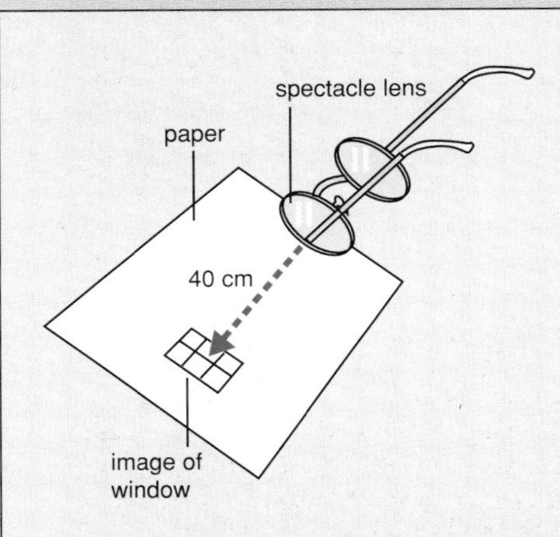

4a The diagram on the right shows part of an optical fibre.

Copy the diagram and draw the path of the light ray through the fibre.

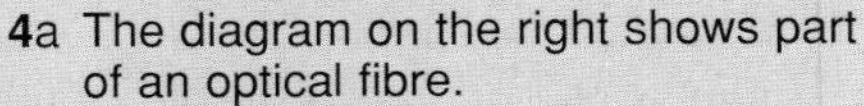

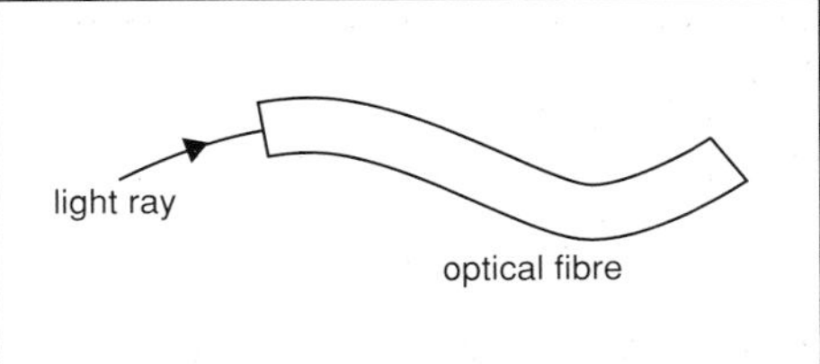

b Surgeons use optical fibres.

Explain how the fibres X and Y shown below allow a surgeon to see a tumour in a patient's stomach.

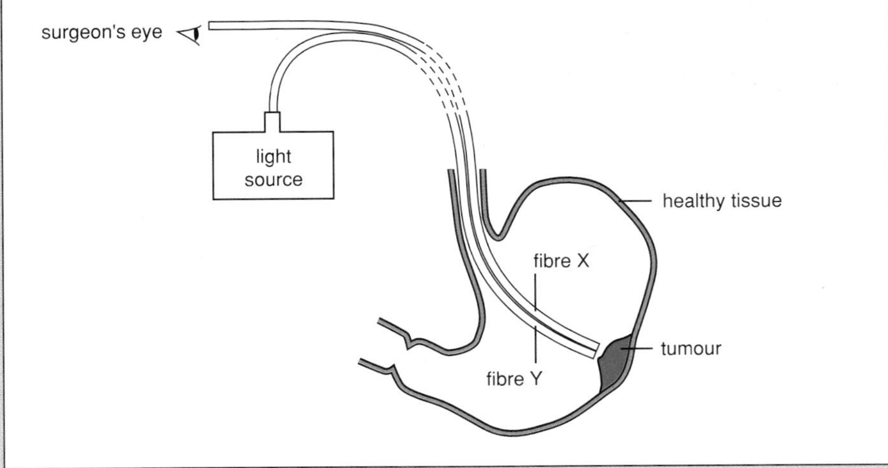

C5 Healing with light

A whole family of waves can be used to aid medical science.

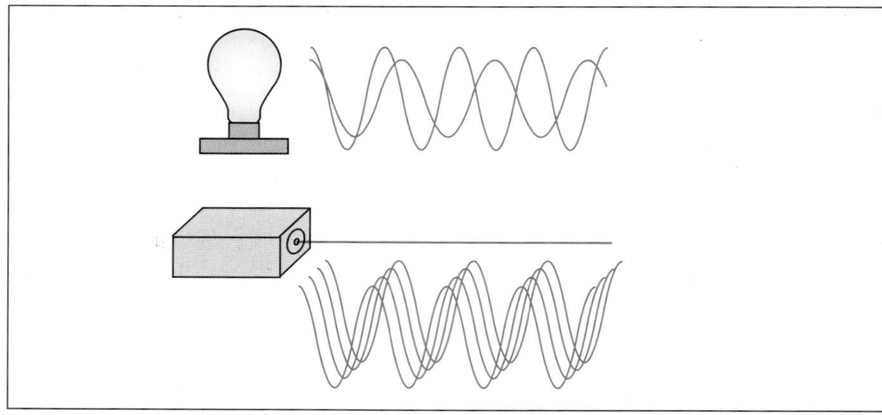
Picture 1 Laser light consists of waves that are 'in step' with each other.

Pure colour

When we pass white light through a prism, as in picture 1 page 184, it spreads out into a band of colours – the **spectrum**. So-called 'white' light is actually a mixture of different colours of light. Light is an electromagnetic wave, and as it passes through the prism, it is refracted. The different colours of light have different frequencies (and therefore wavelengths), and they are refracted by different amounts.

A red light bulb seems to give off light of one colour, but it will still be a mixture of different reds. If we were to pass it through a prism, it would still separate into different frequencies. A 'pure' red light would consist of waves which all had *exactly* the same frequency and wavelength. Such light is called **monochromatic** – 'one colour'.

In 1960, an American scientist called Theodore Maiman produced a light like this, where the waves were all of one frequency, and all marched 'in step' with each other. He had built the first **laser**. Picture 1 illustrates the difference in behaviour between ordinary light and laser light. When the waves of light are 'in step' or 'in phase' with each other, we say they are **coherent**.

Many materials can produce laser light. The first laser used a rod of synthetic ruby crystal, but gases such as carbon dioxide or argon can be used. Dye lasers use a liquid dye which can produce different wavelengths, and chemical lasers use the energy from chemical reactions to produce laser light.

Laser light is very intense, and can be used in medicine to destroy or cut tissues, or to make tissues stick together.

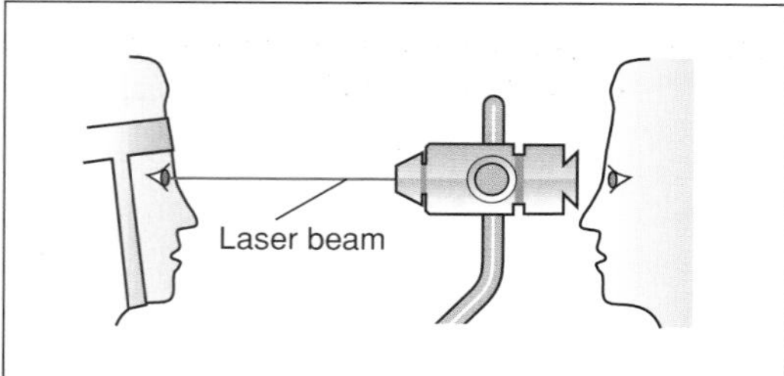

Picture 2 This diagram shows a laser beam being shone into a patient's eye. The patient wears a special kind of contact lens which allows the doctor to see into the eye and focus the laser beam on exactly the right part.

Eye surgery

The eye was the first organ in the human body to be treated with lasers (see pictures 2 and 3). Let's look at an example. Sometimes a hole develops in a person's retina. Fluid in the eyeball gets through the hole and lifts the retina away from the tissue underneath. This is called a **detached retina**. If nothing is done about it, the person may become partially blind.

Detachment of the retina can be treated by laser surgery. Short pulses from the laser are sent into the eye, one after the other, and focused on the retina. The patient wears a special kind of contact lens which allows the doctor to see into the eye and focus the laser beam on exactly the right point.

The pulses are not all directed at the same spot, but form a ring round the hole in the retina. It's like firing a gun at a target, but instead of aiming at the bull each time, you aim slightly to one side and make a circle round the bull. The laser beam makes the retina stick to the tissue behind it, and stops it coming off. It 'welds' it into position.

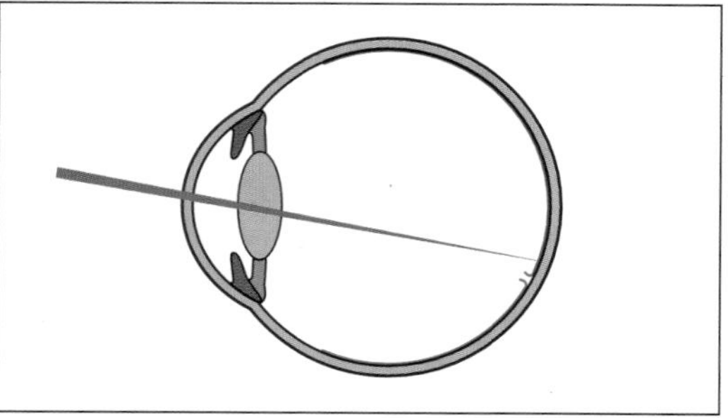
Picture 3 A laser beam being used to stick back a detached retina.

The beam is so fine that very few sensory cells in the retina are damaged – ertainly not enough to affect the person's eyesight. The pulses are extremely uick – each one lasts only a tenth of a second, and the patient hardly feels nything at all.

Jlcers

Jlcers are damaged parts of the stomach or intestine. A green argon laser beam an be sent down an optical fibre in an **endoscope** (see page 80), and aimed at he blood vessels surrounding the ulcer (see picture 4). The beam burns the issue and produces a small scar which seals the blood vessels, preventing the lcer from bleeding. A similar technique can be used to destroy cysts and other rowths which form on organs. If the laser is being used as a scalpel, to cut into issue, the heat of the beam automatically seals off blood vessels as it cuts. This s often called 'bloodless surgery'. There is very little pain involved in this type of treatment, and healing often takes less time.

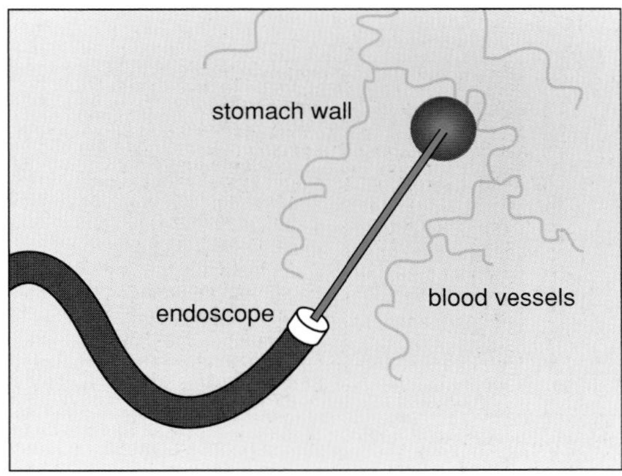

Picture 4 Laser surgery treating an ulcer.

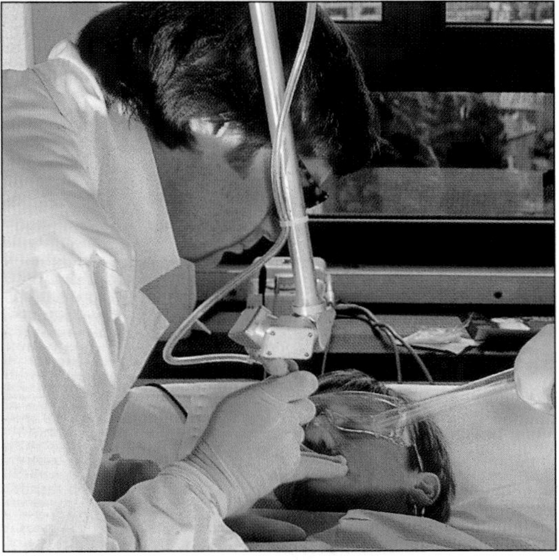

Picture 5 Lasers can be used to remove tattoos and portwine stains.

Cancers

Vhen injected into the body, a chemical compound called **HPD** stays longer in ancerous cells than in normal cells. It glows red when a violet laser beam is hone on it, allowing doctors to identify tumours. If red laser light is then shone onto the HPD, this triggers a chemical reaction. It breaks down into a poison which kills the cancer cells. The healthy tissue is unharmed.

Skin treatment

A very thin laser beam can be used for precision work, such as in cosmetic urgery, where growths such as warts can be removed. Lasers can remove skin ayer by layer.

Tattoos and marks, such as 'port wine stain' birthmarks, can be treated with aser light. The green argon laser is absorbed more by the dark areas of skin. A iny area of marked skin can be burned away, allowing new skin to replace it.

Dental treatment

Laser treatment can now be used as an alternative to the noisy and painful lentist's drill. Patients and dentists have to wear goggles to protect their eyes against the laser light, but anaesthetic is not necessary. The laser light travels lown a fibre-optic tube to the dental instrument. It cuts away decay with a greater accuracy than a drill, and sterilises the tooth area as it does so. The laser can also be used to roughen the tooth enamel, giving a surface to which fillings can be bonded.

Picture 6 Energy beyond the visible spectrum.

Invisible 'light'

Infra-red

In 1800, Sir William Herschel was measuring the heating effect of different parts of the spectrum, using a blackened thermometer bulb. To his surprise, when he placed the thermometer beyond the red end of the spectrum, where no light was visible, the reading on the thermometer *increased* (picture 6).

Red light has a lower frequency than blue light. Obviously, Herschel concluded, there must be waves which our eyes cannot detect, and which have a *lower* frequency and *longer* wavelength than red light. These waves are called **infra-red**.

Infra-red radiation is sometimes called heat radiation, as it is easily absorbed by atoms and molecules. The energy transferred causes them to vibrate more rapidly, which shows as a temperature increase.

Objects also give out infra-red radiation, which can be detected with special films or cameras. A **thermal imaging** camera is used by the emergency services to locate people trapped under the rubble of a collapsed building. The temperature of their bodies is higher than their surroundings, and forms a brighter image on the camera screen. The police can use this technique to detect suspects hiding in darkness.

The engine of a car driven at high speed gets very hot. In a picture taken from a police helicopter by an infra-red camera, the engine seems to glow.

Infra-red sensitive film will produce images when connected to a computer where the colours represent different temperatures. In medicine, infra-red photographs called **thermograms** (picture 7) show differences in temperature on different sections of the body. Unhealthy tissue, for example a tumour, may be warmer than normal tissue. This can be detected on the film.

Infra-red lamps are used in physiotherapy. The warmth of the radiation helps to heal damaged muscle tissue.

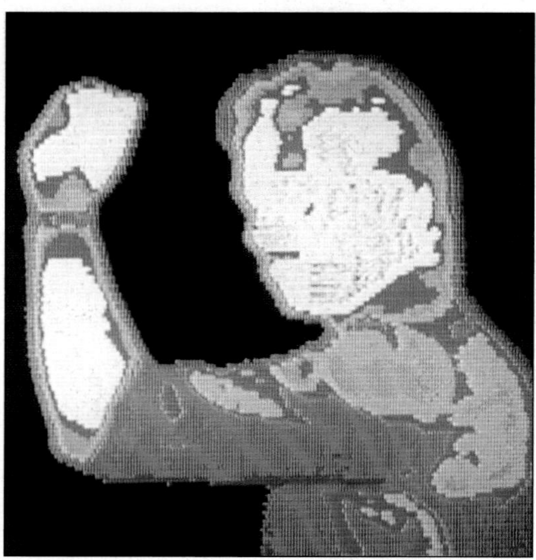

Picture 7 A thermogram shows the level of infra-red radiation emitted by the body.

Ultra-violet

When infra-red was discovered, people naturally wondered if there could be an unseen radiation beyond the other end of the visible spectrum. In 1801, a German physicist, Johann Wilhelm Ritter, discovered that the compound silver nitrate would break down quickly if placed beyond the last colour of the spectrum, violet. The radiation producing this effect was named **ultra-violet**.

Ultra-violet (or UV) has a *shorter* wavelength and *higher* frequency than violet. The Sun gives off UV, but much of it is screened out by the ozone layer in the atmosphere. This is just as well, as exposure to UV can cause skin cancer. Fair-skinned people are particularly at risk. UV produces a change in chemicals in the skin, which darken to produce a tan. Doctors warn that the popularity of sunbathing while on holiday in a hot climate will lead to an increased risk of skin cancer.

The dangerous properties of UV can be turned to advantage by using it to kill harmful bacteria. In controlled conditions in hospitals it can also be used to treat skin problems (picture 8). We also benefit from some exposure to sunlight as our skin needs to absorb some UV to produce vitamin D. This vitamin is essential for strong bones.

In 1860, Maxwell predicted the existence of an **electromagnetic spectrum** (see page 190 of topic G3). Visible light, infra-red and ultra-violet are all members of a family of waves. Heinrich Hertz discovered **radio** waves, which have a longer wavelength than infra-red waves. The discovery of waves with a higher frequency and shorter wavelengths than UV did not occur until 1895. It was a discovery that produced one of the greatest ever advances in medical diagnosis – **X-rays**.

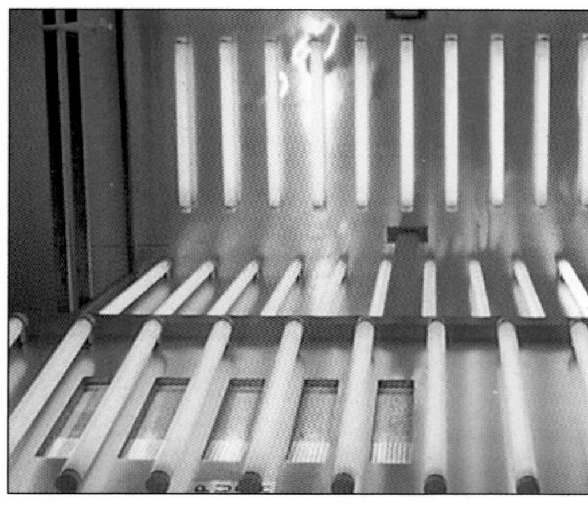

Picture 8

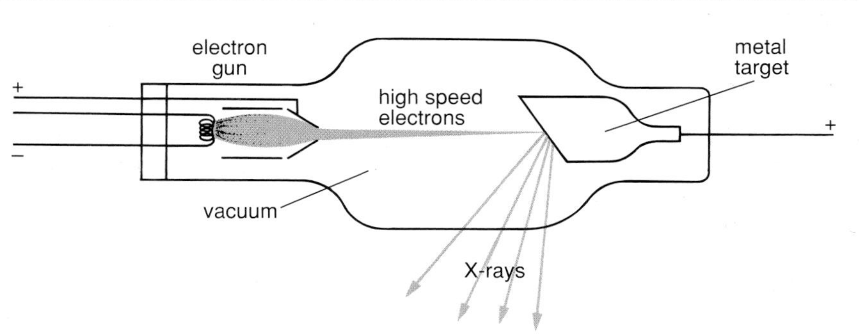

Picture 9 An X-ray tube. The faster the electrons, the more penetrating the X-ray.

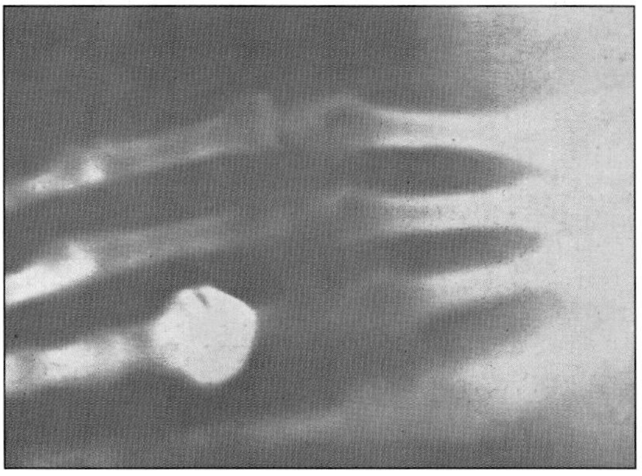

Picture 10 An X-ray shadowgraph of Mrs Roentgen's hand

ooking through you

-rays are yet another example of a scientific discovery made by accident. A erman physicist, Wilhelm Konrad Roentgen, was investigating electron streams vhen he noticed that a sheet of paper was glowing. This was not too unusual, as he paper was coated with a chemical which glowed if struck by electrons. The trange thing was that it was on the other side of the lab. It was much too far away or any 'leakage' of electrons to get to it through the air. Roentgen brought the heet closer and found that it glowed even brighter. After testing further he roved that the glow wasn't being caused by electrons but by an unknown kind f radiation. Because he didn't know what it was he called it 'X' rays.

Roentgen worked out that the X-rays are produced when a fast stream of lectrons hits glass or metal (picture 9). Then he discovered the most nteresting property of X-rays. When he put his hand in the path of the rays he aw that they cast a shadow on the screen. The shadow of his hand was a very trange one. *It showed the bones as well as the flesh* (picture 10).

Within a few weeks of this discovery in 1895, X-rays were being used in ospitals to look for broken bones, swallowed pins, blocked intestines and lamaged lungs. X-rays offered a new tool for medical diagnosis, for they enetrated the soft fleshy tissues of the body quite easily, but some were bsorbed as they passed through bone. Photographic film turned black when truck by the rays, so that areas of film shielded by bone or metal objects emained white. Picture 11 shows X-rays of an artificial hip joint and an artificial nee. The steel and plastic components show up clearly.

What if we need information about a part of the body, such as the gut, which s mostly soft tissue? The answer is to get the patient to drink a substance called arium sulphate. This is commonly called a 'barium meal'. Picture 12 shows an -ray photograph of the gut after the drink has been taken. The barium sulphate ills the gut and absorbs X-rays, so that the parts of the gut show up clearly.

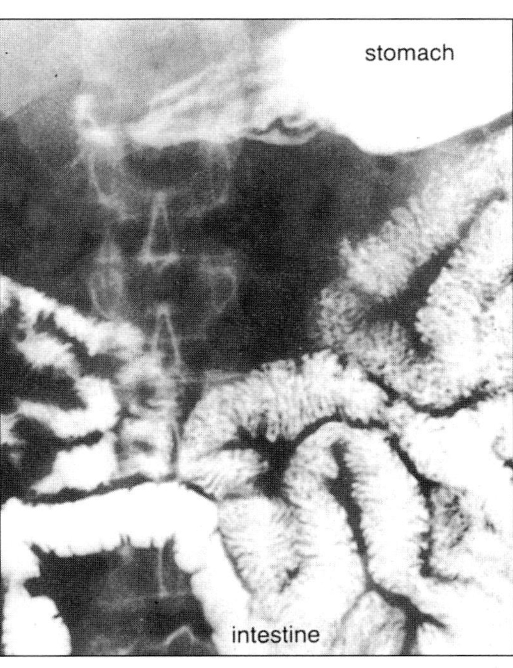

Picture 12 An X-ray photograph of the human gut taken after the patient had been given a barium meal.

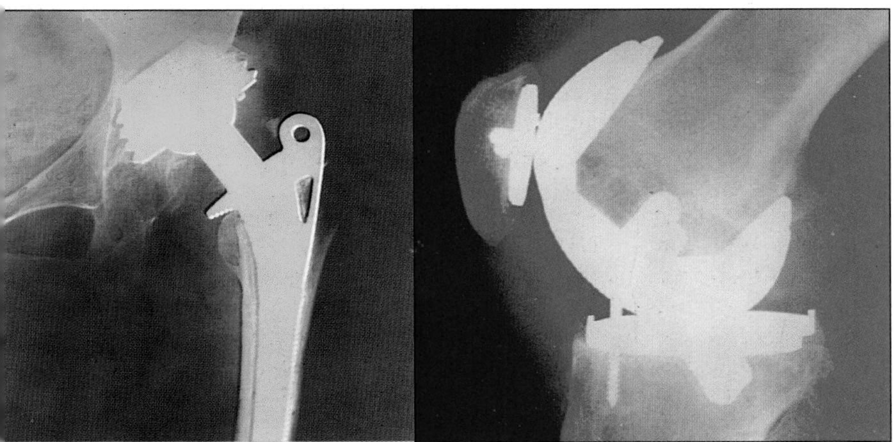

icture 11 X-rays of an artificial hip joint (left) and an artificial knee (right).

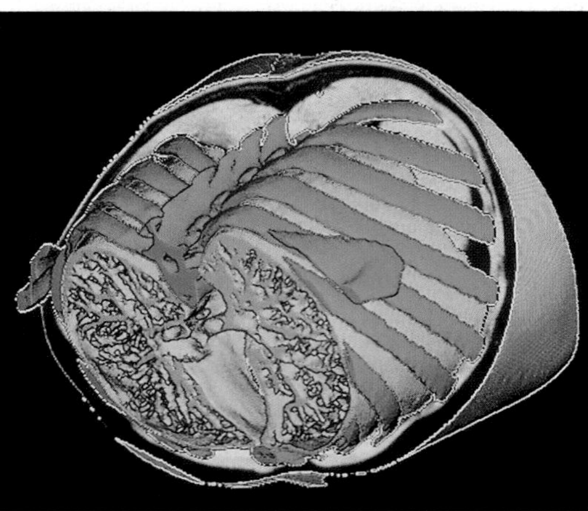

Picture 13 A CAT Scanner gives a 3D image.

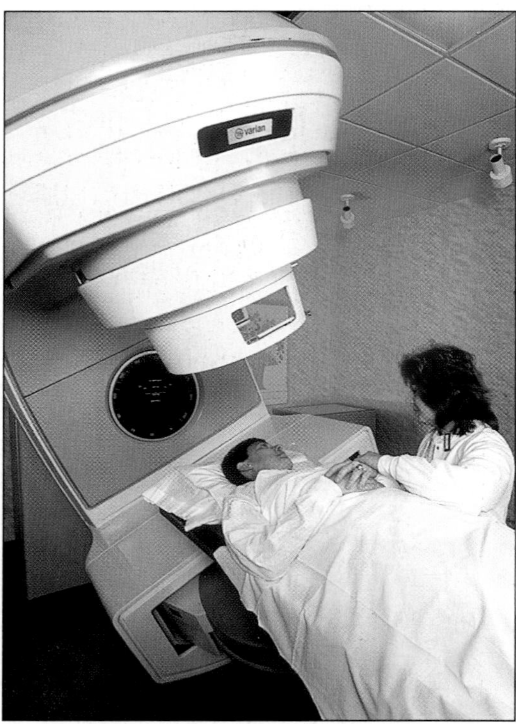

Picture 14 Only the tumour receives a lethal dose of X-rays.

Continuous 'moving' X-ray pictures can now be used in hospitals. Medical sta can view these on a television screen, and the images can be stored in computer.

Advances in computer technology now allow the information from an X-ra scan to be displayed in three dimensions. The **CAT scanner** (**c**omputer **a**xi **t**omography) scans the body in a complete circle, and detectors feed th information to the computer. Different 'slices' of the body are scanned, and th pictures assembled to make an image which the computer can rotate on scree This allows doctors to view a part of the body from any angle (picture 13). Th images are more highly detailed than ordinary X-ray pictures, and can show clea differences between body tissues.

Just as with static electricity 200 years earlier, some people went mad abou X-rays. They had 'skeleton pictures' taken of themselves and their families. The tried to use X-rays to cure all kinds of diseases.

It took 20 years for doctors to notice that people who used (and misused X-ray machines tended to get serious cancers. X-rays are invisible, highl energetic electromagnetic radiation. They can kill the delicate cells of livin matter. But they can also alter the cells, making them turn into cancer cells. W know now how to manage X-rays so that the 'dose' given to people is as sma as possible. Nurses and technicians who operate the machines are well shielde from them. X-rays are only used on people when it is medically necessary, afte carefully weighing up the balance between harm and benefit.

X-ray treatment

The fact that X-rays can kill cells can be used in treatment. A beam which ca travel inside the body and kill cells which are diseased is a very powerful medic tool. X-ray therapy has been used to destroy tumours which are difficult to reac by normal surgical techniques. A brain tumour, for example, can only b removed by opening the patient's skull and cutting into brain tissue. This migh cause damage which would prove fatal. Using a beam of X-rays, as shown i picture 14, the tumour cells can receive a lethal amount of radiation while th healthy brain tissue is exposed to much smaller doses. As the X-ray sourc rotates, the tumour is always at the centre of the circle, while the X-rays pas through the other tissues briefly.

New radiations

Roentgen's discovery of X-rays excited many scientists, who proceeded to tr experiments of their own. This led directly to a discovery of new and eve stranger forms of radiation, which seemed to come from atoms themselves. Yo can read about this in the next topic.

Questions

1 Read the following passage.

'Come in, Chris,' said the doctor. 'We are going to take a thermogram of your hand.'

'What's a thermogram?' asked Chris.

'Your body gives out radiation, called infra-red,' explained the doctor. 'This is similar to light but it has a longer wavelength. We have a special camera which makes use of this radiation to take a photograph of your hand. The photograph is called a thermogram and is similar to the one shown in the diagram.'

'What are the different patches in the photograph?' asked Chris.

'In a real thermogram,' answered the doctor, 'your hand will show up as patches of different colour. Each colour is due to a different temperature. The coldest parts are blue and the hottest parts are white. We can use the thermogram to detect unhealthy tissue since it is warmer than healthy tissue and so shows up as a different colour.'

a Name the type of radiation given out by the human body.

b How does the wavelength of this radiation compare with that of light?

c If Chris did have unhealthy tissue in his hand, suggest how this would be detected on the thermogram.

2a X-ray machines are used to destroy cancerous tissue in the body of a patient. The X-rays produced by the machine reach the patient from different directions by rotating the machine around the patient's body.

In this treatment, the X-rays are not fired continuously in one direction. The different paths of the X-rays through the patient's body are shown in the diagram above.

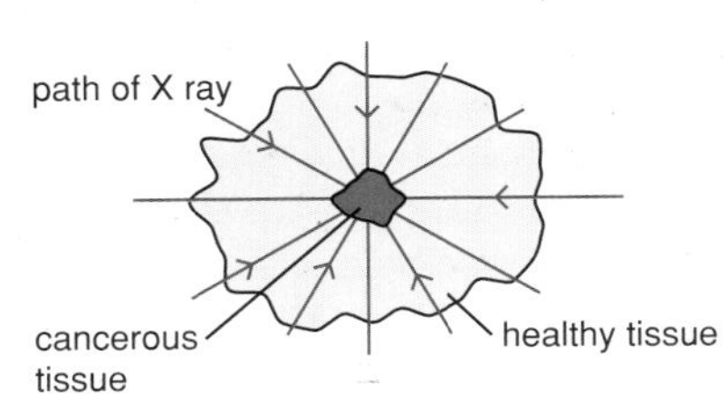

i) Explain why rotating the X-ray machine provides a safer way of ensuring that the cancerous tissue receives the maximum dose.

ii) Why is it important that the patient keeps still during the treatment?

3 In some parts of North America, a daily ultra-violet index is published to give a guide to the amount of time that a person can sunbathe safely. The table shows such an index. The chart shows how the index changed during a week in May.

Ultra-violet index	Time to sunbathe
Greater than 9	15 minutes
7–8.9	20 minutes
4–6.9	30 minutes
0–3.9	1 hour

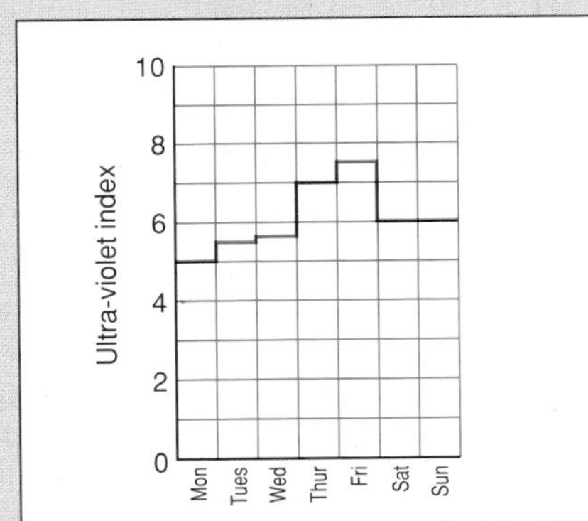

a Use the chart and the table to estimate the maximum safe time allowed for sunbathing on Friday of that week.

Carefully read the following information.

Special creams and liquids called sunscreens are used to protect the skin from the harmful effects of the ultra-violet radiation (UV) from the Sun. The sunscreens absorb some of the UV and prevent it reaching the skin.

Ultra-violet radiation with wavelengths in the range 315–400 nm is called UVA. Radiation with wavelengths in the range 280–315 nm is called UVB.

The longer wavelength UVA can cause wrinkles and premature aging of the skin.

The shorter wavelength UVB gives a long-lasting tan but UVB causes sunburn.

Both UVA and UVB increase the risk of skin cancer.

Table 1 below gives some properties of sunscreen chemicals P, Q, R and S at different wavelengths.

b Give **two** reasons why most sunscreens are made from a mixture of more than one of these chemicals.

c Which chemical gives more protection against premature aging of the skin?

d Sunscreens containing only chemicals listed in the table do not give complete protection against both aging and burning. Give a reason for this.

e Although UV can harm our skin it can be used to our benefit. Name **one** use of ultra-violet radiation in medicine.

4 Table 2 below gives information about the wavelength and output power of some types of laser.

The visible spectrum has wavelengths ranging from 4.0×10^{-7} m to 7.0×10^{-7} m.

a Which laser emits infra-red radiation?

b Name **one** medical use of infra-red radiation.

c Calculate the frequency of light from the helium–neon laser.

d Light from an argon laser is used to treat a patient's eye. During the treatment, the laser fires 15 short pulses of light. Each pulse lasts 0.2 second.

Use the formula energy = power × time to calculate the energy given out by the laser during the treatment.

Table 1

Sunscreen chemical	Range of wavelengths absorbed	Effect of water
P	250–320 nm	does not dissolve
Q	290–320 nm	dissolves
R	280–360 nm	dissolves
S	295–315 nm	dissolves

Table 2

Type of laser	Wavelength (m)	Output power (W)
Excimer	3.2×10^{-7}	20.0
Argon	4.9×10^{-7}	2.0
Dye	5.5×10^{-7}	0.5
Helium–neon	6.3×10^{-7}	0.005
Nd–YAG	10.6×10^{-7}	50.0

C6 Radioactivity

One of the great discoveries of the 20th century was that atoms themselves gave off 'rays'.

Picture 1 shows a group of people protesting against plans to build a nuclear power station. Many people are opposed to nuclear power because it involves the use of large quantities of material which are **radioactive**.

Picture 1 Not everyone wants to use nuclear energy.

Radioactivity

Radioactivity was discovered in 1895 by a French scientist called Antoine Henri Becquerel. He had been intrigued by the discovery of X-rays, and had an interest in **fluorescent** materials. These are substances that glow when light strikes them. Roentgen discovered X-rays because they made a fluorescent screen glow, and Becquerel wondered if these materials themselves might give off X-rays when exposed to sunlight. His first experiments produced blackening, or 'fogging' of some photographic plates.

He wrapped up some more plates, and put them in a drawer underneath a fluorescent mineral. He intended to wait for a sunny day, to repeat his experiment. After several dull days, he grew frustrated and decided to develop the plates anyway, to check whether any tiny amount of fluorescence was left in the rocks from their previous exposure to sunlight. He expected to get no result, or perhaps a faint amount of fogging. He was astonished to find that the plates were strongly blackened. Obviously radiation was being emitted that did not depend on sunlight. It was coming from the mineral itself.

A radioactive substance is one that sends out very energetic rays. There are three types of ray. All of them can damage living things, but they are also very useful. When they were first discovered, nobody knew exactly what they were, so they named them **alpha** (α), **beta** (β), and **gamma** (γ) rays, after the first three letters of the Greek alphabet.

Alpha, beta, gamma

Table 1 summarises the properties of these rays. It took scientists 20 years after they were first discovered to work out what the radiations actually were, and that they were coming from the **nucleus** of the atom. The structure of the atom is summarised in picture 2.

One property that these radiations possess is their ability to **ionise** atoms and molecules. The radiations knock electrons out of the atoms to turn them into **ions** (picture 3). The atoms and molecules become positively charged. Thus the radiations are called **ionising radiations**.

The reason they are dangerous to life is that they ionise atoms in living cells, which can kill the cells.

The radiations travel at high speeds, as if they are shot out of the nucleus like a bullet from a gun. What was puzzling to the scientists who first worked with these radiations was where they got the energy from to do this. We now know that it comes from the conversion of matter into energy.

Table 1 Nuclear radiations.

Radiation type	What are they	Range in air	Stopped by	Comments
ALPHA	Positively charged. NUCLEI of helium ($^{2}_{4}He$)	A few centimetres	A sheet of paper	Because they are so massive and carry a double positive charge they easily affect atoms. They make lots of ions and don't travel far. Alpha emiters are quite safe unless they get into the body.
BETA	Negatively charged. Fast-moving ELECTRONS	A few tens of centimetres	A few millimetres of aluminium	Electrons are so small and can travel further than alpha particles as they don't collide as often. Dangerous but easily stopped.
GAMMA	Unchanged. Very short wavelength ELECTROMAGNETIC WAVES (high-energy photons)	They go on indefinitely	A metre or two of concrete	These are genuine 'rays'. They don't ionise atoms very easily and so travel a long way. They travel at the speed of light. Dangerous because they are hard to shield against.

Detecting the radiations

We detect the rays from atoms using the fact that the rays ionise other atoms. Picture 4 shows the tracks of alpha particles travelling through damp air. The water vapour in the air condenses as droplets on the **ions** made from the air by the alpha particles. This leaves a 'vapour trail' like the ones made by high flying aircraft. This picture was taken as the alpha particles travelled through a special 'cloud chamber'. This contains cool damp air, which is good at making clouds and vapour trails.

Picture 5 shows another detector which makes use of ionisation.

It is a GM tube, or **Geiger–Muller tube**. It contains a gas at a low pressure. The inner wire is at a high voltage. When some ionising radiation goes into the tube it makes ions in the gas. The wire attracts them and so there is a short pulse of current when the ions hit the wire. This is amplified and can be counted by an electronic **pulse counter**. Thus each time a 'ray' gets into the tube it produces a pulse which can be counted.

Geiger counters like this are the most common way of finding out how much radioactivity is present.

Alpha particles

Alpha particles are very good at ionising other atoms. This suggests that they carry a lot of energy. This is movement energy (kinetic energy).

But they don't travel very far in air. They barge through the air like a bull in a china shop, hitting lots of air molecules and knocking electrons off them (picture 3). As they do this they lose energy quite rapidly, so they soon slow down.

If we put a piece of paper in the way the alpha particles can't get through it! This is because they hit a lot of atoms in the paper.

Alpha particles are electrically charged, carrying 2 units of positive charge. This is twice as much as the (negative) charge carried by an electron.

Because alpha particles are positively charged they are affected by both electric and magnetic fields. Scientists have worked out exactly what alpha particles are by measuring how strongly they are affected by these fields.

These measurements show that alpha particles are in fact **helium nuclei**, which are four times as heavy as hydrogen nuclei. They have, therefore, an atomic mass of 4. They are made up of two protons (positive particles) and two neutrons, joined very firmly together (picture 6).

Beta particles

Beta particles do not cause as much ionisation as alpha particles. Also, they travel much further in air before running out of energy. This suggests that they are lighter and smaller than alpha particles. They carry a single unit of negative charge. Measurements using electric and magnetic fields show that they are in fact **high-speed electrons**. An alpha particle is 7333 times as massive as a beta particle.

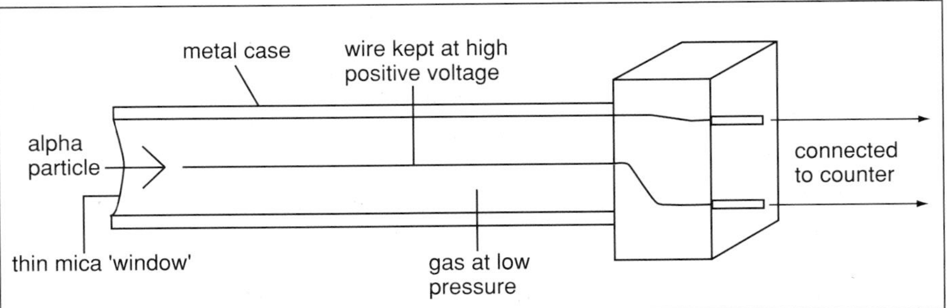

Picture 5 A GM tube. When an alpha particle, for example, enters the tube, it ionises the gas inside. This triggers off a sudden flow of freed electrons to the wire. This registers as a 'count' or a 'click'.

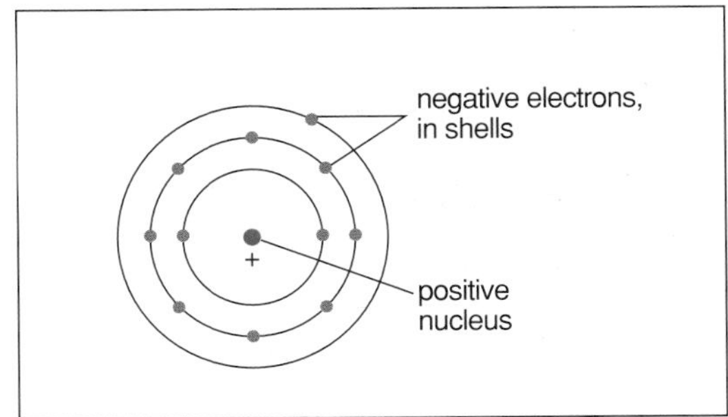

Picture 2 Rutherford's model: a nuclear atom.

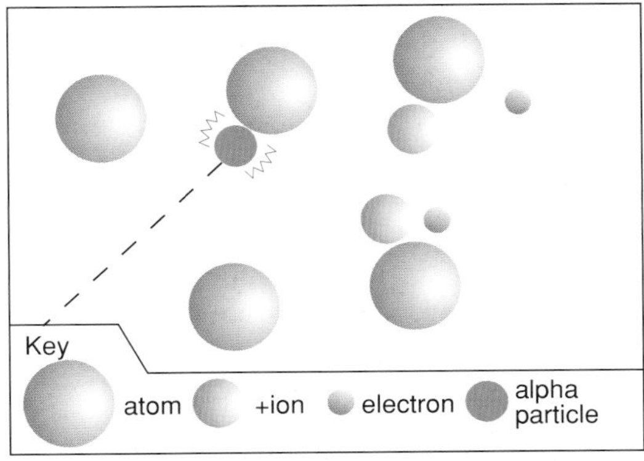

Picture 3 How alpha particles ionise atoms.

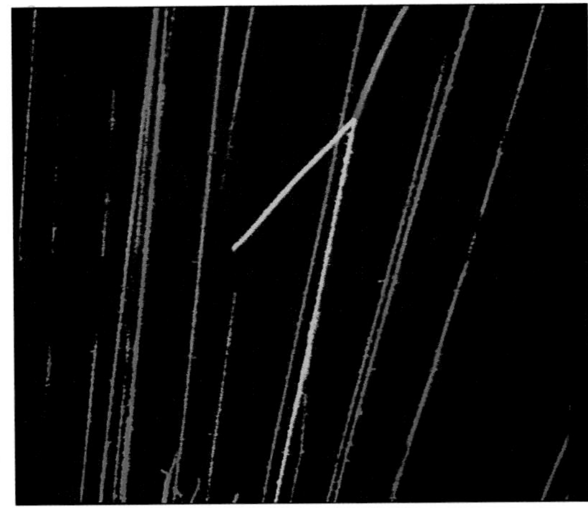

Picture 4 The tracks of alpha particles in a 'cloud chamber'.

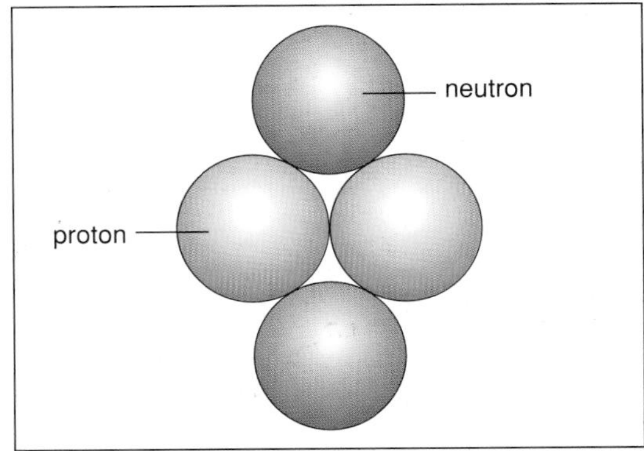

Picture 6 A helium nucleus.

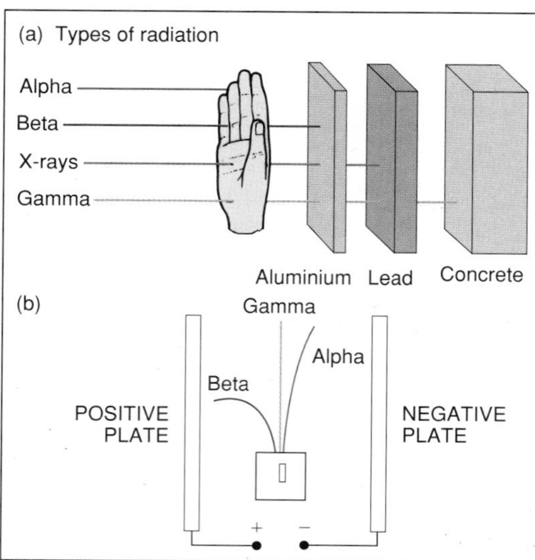

Picture 7 (a) What stops the radiations – or doesn't! (X-rays are shown for a comparison.) (b) What happens to the radiations in an electric field.

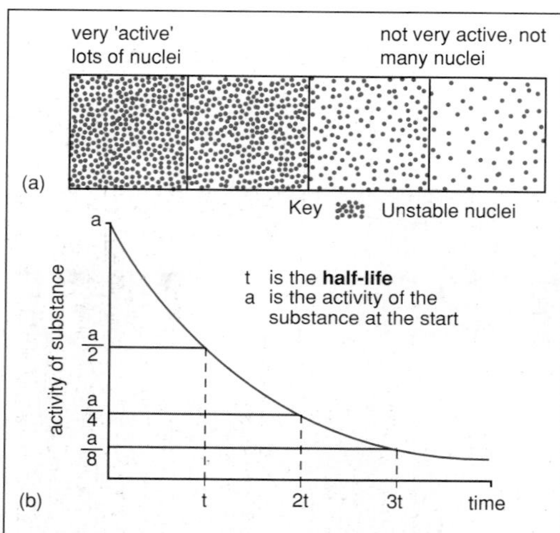

Picture 8 (a) Radioactive decay. The activity of a radioactive substance gets less all the time. This is because the number of unstable, active nuclei gets less. But there is a catch – the new nuclei may also be unstable! (b) A half-life graph.

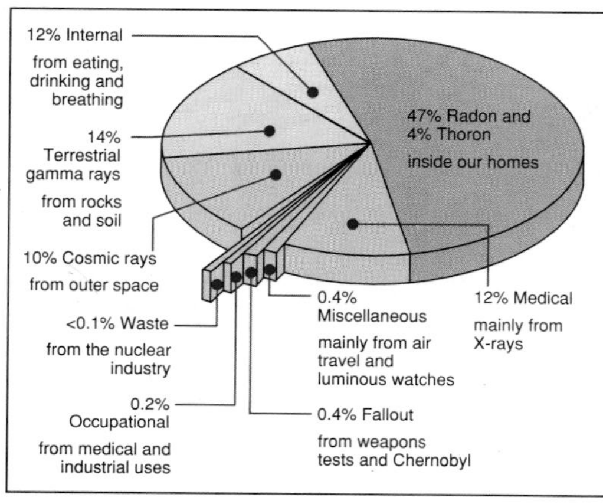

Picture 9 Where background radiation comes from.

Because they are so small, beta particles can travel through matter more easily than alpha particles can. But a few millimetres of aluminium will stop them.

Gamma rays

Gamma rays do not cause much ionisation and they travel quite freely, through air. They carry no charge and so are not at all affected by electric or magnetic fields. This means that they are very **penetrating**. They can travel through thick blocks of concrete, and it takes up to a centimetre or so thickness of a heavy metal like lead to cut down the radiation by a half.

Gamma rays are different from the alpha and beta particles because they have no mass. They travel at the speed of light, and are a type of **electromagnetic radiation**, like light and X-rays. But they carry more energy than X-rays do.

Picture 7 shows how the three kinds of radiation compare in their ability to pass through matter, and what happens to them in an electric field.

Half-life

Radiations are given out by decaying atoms. As the atom decays to something else, it 'spits out' the radiation. In a sample of uranium the nuclei don't decay all at once. In fact, only a very tiny fraction of the nuclei in the sample decay each day. It will take four and a half thousand million years for just half of the nuclei in a lump of uranium (U) to decay.

On the other hand, it will take only 52 seconds for half of the nuclei in a sample of radon gas (Rn-220) to decay. These times are called **half-lives**, and we can measure them very accurately.

Picture 8(a) shows how the number of undecayed nuclei left in a sample of a radioactive element changes with time. Picture 8(b) shows this in the form of a graph.

The **count rate** is a measure of the number of rays given out per second. One count per second is known as one **becquerel** (Bq), and the **activity** of a radioactive source is usually measured in **megabecquerels** (MBq). As time goes on this count rate will go down, as more and more of the nuclei have decayed.

Your teacher should be able to show you an experiment about how the rate of radioactive decay gets less as time goes on. You should be able to get results to allow you to measure the half-life of a radioactive material.

Background radiation

Nuclear radiation is all around us. It comes from the rocks and the soil; it comes from plants and even animals. This is because they all contain tiny amounts of radioactive materials that are naturally present on Earth. Some comes from elements made radioactive by radiation from outer space, some from atomic weapons testing 30 or 40 years ago. A small amount comes from the operation of nuclear power stations. Also, the nuclear accident in Russia (at Chernobyl) in 1986 produced radioactive 'fall out'.

Background radiation must be taken into account when measuring the activity of a source by experiment. Subtracting background radiation from the measurement gives us the *corrected* count rate. Picture 9 summarises where this background radiation comes from. It is too low to have a serious effect on health, but it does have some effect. Doctors estimate that background radiation causes 1200 deaths from cancer per year in Britain. It is also likely that this radiation affects the genes in sex cells, so causing slight changes from one generation to the next. This may be one of the main causes of biological **variation**, which is necessary for evolution to occur.

Radioactive dating

Radioactive elements decay into lighter elements. They decay at a known rate. So, using a special machine called a mass spectrometer, scientists can measure how much of the original radioactive element is left and how much of the new, lighter elements are present. The ratio of the two gives a fairly accurate estimate of the age of the rock.

For example, potassium-40 (K) has a half-life of 1.3 billion years (1.3×10^9 years). It decays, eventually, to a stable isotope of argon (Ar). A sample of rock is found to have three times as many argon atoms as potassium atoms. We can work out how old the rock is as follows.

Suppose there were 1000 potassium atoms to start with, when the rock was newly made.

Time in half-lives	Number of K atoms	Number of Ar atoms
start	1000	0
1	500	500
2	250	750

So it takes two half-lives to produce three times as many argon atoms as there are potassium atoms left. This means that the rock is 2.6 billion years old.

Radioactive dating has been used to measure the age of meteorites and moonrocks. These measurements suggest that the whole Solar System, Earth, meteorites and the Moon were formed at the same time – 4.6 billion years ago. For the first four billion of those years, there was no life as we know it, and people have only been on the Earth for the last 0.003 billion years.

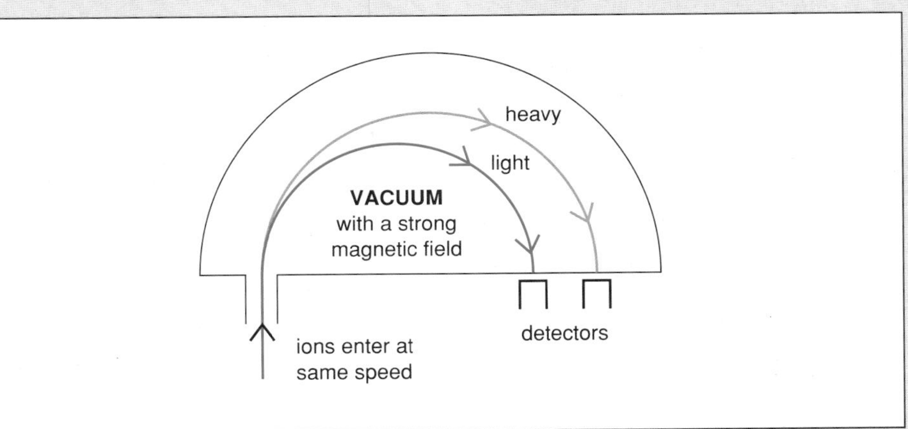

Picture 1 **The principle of the mass spectrometer.** The atoms being investigated are ionised and accelerated by an electrical field into a vacuum chamber containing a strong magnetic field. The magnetic field makes the ions move in circular paths. The more massive atoms (red path) don't curve as much as lighter atoms (green path). The machine can therefore separate atoms of different mass – and uses electronics to count how many of each there are.

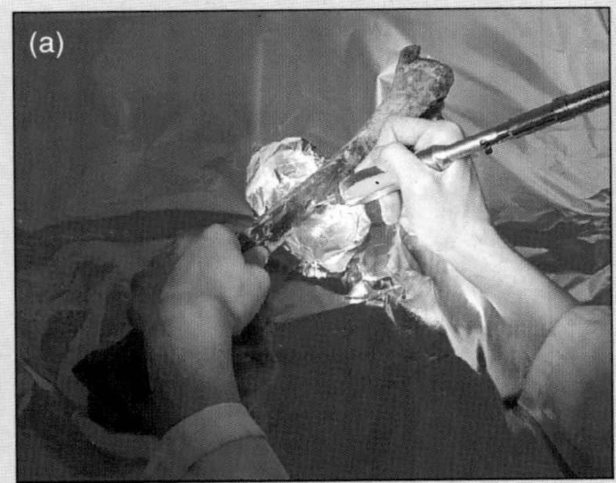

Picture 2 Radiocarbon dating using carbon-14.
(a) Scientists use very small samples – here being taken from a reindeer bone.
(b) The bone samples are dissolved in a solvent to release the amino acids containing carbon.

Carbon-14 dating

Carbon-14 is a **radioisotope** of carbon (see page 93). All living things are made of carbon atoms, and all contain a certain percentage of these radioactive carbon-14 atoms. The carbon in the bodies of living things is continually being exchanged with the environment. For example, plants take in carbon dioxide, and animals eat plants and other animals. They then breathe out carbon dioxide.

When living things die, the carbon in their bodies (including carbon-14) is no longer being replaced. The carbon-14 decays radioactively, and so the level of radiation in the dead material gradually decreases. Scientists can measure the activity of the carbon-14 in samples from dead animal or plant matter, and calculate when the organism died.

C7 Radiation and life

Ionising radiations are all around us. Only a small amount is due to human activities.

Picture 1 A granite outcrop. Granite often contains radioactive elements.

Why is radioactivity dangerous?

The alpha, beta and gamma radiations from a radioactive material travel at high speeds. Also, alpha and beta particles are electrically charged. When they go into living cells they can kill or damage them. They can do this because they ionise molecules that are vital to life. A large 'dose' of radiation kills so many cells that the effect is like being burned by fire.

Alpha particles are easily stopped. Even a sheet of paper is enough. But beta and gamma radiations can get deep into the body so that cells in internal organs are damaged.

For low levels of radiation you lose just a few cells. This in itself is not dangerous. After all, our bodies contain lots of cells. The danger comes from the fact that the radiation can *change* some of the chemicals we have in cells. These are the complex molecules of DNA and RNA that control how the cell works.

As a result, the cell may go out of control. It grows and divides just as if it was an independent organism that feeds on our bodies. It becomes a group of **cancer cells**.

Also, if sperm or ova cells in the reproductive system are changed, the result could be children with birth defects. They could be born with badly formed or missing limbs, or brain damage.

Table 1 Exposure to radiation in everyday situations.

	Type of exposure	Microsievert
1	radiation due to nuclear power stations for a year	10
2	watching television for a year	10
3	wearing a radioactive luminous watch for a year (now not very common)	30
4	having a chest X-ray	200
5	exposure to fall-out in Britain from nuclear bomb testing in 1959	350
6	radiation from a brick house, per year	750
7	working for a month in a uranium mine	1000
8	typical dose received by a member of the general public in a year	1500
9	maximum dose allowed to general public per year	5000
10	maximum dose allowed to workers exposed to radiation per year	50 000

Picture 2 Nuclear waste transporter.

Table 1 shows the radiation doses you might get in different situations, together with the allowed doses for ordinary people and workers in the nuclear industries. We cannot measure dosage in **becquerels**, as the effects produced by radiation depend on the type of radiation, the type of body tissues affected, and the total amount of energy absorbed.

The **dose equivalent** measures the *biological risk* of radiation, in units called **sieverts** (Sv). A sievert is a very large dose of radiation, and so normal doses are usually expressed in **millisieverts** (mSv), or as in the table, **microsieverts** (μSv). People who live in areas such as Aberdeenshire, where the rocks are mainly granite, are exposed to a higher background radiation level. Granite contains more than the average amount of radioactive elements (picture 1).

Workers in the nuclear industry, or those using radioactive materials in medicine, must observe strict safety precautions. All nuclear workers wear a special badge called a **dosimeter**, containing a type of photographic film. This records the amount of radiation the worker receives over a certain period.

Radioisotopes

In some elements, a number of the atoms are slightly different from the others. They behave in the same way in chemical reactions, but the nucleus may be slightly larger or smaller. Carbon, for example, usually has 12 particles in the nucleus – 6 **protons** and 6 **neutrons** (picture 3). Some carbon atoms have two *extra* neutrons, and this version of carbon is known as **carbon-14**, or **C^{14}** (see page 91). Different versions of atoms are known as **isotopes**, and if they are radioactive they are called **radioisotopes**. Radioisotopes are used in medicine as aids to diagnosis and treatment.

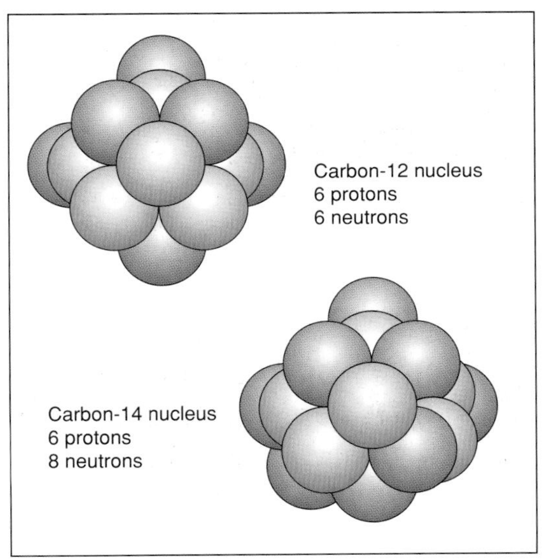

Picture 3 Carbon 14 has two extra neutrons in its nucleus.

Radiotherapy

When radioisotopes are used in treatment or **therapy**, they are employed to kill cells which are cancerous. A radioisotope of cobalt, called **cobalt-60**, emits gamma radiation. As we have seen, alpha and beta radiation can not penetrate the body. Gamma rays are very penetrating, and so they can be directed at internal tumours. As with X-rays, care must be taken to ensure that only the cancerous cells receive a dangerous level of radiation. The equipment is rotated in a circle, with the tumour at the centre (picture 4).

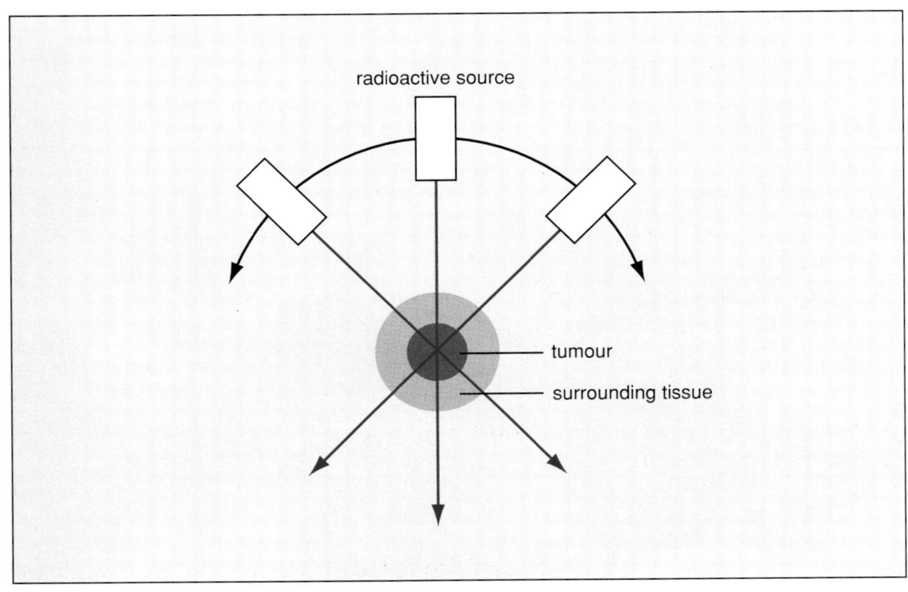

Picture 4 Gamma rays can be used to treat cancer.

When working normally, some organs in the body use particular chemicals. The **thyroid gland** helps to control growth, and needs the element **iodine**. If tadpoles do not receive iodine in their diet, they do not develop legs and grow into frogs. Iodine from our natural diet is concentrated in the thyroid gland.

Different radioisotopes of iodine can be produced by the nuclear industry for use in medicine. The radioisotope iodine-131 emits beta particles. If injected into a patient, it will concentrate in the thyroid, and the beta radiation will destroy cancerous cells in the gland.

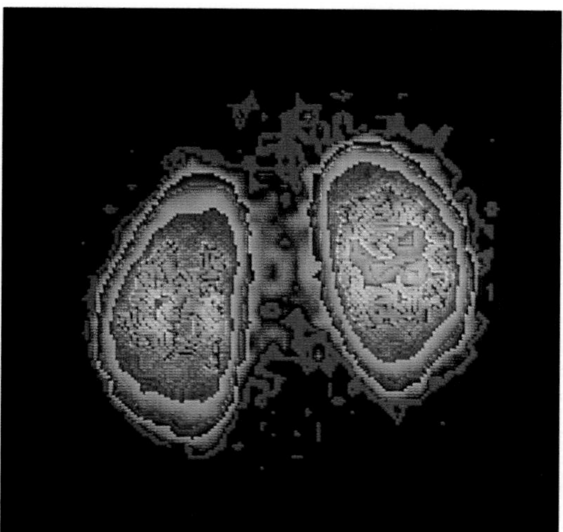

Picture 5 Different levels of radioactivity show which sections of an organ are working properly.

Diagnosis

Just as some parts of the body need certain chemicals to function normally, *unusual* levels of substances may indicate a problem.

If we introduce a radioisotope into a substance, and then inject it into the body, we can follow the path of that substance by following the patterns of radioactivity. We say we have added a radioactive **tracer**, and that the substance has been **labelled**. If the results show high or low levels of radioactivity in a particular organ (picture 5), this can help the doctor with a diagnosis.

A diagnostic examination should not do harm to the patient, so it is important that these radioisotopes have very *short* half-lives. This ensures that the level of radioactivity inside the patient drops very quickly.

A radioisotope, which was a **beta** emitter (or alpha), would also be unsuitable for diagnosis. Firstly, the beta radiation could damage nearby healthy tissues. Secondly, very little would escape the body to be detected. The most suitable radioisotopes for use in diagnosis are those which emit gamma rays.

The gamma camera

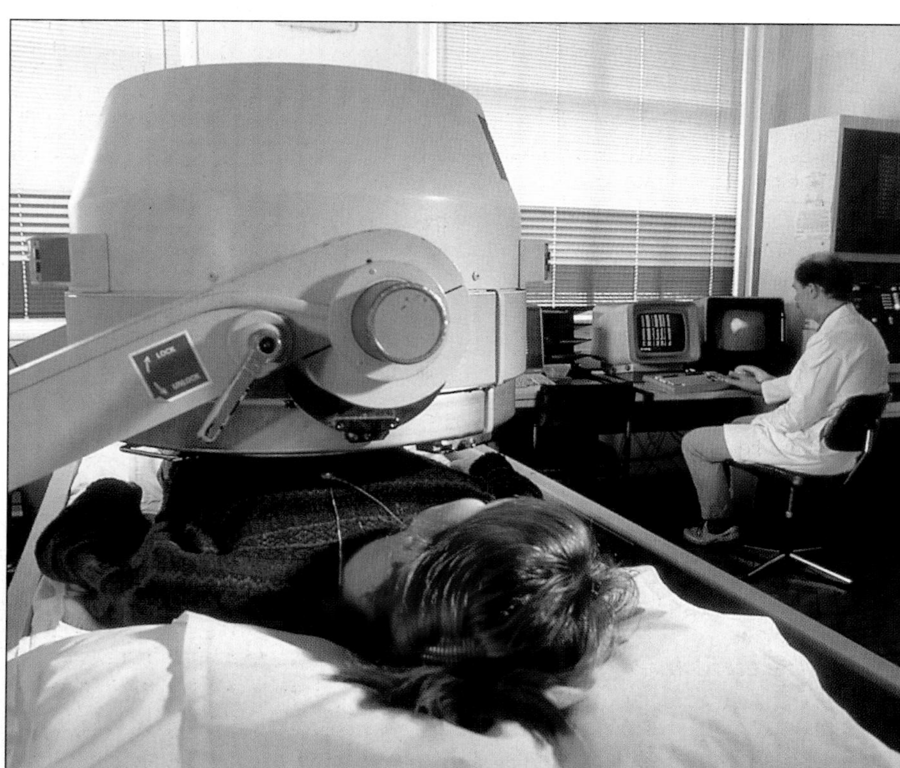

Picture 6 A gamma camera in use.

The gamma camera (picture 6) detects the gamma radiation being emitted from the patient's body. The gamma rays spread out in all directions, but a section called the collimator only allows through those which are travelling directly towards the camera. The detector is a device called a **scintillation counter**. When gamma rays strike a crystal, it emits a flash of light. This very faint flash is boosted by a **photomultiplier** tube, and the position of the flash is recorded and stored by a computer. The pattern of flashes can be displayed on a screen, (picture 7) showing the different concentrations of the radioactive tracer in the body.

Picture 7 A computer converts the pattern of gamma rays into a picture.

Questions

1 A sample of air containing a radioactive gas was collected from a house in Cornwall. The sample and a detector were put into a sealed lead container. A cutaway section of the container is shown below. The count rate for the sample was found at various times.

a i) Why were the sample and detector enclosed in a thick lead container?

ii) The measurements of count rate for the sample as time passed are shown below.

Time (h)	Count rate (counts /min^{-1})
0	42.0
30	33.5
60	26.7
90	21.3
120	17.0
150	13.6
180	10.8

Use the figures in table 1 above to give an **estimate** of the half-life of the radioactive gas.

b Such gas samples from Cornwall emit radiation which gives a high density of ionisation compared with the other two types of radiation emitted by natural substances.

i) What does *ionisation* mean?

ii) What kind of radiation is the sample emitting?

iii) Explain why this gas is dangerous if it is breathed in.

2a A teacher set up an experiment, as shown in the diagram below, to determine the half-life of a radioactive source.

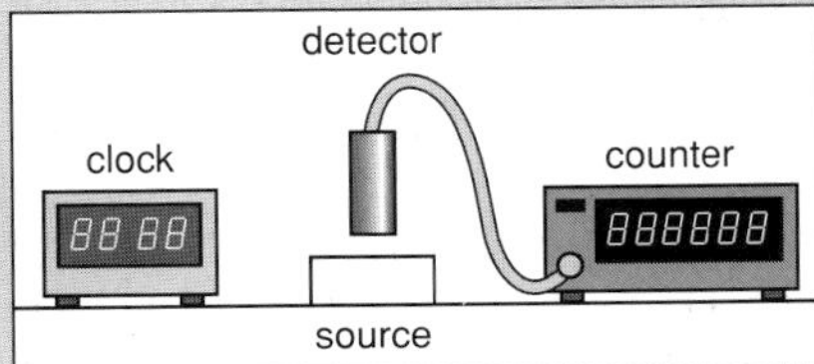

b The source used in the above experiment had an original activity of 800 kBq and a half-life of 30 s.

Calculate the activity of the source after 2 minutes.

3 A hospital technician measures the half-life of a radioactive element which emits beta radiation and finds this to be 20 minutes.

a The sample of radioactive element she is working with has an activity of 2000 Bq at the start of her measurement.

What will be the activity of the sample after 1 hour?

b While working with radioactive substances, the technician wears a film badge similar to that shown in the diagram below. A photographic film, protected from light, is placed behind the windows in the badge.

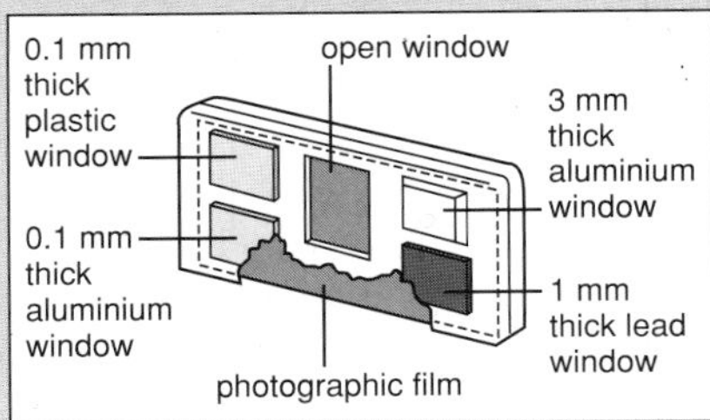

If the technician was exposed accidentally to too much beta radiation, which part or parts of the film would **not** be affected?

Explain your answer.

c When hospital technicians are making up doses of radioactive chemicals for patients, they wear detector badges on their gloves rather than on their laboratory coats.

Suggest a reason for this.

4 A patient is examined to find out if his kidneys are working properly. A liquid containing some gamma emitting radioactive material is injected into the patient's bloodstream. This radioactive material and other impurities should be absorbed by the kidney and then passed to the patient's bladder. A gamma camera is used to detect the radiation coming from the patient's kidneys. The gamma camera produces images of the patient's left and right kidneys on a monitor as shown below.

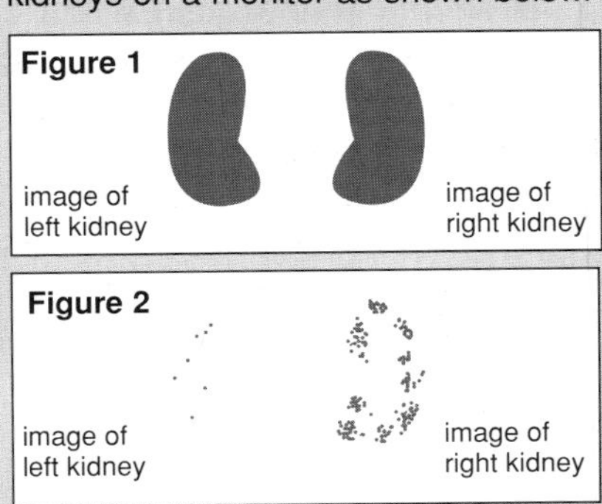

Figure 1 shows the image produced 2 minutes after the injection and figure 2 shows the image 10 minutes after the injection.

a Which kidney is not working properly? Explain your answer.

b The half-lives of four gamma emitters W, X, Y and Z are listed in the table below.

Gamma emitter	Half-life
W	1 minute
X	5 minutes
Y	5 hours
Z	5 days

The examination of the patient lasts for 15 minutes.

Which one of the above gamma emitters would be most suitable for use in the examination?

c Alpha emitting materials are never injected into the body in order to obtain images of parts of the body.

State **two** reasons why alpha emitting materials are unsuitable.

5 A radioactive element emits gamma radiation. The graph below shows how the activity of the element decreases with time.

a What is the half-life of the radioactive element?

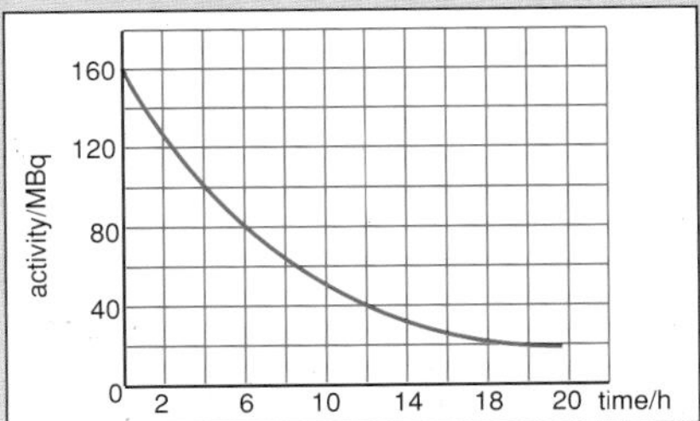

b When radiation is absorbed in tissue, the effect depends on the tissue and the type of radiation. A measure of the effect of the radiation on tissue is given by the dose equivalent.

State the unit of dose equivalent.

D1 Electronics

Electronic systems operate in three simple stages.

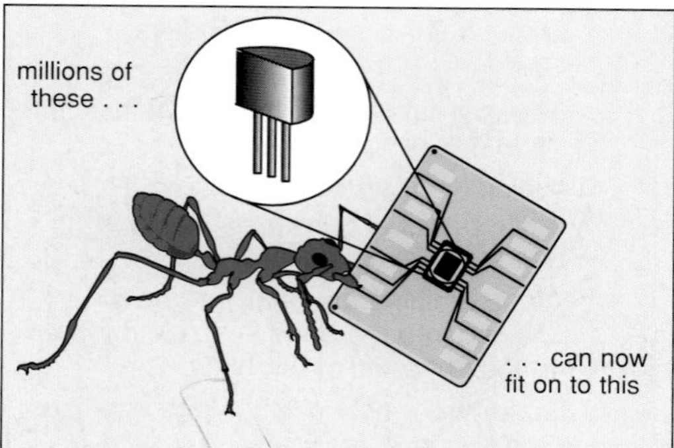

Picture 1

The modern world relies more on electronics than on any other type of technology. In almost anything we do, from designing a jet plane to using a calculator for our Physics homework, we use tools containing electronic components.

An **electrical** appliance performs a task by using electrical currents to carry energy, which the appliance converts into other forms. A cooker converts electrical energy to heat, while a vacuum cleaner changes electrical energy to movement energy.

An **electronic** device also uses electricity, but mainly to carry **information**. Energy conversions are involved, but usually to change information into a form that we can understand – for example, sound energy must go *in* and come *out* of the telephone before we can have a conversation.

The components of an electronic system include resistors, transistors, diodes, and capacitors. All these components change the *patterns* of the currents and voltages in a system, so that information can be altered or transmitted.

Over the last 40 years, components have become smaller and smaller, until we can now pack millions of them into a tiny space. In the 1950s a computer might fill two entire rooms in a building. With the latest developments in miniaturisation, such a computer could soon be fitted into a full stop on this page!

These components are **integrated circuits**, or what we commonly call **'silicon chips'** (picture 1), and they have started a revolution that continues to affect every aspect of our daily lives. Let us start with some simple rules describing what an electronics system does.

INPUT – PROCESS – OUTPUT

Imagine you are a tennis player (picture 2). Your opponent hits the ball towards you and your eyes follow it. The information from your eyes travels to your brain, which works out the direction and speed of the ball. The brain makes decisions, based on this information and sends out signals to the muscles of your body. You run, stretch your arms and hit the ball past your opponent to score a point – game, set and match!

Living things do this all the time.

- Our senses detect events around us and produce signals that form the **input** to our brain.
- It is important that the brain gives the body correct instructions, (for example, it would not be a good idea to start walking across the road if the crossing light is at red!) so it makes decisions based on rules that are built-in or learned from experience. We say it **processes** the information.
- It then produces a set of instructions for our body that will produce the desired result (for example, wait for the 'green man', *then* you walk across the road). These instructions are the **output** signal.

Electronic systems work by the same method.

- A computer system has a keyboard and a mouse, which are the **input** sections.
- The computer itself (called the **CPU** or central *processing* unit) translates these signals into instructions.
- The **output** sections are the screen or printer, which display the result.

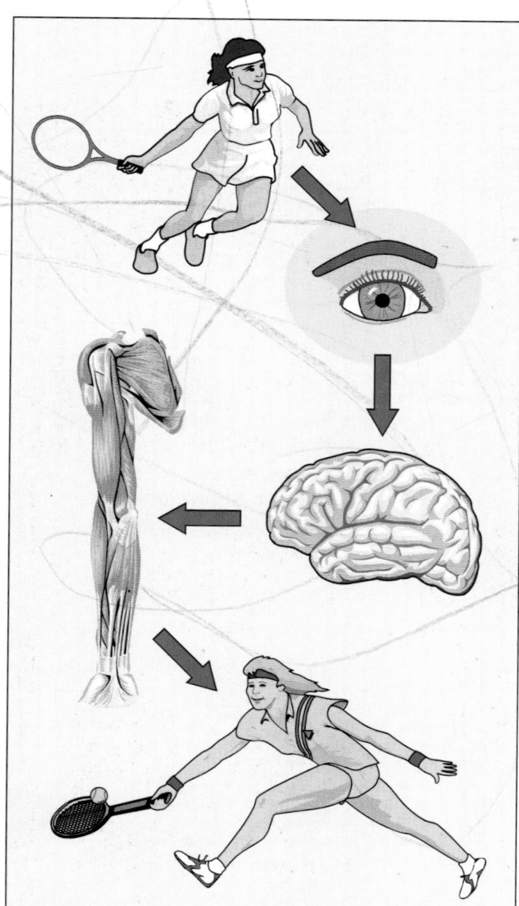

Picture 2

These three stages are the same for all electronic systems, so we can show any particular system as a **block diagram** (picture 3).

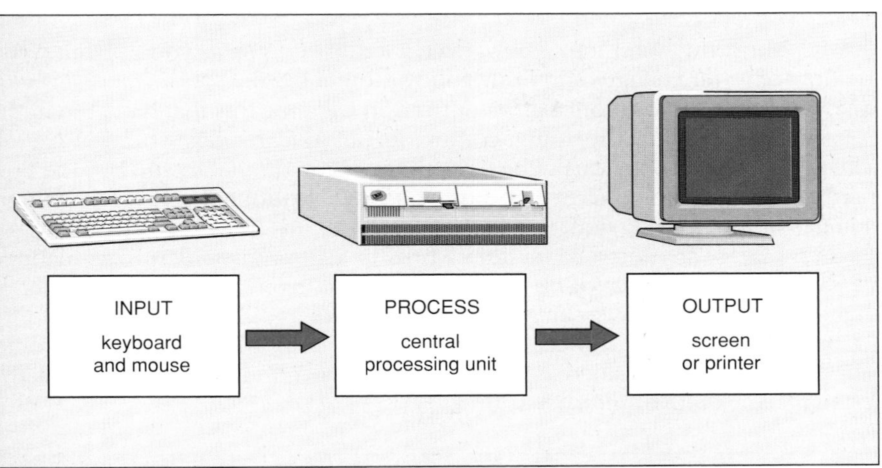

Picture 3

The block diagram shows which way the information flows in an electronic system. Systems may have several different input and output devices, so block diagrams are a useful method for making sense of complicated equipment.

Modern homes contain many electronic devices, from large installations such as burglar alarms and automatic central heating systems, to small items such as portable phones and personal stereo players.

Many of these are *programmable*; that is we can set times for heating to come on, select a particular temperature and spin for our washing, tell the microwave what settings to use to cook a meal, or tell the CD player to play certain tracks in a particular order.

Questions

1a List these parts of a sound system shown in the diagram below according to whether they are input, process, or output devices.

b Draw a block diagram of the assembled system.

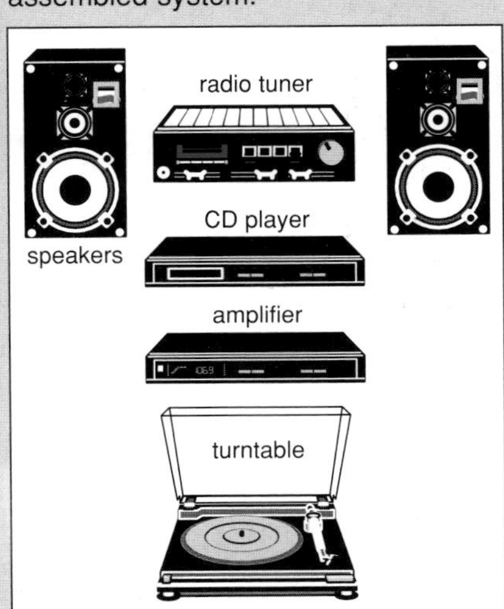

2 Copy and complete this table, selecting the correct items from the diagram below.

System	Input device	Output device
burglar alarm		
karaoke system		
lift controls		
central heating		

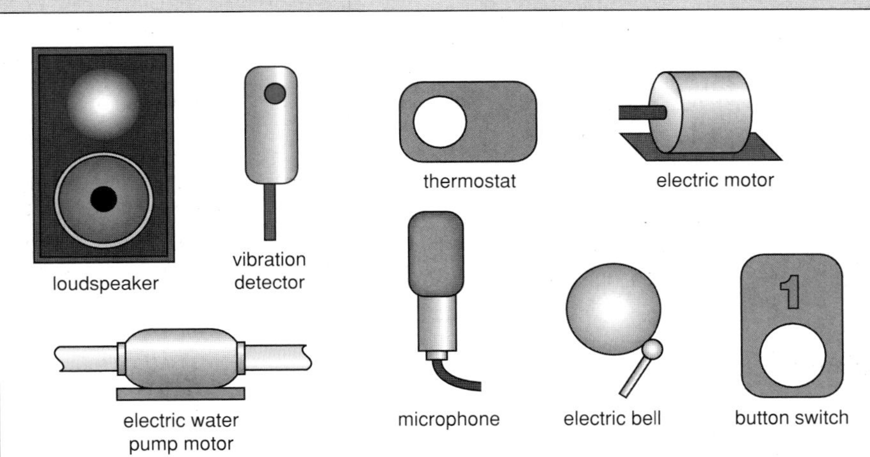

D2 Output devices

How does an electronic system produce a result?

Analogue and digital

Slowly pour some water into a bowl from a kettle or a jug: as you tip your wrist the flow of water changes smoothly and without a break.

Now take the same amount of water from an ice-cube tray that has been in the freezer. As you pour, the water comes out in solid blocks. There is no 'in between' here – you get one cube or nothing. If you tip the jug further, the flow increases in steps of 1, 2 or 3 cubes at a time, without the smooth gradual changes of the pouring liquid.

When part of an electronic system works in a smooth **continuous** manner we say that it is an ***analogue*** device. If it functions in an 'on/off' fashion, or changes in fixed steps, we say it behaves ***digitally***.

Compare the output devices shown in picture 1. Both clocks are electronic but the digital display increases by steps of one minute. The hands on the analogue clock move smoothly round.

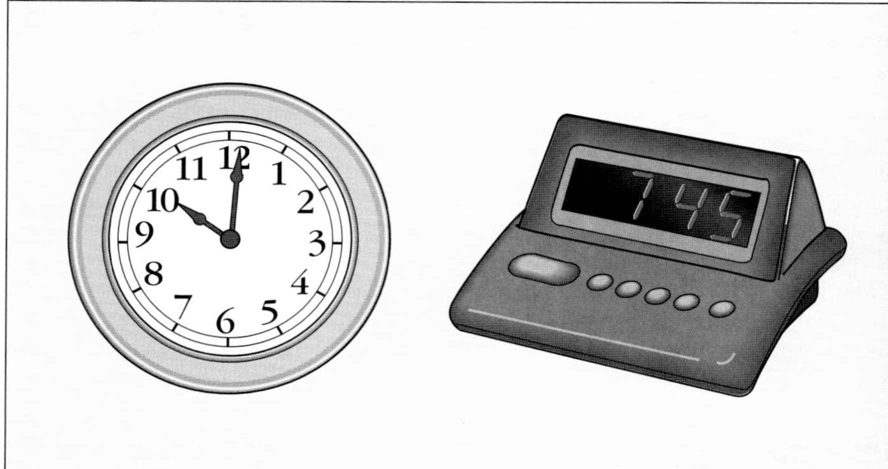

Picture 1 Analogue and digital displays.

Output devices are the parts of a system that make things happen, usually by converting a signal from one form of energy to another. Such energy changers are called **transducers**.

An alarm buzzer changes electrical energy into sound energy. The output signal to the buzzer, shown on an oscilloscope, is either *high* or *low*, corresponding to on or off.

A loudspeaker performs the same energy conversion, but can produce a range of frequencies, depending on the signal fed in to it. When displayed on an oscilloscope, we see an unbroken, continuously varying pattern.

More examples of output transducers are shown in pictures 2 and 3. Try to decide whether they are *digital* or *analogue*, and try to state the energy change involved in their operation.

A **solenoid** is an electromagnetic device which moves a metal rod backwards or forwards. Solenoids can operate the steering in radio controlled models. An **electric motor** can switch on or off, or can speed up or slow down according to the voltage supplied to it. It can be used to accelerate or decelerate a model racing car.

A **relay switch** is operated by an electromagnet. When a signal is sent to the relay, it can open or close a switch in a circuit carrying a much higher current than the control circuit. It can also be used to operate machinery remotely, to avoid placing humans in dangerous situations, for example in a nuclear power station.

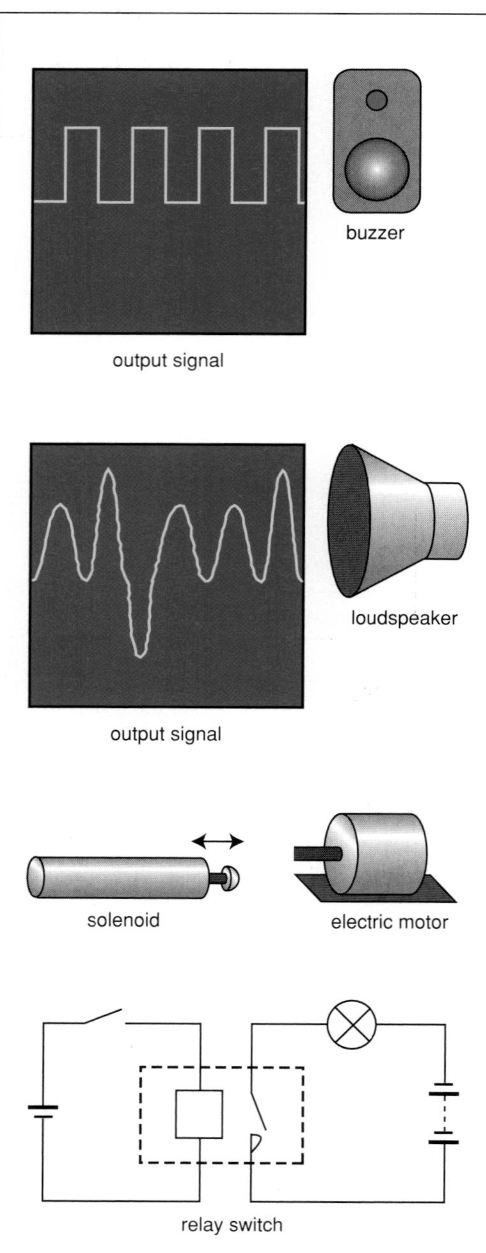

Picture 2 Analogue and digital outputs.

A lamp, such as an ordinary torch bulb, can be *on* or *off*, but can also get *brighter* or *dimmer*. In the theatre, large lamps are used in stage lighting. When a scene changes, the brightness of the lamps increases or decreases.

A Light-Emitting Diode, or **LED**, is usually operated at a set voltage and is either on or off. If we need to display changes in the level of a signal, banks of LEDs are used, as in the recording level indicators on a tape deck.

A Liquid Crystal Diode, or **LCD**, changes when switched on so that it absorbs light and thus appears dark against its background. No energy is given out – the energy change occurs inside the structure of the crystal itself.

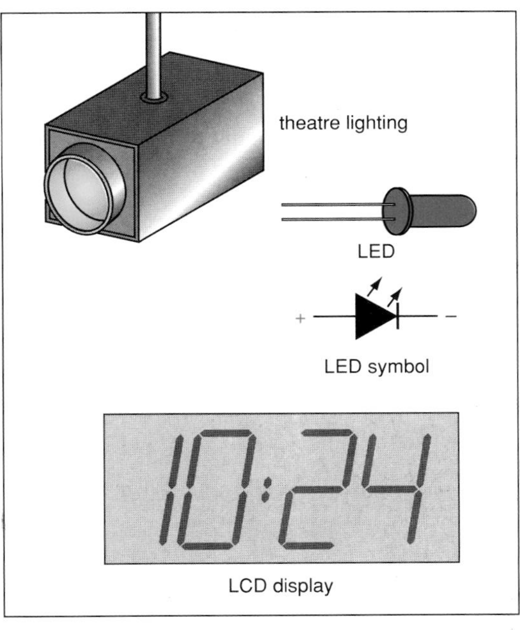

Picture 3 Analogue and digital output.

LEDs

Over the last 20 years, LEDs have become used as simple on/off indicators in a wide range of devices, such as computer disk drives, alarm systems, battery chargers, radios and televisions.

A **diode** only allows current to flow through it in *one* direction, so an LED must be connected the correct way in a circuit (see picture 3).

An LED will only work within a small current range, typically 30 mA maximum. This means that it must have a resistor connected in series to ensure that it is not damaged by excessive current.

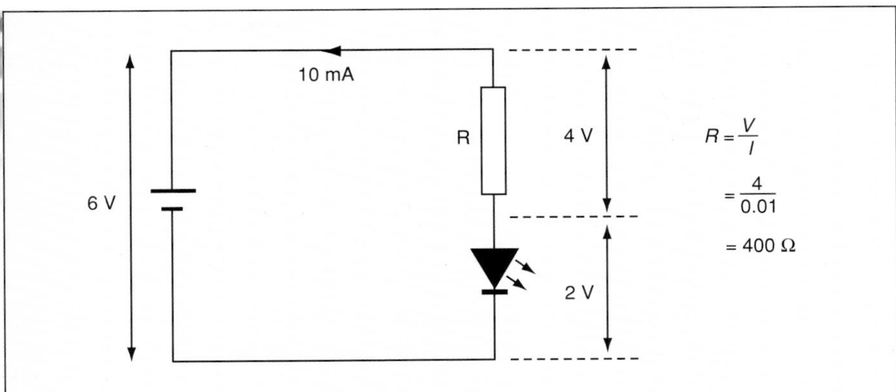

Picture 4 An LED needs a protective resistor.

For example, in picture 4 an LED is to work from a 6 V supply, and its normal operating current is 10 mA at 2 V. The voltage across the resistor must be 4 V.

Many people first encountered LEDs in early calculators, where they were used to display numbers. This can be done by using seven bar-shaped LEDs arranged as shown in picture 5; we call this a **seven-segment display**. Any number can be represented by switching on different combinations of the LEDs in the display.

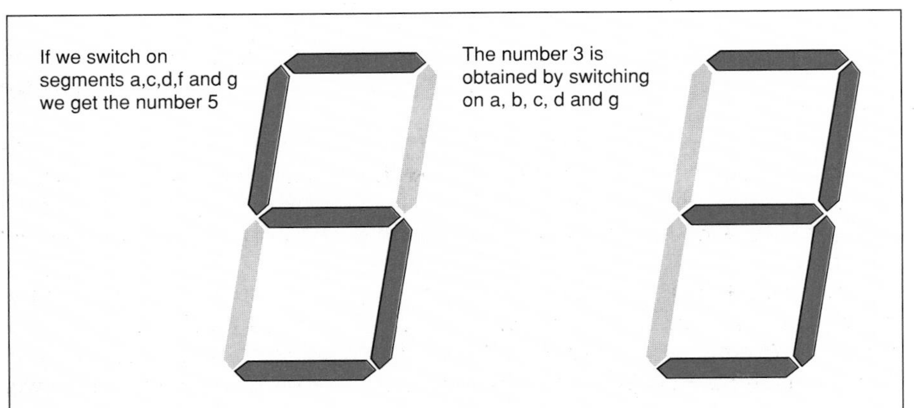

Picture 6 Different combinations of LED segments.

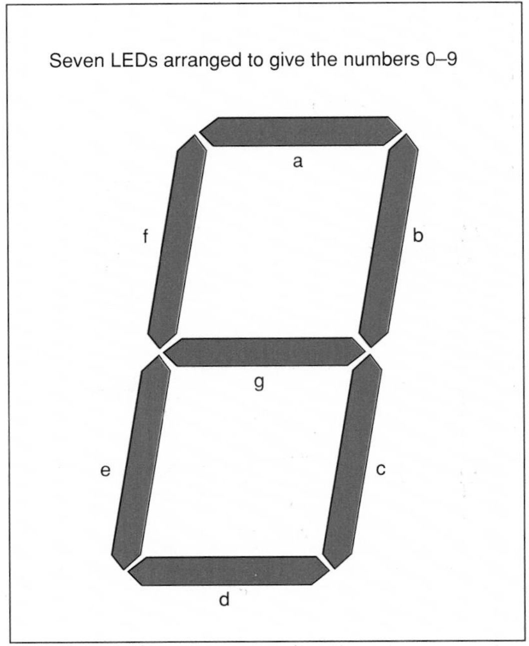

Picture 5 The seven-segment display.

Numbers can also be represented by simply using two characters, or *digits*: '1' or '0'. This is called the **binary system**. As digital electronic systems operate in an on/off manner, then the binary system is ideal for electronic calculations, where 'on' represents '1', and 'off' represents '0'. When 'on' and 'off' signals are instructions, rather than numbers, they are usually referred to as 'logic 1' and 'logic 0'.

Any decimal number can be calculated by adding powers of 2. For example, the number 7 can be found by adding

$$4 + 2 + 1$$

which are

$$2^2 + 2^1 + 2^0$$

A **binary number** is a pattern containing 1 or 0. Each position in the pattern represents a different power of 2. If there is a **1** at that position, the power of 2 is added to the total:

Decimal numbers	8		4		2		1	
Powers of 2	2^3		2^2		2^1		2^0	
Binary number	1		0		0		1	
Powers of 2 added	2^3	+	0	+	0	+	2^0	
Decimal total	8	+	0	+	0	+	1	= 9

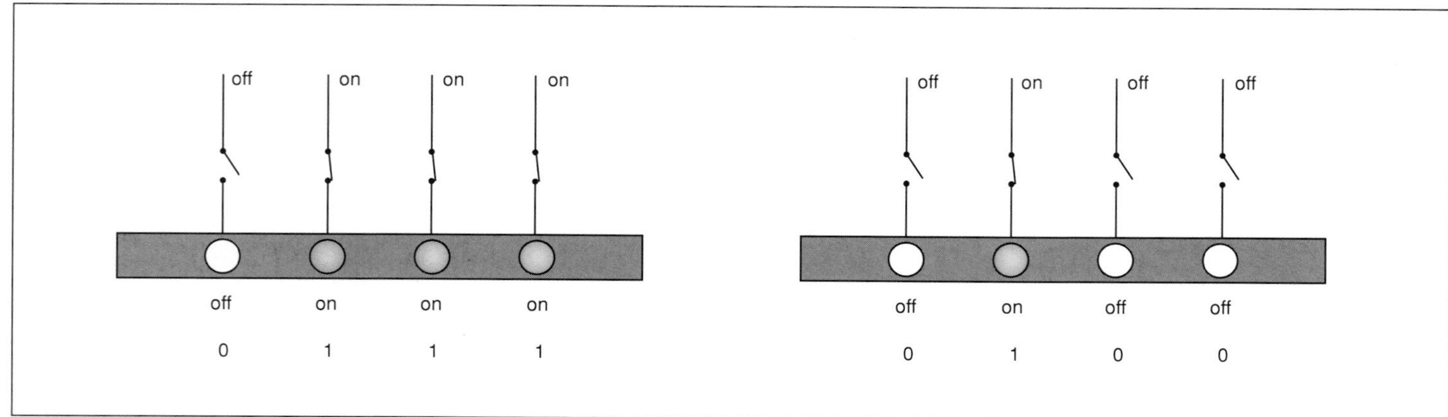

Picture 7 Binary numbers can be produced by on/off signals.

Thus 7 would be represented in binary as 0111, while 4 would be 0100. These could represent the on/off positions of switches connected to LEDs, as shown in picture 7. If the LED on the panel of the binary counter is ON, then the corresponding binary digit is a 1. If the LED is off, then that is binary 0.

Unfortunately, not many people are skilled at reading binary! To represent these numbers quickly and clearly in decimal, the signals are then sent to a decoder, which converts them into instructions for the seven-segment display.

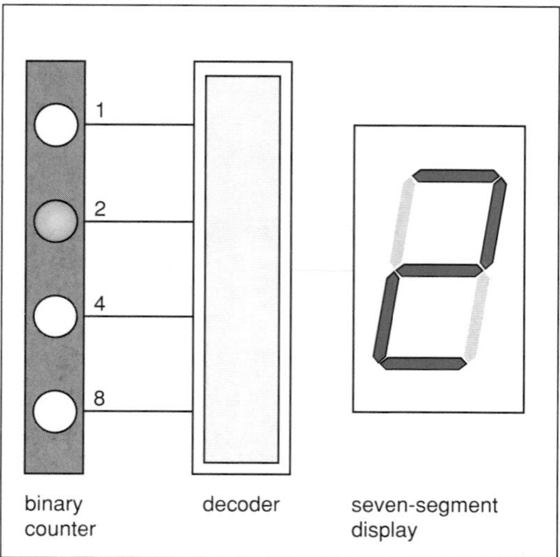

Picture 8 Converting binary to decimal.

Questions

1 Which of the LEDs in a seven-segment display would have to be on to give us the numbers shown below?

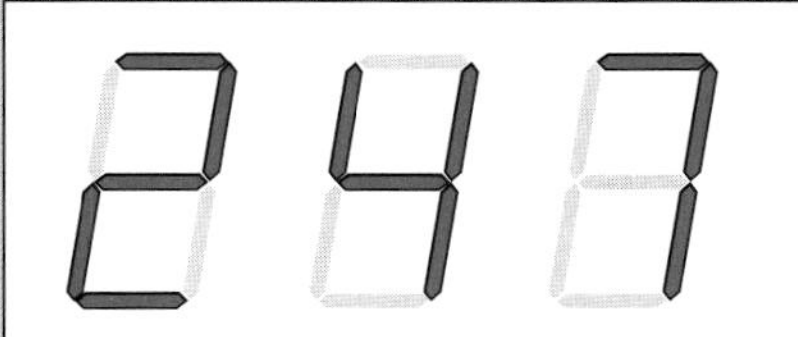

2 Which numbers would be produced by these combinations of LEDs?

a **a**, **b**, **c**, **f**, and **g**

b **a**, **c**, **d**, **e**, **f**, and **g**.

3 In the circuit shown below, which of the LEDs would light when switch S is closed?

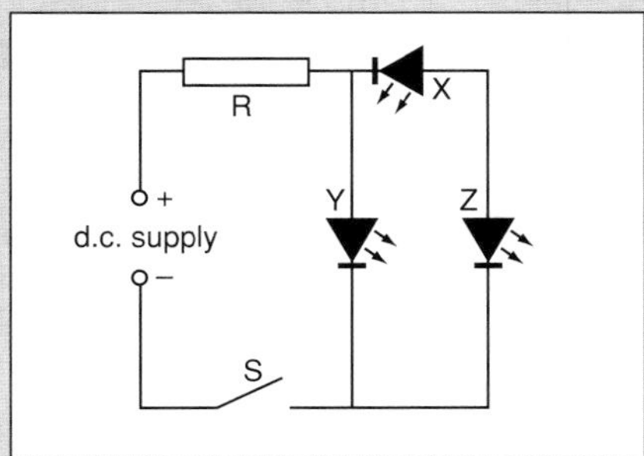

4 These output devices have been mentioned in this section: buzzer, loudspeaker, solenoid, motor, lamp, LED, relay switch.

a Group them in a simple table, under the headings *Analogue* and *Digital* (some may appear in both columns).

b From the list, choose which devices a car manufacturer could use in the following sections of the vehicle:

central door-locking system; in-car stereo system; oil warning indicator; electric windows; glove compartment light; seat-belt warning; starter motor circuit.

5 Picture 8 (page 100) shows a binary counter display connected to a decoder and seven-segment display.

Sketch the appearance of the binary counter when the numbers **1**, **3**, **6**, and **9** are shown on the decimal display.

D3
Input devices

Electronic systems can only function if they are supplied with information.

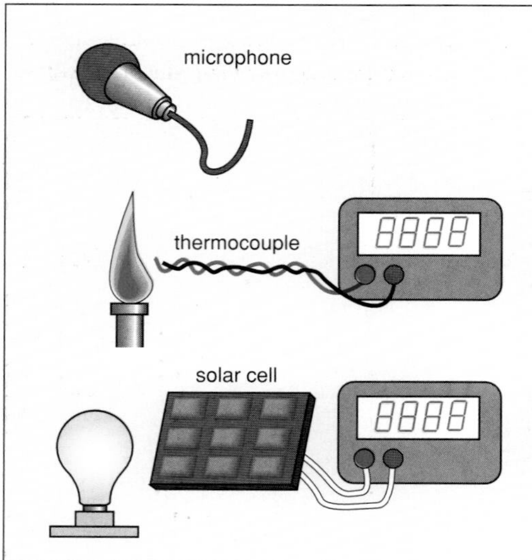

Picture 1

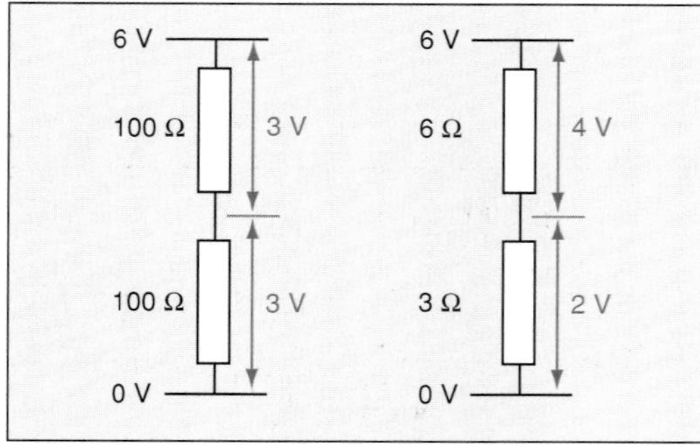

Picture 2 Using resistors to divide voltages.

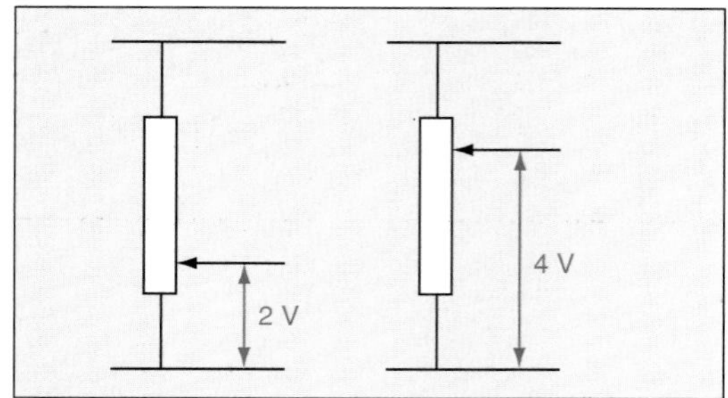

Picture 3 A potentiometer can alter voltages.

Inputs

Living things respond to changes in their environment. These changes may be gradual, such as the seasonal increases in temperature and light which tell plants that spring has arrived. They may also be sudden, such as the abrupt change in noise level when the alarm clock wakes us up on a winter morning.

Electronic systems can also be affected by events, such as the closing of a switch by a human finger. At other times, we wish the system to react to a change in the environment, and to do this automatically in our absence.

Some systems use components which respond to a particular form of energy. To supply an input to the system, they convert this into electrical energy, that is they are **transducers** (see picture 1). Other components do not *convert* the energy reaching them, but their *properties* change in response to a change in energy levels.

As humans detect changes through their senses, both types of input device can be grouped under the heading of **sensors**.

A **microphone** is the sound sensor most familiar to us. The **electret** microphone (see topic A4) changes a sound signal into an electrical signal.

A simple **thermocouple** can be made by wrapping two different wires together. When heated, it produces a voltage that increases as the temperature rises. Thermocouples are extremely useful for measuring high temperatures in inaccessible spots, such as a furnace.

A **solar cell** is a device which converts light energy into electrical energy. The greater the intensity of light falling on the cell, the bigger the voltage signal that it can produce.

The potentiometer

If two resistors are connected in series, then the voltage of the supply is divided proportionally across them, according to the value of their resistances. For example, if two *equal* resistors of 100 Ω each are connected to a 6 V supply, as in picture 2, then the voltage across each resistor is 3 V – the supply voltage is divided *equally* between them.

In the second example, one resistor is *twice* the value of the other. The supply voltage is divided into 4 V and 2 V. Using resistors as voltage dividers is also dealt with in topic B3. Note that it is not the actual *values* of the resistors that are important, but the *ratio* of their sizes:

$$\frac{V_1}{V_2} = \frac{R_1}{R_2}$$

In picture 3, a **variable** resistor is used to alter the voltage ratios, without the need to disconnect and reinsert different resistors. As the sliding contact of a variable resistor is moved, the resistance values of the different sections are altered. This means that the voltages across the terminals alter accordingly.

When used to alter voltages, a variable resistor is known as a **potentiometer**, and can provide an input voltage for an electronic system. The volume control of an amplifier is an example of how a potentiometer can be used in this way. A potentiometer can also be used as a position or movement sensor, for example in the 'joysticks' which control computer games.

LDRs and thermistors

When the amount of light falling on a **light-dependent resistor** (LDR) *increases*, its resistance *decreases*. In the dark, a typical LDR may have a resistance of 100 000 Ω (100 kΩ). In bright sunlight, its resistance could fall to about 100 Ω.

A **thermistor** behaves in a similar way, but it responds to heat energy. As its temperature *increases*, its resistance *decreases*.

Although these devices do not *convert* energy in the way that solar cells or thermocouples do, they are very useful. When connected into a circuit, the behaviour of the circuit will change according to the amount of the light falling on the LDR, or the temperature of the thermistor's surroundings.

In picture 5, an LDR is part of a voltage divider. The voltage across the LDR depends on its resistance, which depends on the amount of light falling on it. Both resistors are connected to a 5 V supply. At high light levels, the resistance of the LDR will be low (100 Ω). V_{bc} will be 0.05 V.

If the LDR is now shaded from the light, the resistance may increase to 10 kΩ, and V_{bc} will be approximately 2.6 V.

This circuit gives a raised voltage across bc if conditions are dark.

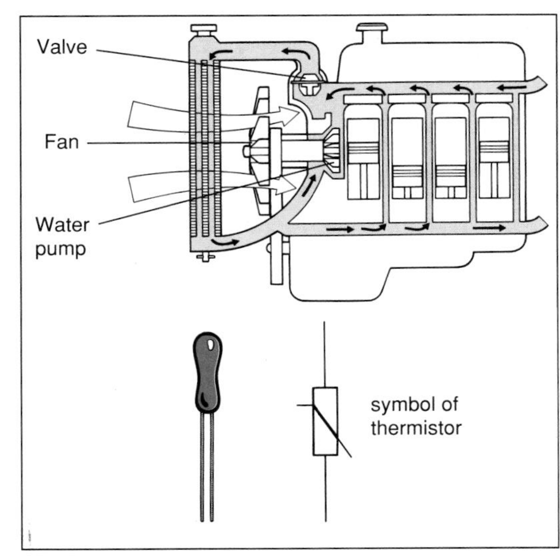

Picture 4 A car cooling system uses a thermistor.

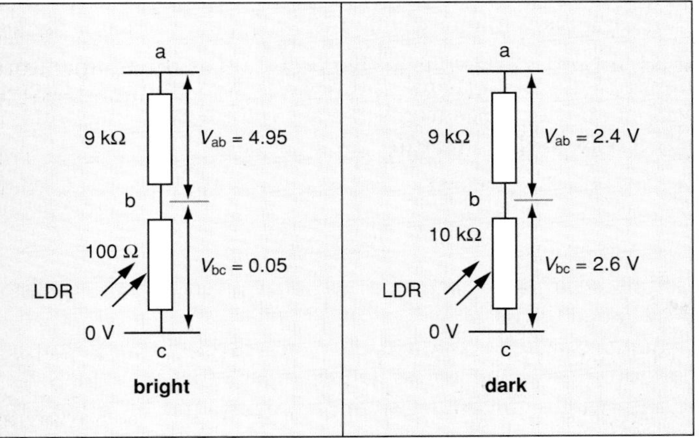

Picture 5 Using an LDR to detect different light levels.

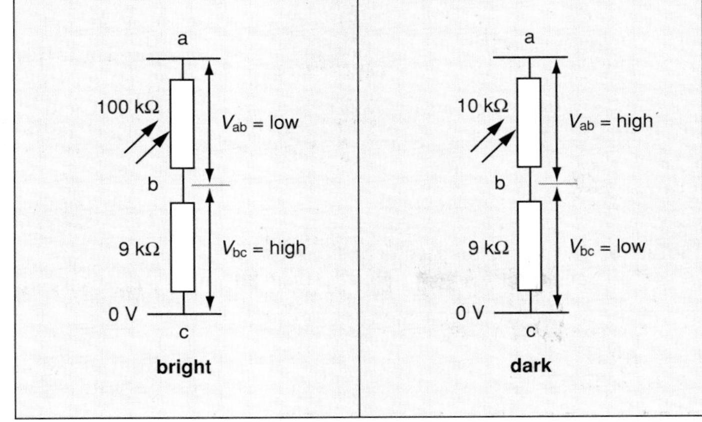

Picture 6

If we reverse the positions of the fixed resistor and LDR, as in picture 6, we have a circuit that gives a high voltage when conditions are bright.

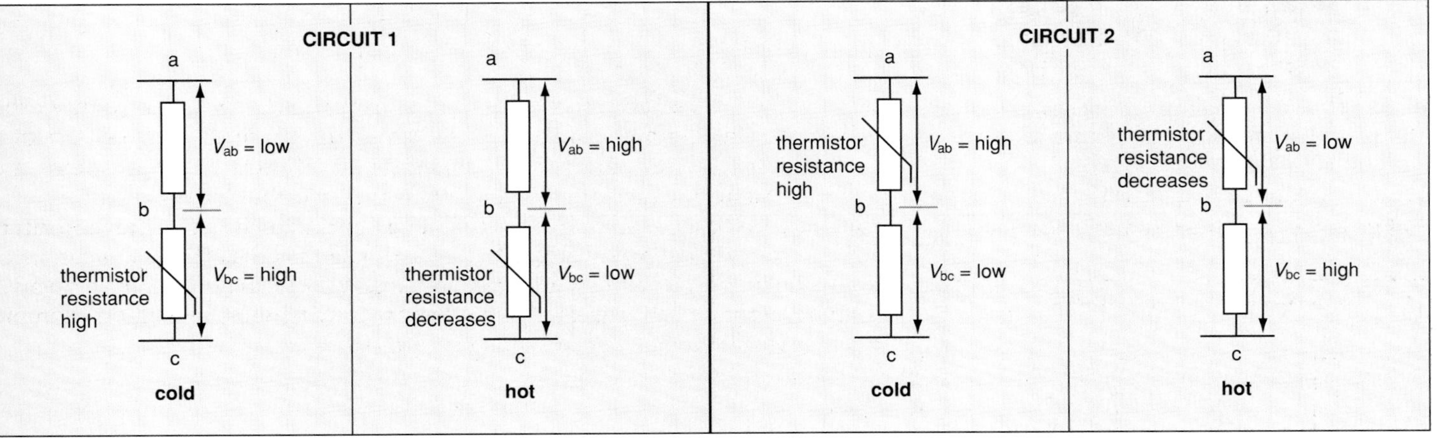

Picture 7

A thermistor behaves similarly, but its resistance varies with **temperature**. Picture 7 shows typical voltage divider circuits. In circuit 1, V_{bc} is high when the temperature is low. In circuit 2, it is high when conditions are warm.

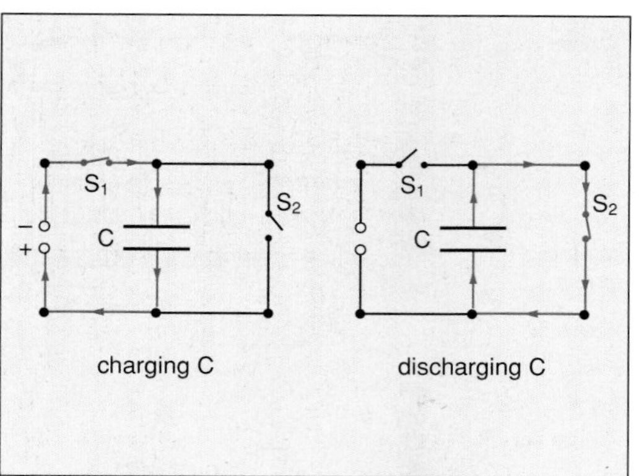

Picture 8 Charging and discharging

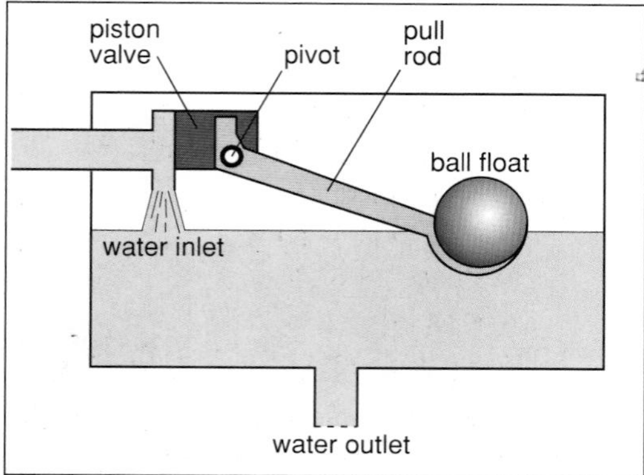

Picture 9 A cistern stores water and releases it quickly

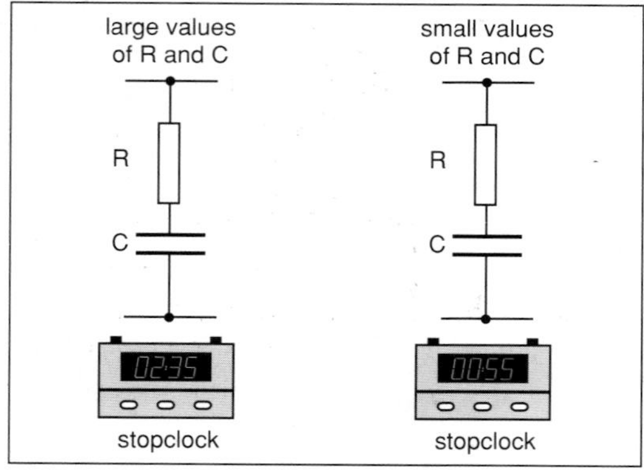

Picture 10 Altering the size of components changes the time required to reach a certain voltage level.

The capacitor

In some cameras, a faint high-pitched whine can be heard as the flash gun gets ready. This happens while the camera battery is charging the **capacitor**. A capacitor is a device which stores electrical energy (see page 51). When a switch is closed, a current will flow until the capacitor is full of electrical charge. At that point, the voltage across the capacitor is the *same* as the supply.

The capacitor can be **discharged** by connecting both sides to a switch. When the switch is closed, a current flows until there is no charge left in the capacitor and the voltage across it is zero. Picture 8 shows both these stages.

Compare this to a toilet cistern which fills until the valve is closed by the float as in picture 9. When the toilet is flushed, all the water that has been slowly stored flows away quickly. In a camera, when the capacitor is discharged, all the energy stored in the capacitor is released quickly through the flash gun, to give a bright light.

If we squeeze a garden hose while filling a bucket, the trickle of water will fill the bucket slowly. If a *large* resistor is connected in the charging circuit, as in picture 10, the flow of current is small. The capacitor is slow to charge up and reach maximum voltage. If we *lower* the value of the resistor, a large current flows, and the charging process takes less time.

If we use a large bucket it takes longer to fill. If we make the capacitor *larger* then it will also take longer to 'fill up'.

By combining different sizes of capacitor and resistor, we can design circuits which will take longer or shorter times to reach a set voltage after the switch is closed: these are called **time delay circuits**.

The switch

A switch can be used as an input device in a way that gives a 'high' or 'low' voltage – a '1' or '0' in digital terms.

In picture 11(a), when the switch is open, there is no current flowing through the resistor, and therefore no voltage across it. This means that V_{bc} equals zero or 'low'. If we close the switch, current flows in the circuit, and V_{bc} equals the supply voltage, giving '1'. If we reverse the components, we can produce the opposite effect.

In picture 11(b) when the switch is open, the voltage across bc is 5 V – 'high' or '1'. When the switch is closed, the switch has no resistance, and all the supply voltage is across the resistor. The voltage across bc is zero – 'low'.

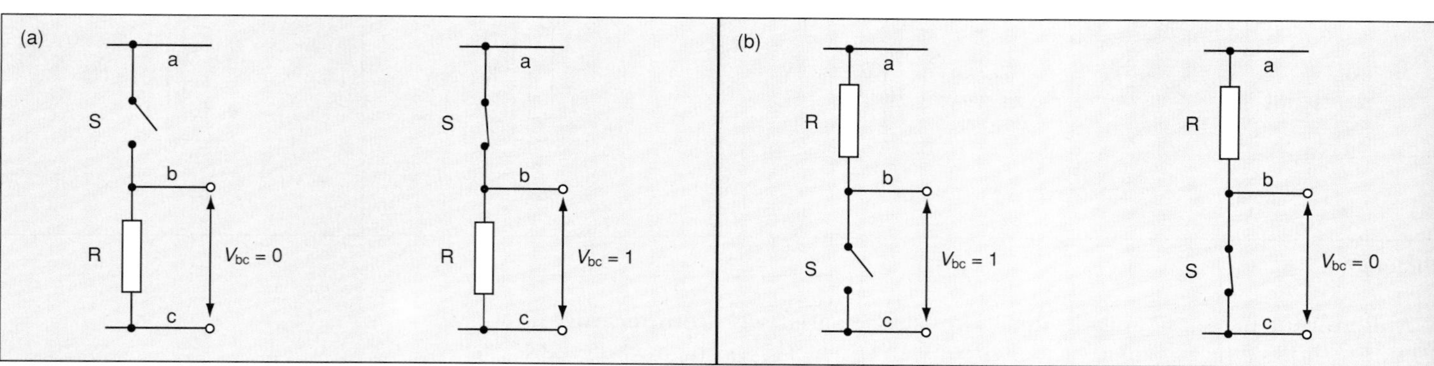

Picture 11 Switches can be arranged to produce a '1' or a '0'.

Questions

1a The resistance of a light dependent resistor (LDR) in light and in dark is given below.

Resistance of LDR in light = 1.0 kΩ

Resistance of LDR in dark = 1.0 MΩ

A 49 kΩ resistor and a LDR are connected to a 5 V d.c. supply as shown in the figure below.

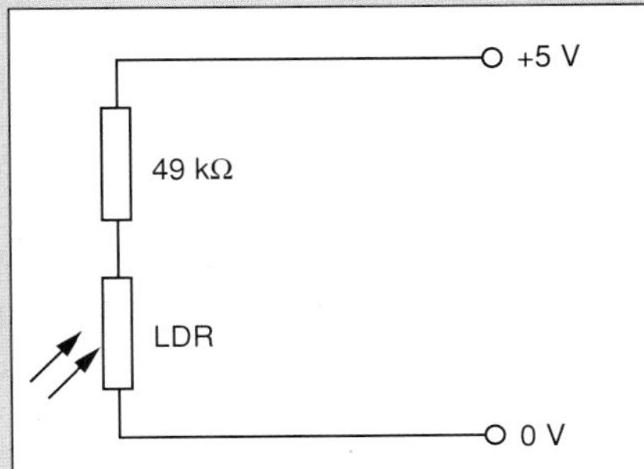

What is the voltage across the LDR when in light?

2 A thermistor is connected to a 3 volt d.c. supply.

The table below gives some information about the thermistor.

Calculate the current flowing when the thermistor is placed in a warm room.

Position of thermistor	Resistance of thermistor (ohms)
Inside a freezer	2000
In a warm room	500
Inside a hot oven	100

3 Three members of a school electronics club are planning their next projects. One project is to build a light meter. A second project is to build a circuit which will control the opening and closing of curtains from a distance. The third project is to build a sound operated baby alarm.

The members use a catalogue to select components for their projects. The catalogue has the following list giving details of input and output devices.

Reference	Device	Details
MIC 1	Microphone	Table type
LDR 70	Light dependent resistor	Resistance in dark – 1 000 000 ohms Resistance in light – 1000 ohms
THERM 94	Thermistor	Resistance at 25°C is 5000 ohms
SOL 2	Solar cell	Complete with leads
MOT 1	Motor	Input voltage 9 volts
LS 3	Loudspeaker	Resistance 3 ohms
SOL (4 cm)	Solenoid	Spring return

a Which of the devices listed in the catalogue is a suitable input device for the baby alarm?

b Name **two** devices in the list which are output devices.

c Name, from the list, a suitable output device for the curtain control circuit.

d State the useful energy change which takes place in the solar cell.

e The light meter project involves the use of the light dependent resistor (LDR) in a circuit as shown below.

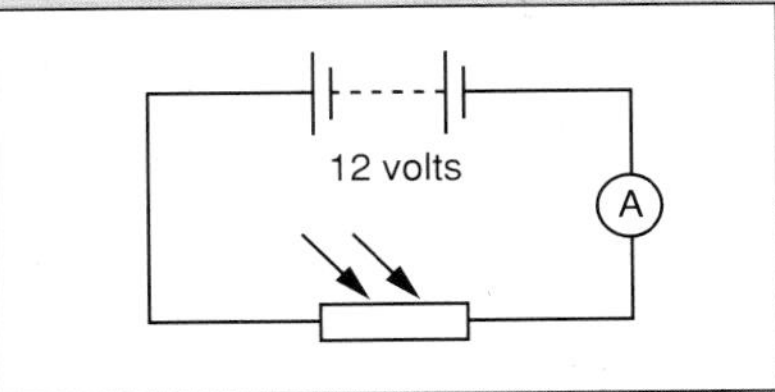

Calculate the current in the circuit when the LDR is exposed to light.

D4
The transistor

A tiny device which conrols the modern world.

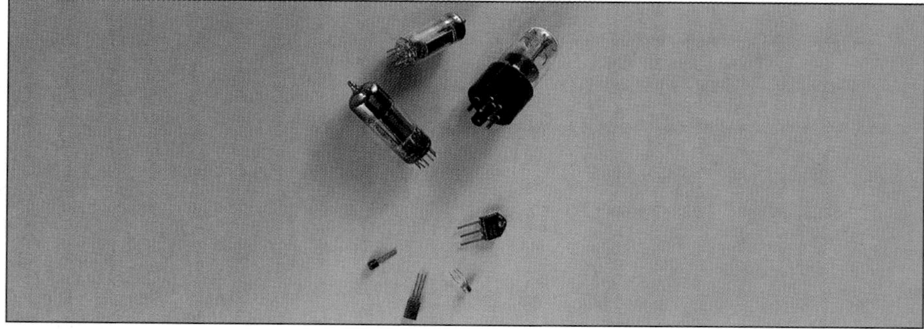
Picture 1 Large valves and small transistors.

The transistor is one of the most significant inventions of the 20th century. Before its development, electronic devices such as radios and televisions contained large fragile components called **valves**, which were made of glass and metal. By contrast, transistors are small solid components made from materials called **semiconductors**.

As the name suggests, semiconductors are neither good conductors nor complete insulators, but fall between these two categories. The two most common examples are **silicon** and **germanium**. Semiconductor materials can be specially treated to improve their conducting properties, by introducing small amounts of impurities. This process is known as **doping**.

If a semiconductor is given extra *negative* charges, it is called **n–type**. If the doping creates a shortage of negative charges, leaving a surplus *positive* charge, the material is **p–type**. Picture 2 shows how these materials can be arranged in a three layer 'sandwich' – either **pnp** or **npn**. The outside layers of the sandwich are the **collector** and **emitter**; the central 'filling' is called the **base**.

When the transistor is connected into a circuit, nothing happens, because no current can flow across the different layers from the collector to the emitter. Yet, as shown in picture 3, if a voltage is applied in the correct way across the **base–emitter** terminals, a small current flows between them. This has the effect of breaking down the 'barrier' in the layers, and current flows from the **collector** to **emitter** in the main part of the circuit: the transistor has been **switched on**.

This can be indicated, as in picture 4, by connecting an LED in the collector–emitter circuit, so that whenever the transistor conducts, the LED is *on*.

Note that although the current in the base triggers the flow of current in the main part of the circuit, in practical terms they are entirely separate. The base current can be much smaller than the collector–emitter current.

Even the tiny amount of electrical activity in the human body can be enough to switch the transistor on. If the base of the transistor in picture 5 is touched by the person's thumb, the transistor allows a current to flow from the battery and through the bulb.

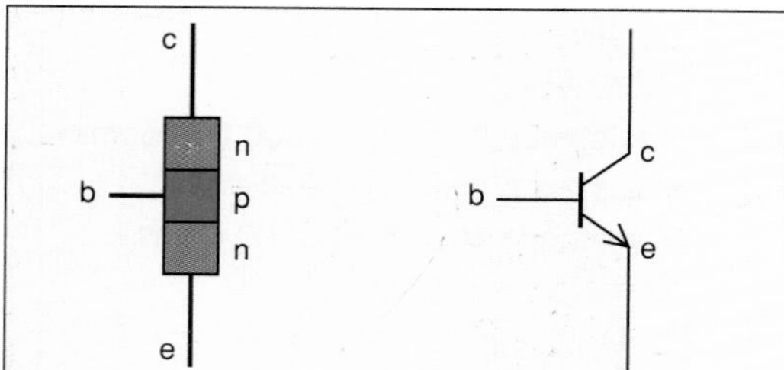

Picture 2 An npn transistor.

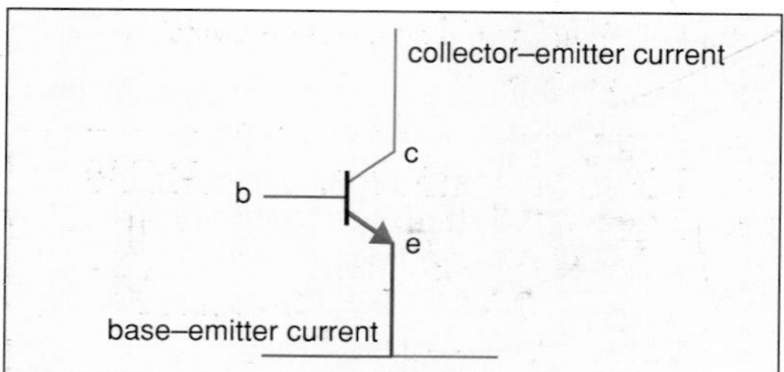

Picture 3 Current flow in a transistor.

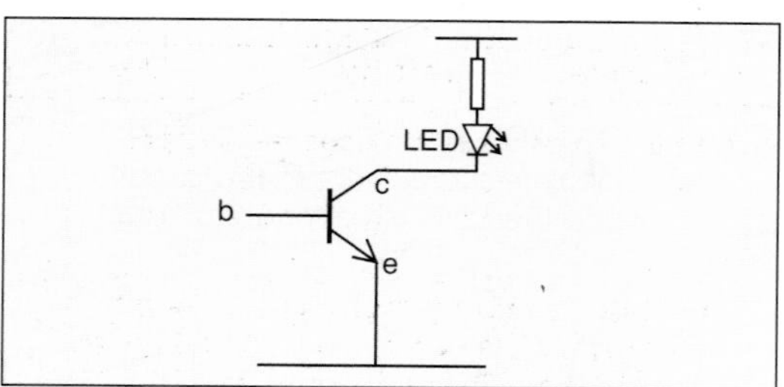

Picture 4 Using an LED as an indicator.

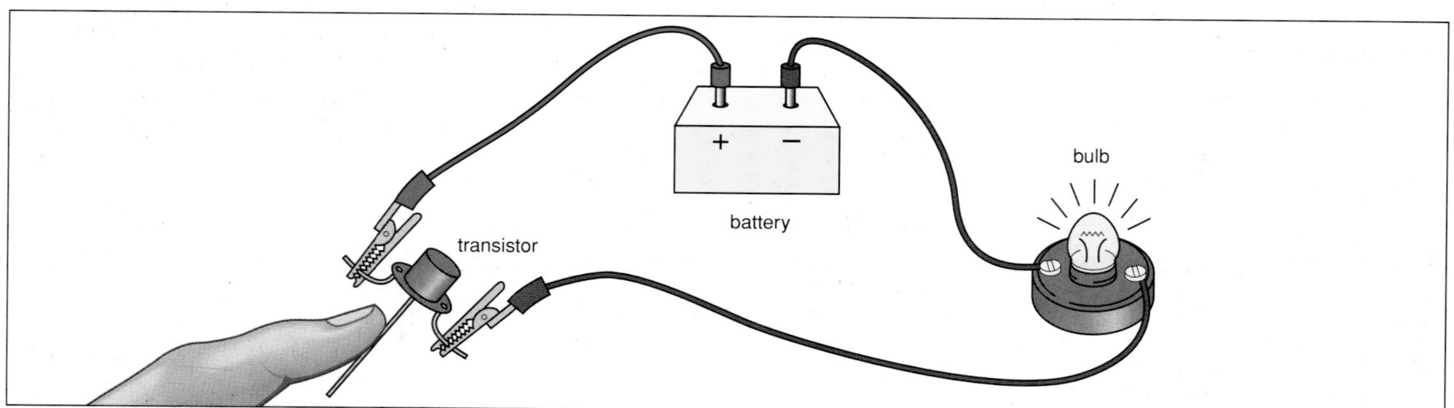

Picture 5 A transistor can be switched on by very small amounts of electricity.

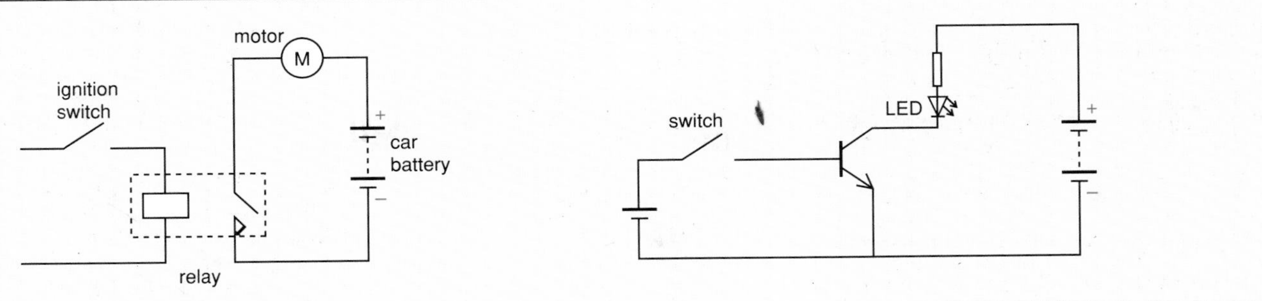

Picture 6 A transistor can be used as a switch.

In picture 6, a relay switch being used to switch on the starter motor of a car. When the ignition key switch is closed, a *small* current flows in the relay switch. It closes and completes the circuit that supplies a *large* current to the motor.

The transistor can be regarded as a switch which operates in a similar manner. A current *only* flows in the main part of the circuit if an **input voltage** produces a **base–emitter current**. We can use the transistor as a **voltage operated switch**. The advantage of such an electronic switch is that it can switch on and off millions of times every second. Computers can therefore do rapid binary calculations, using integrated circuits filled with transistors.

A voltage divider circuit can be used to provide input to a transistor (picture 7). The values of R_1 and R_2 must be chosen to give the required voltage across R_2. The resistor R_b is included to control the size of the base current.

If we connect the base to the variable contact on a **potentiometer**, we can increase the input voltage gradually until the transistor switches on. We find that the transistor starts to work when $V_2 = 0.7$ V.

The transistor is our first example of a *process* device; if it receives the appropriate input signal, it can activate an output device.

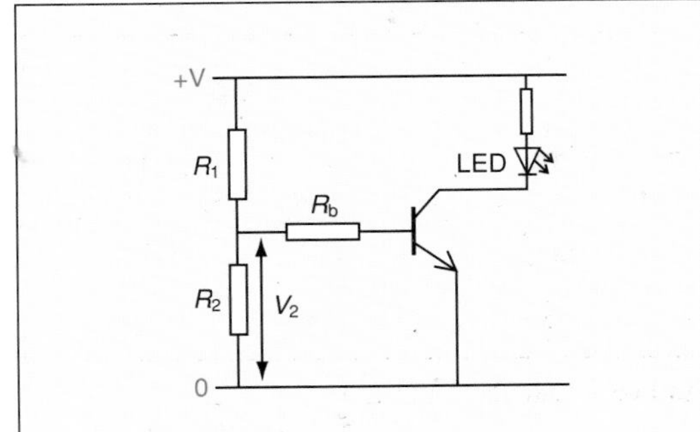

Picture 7 Using a voltage divider to switch a transistor on.

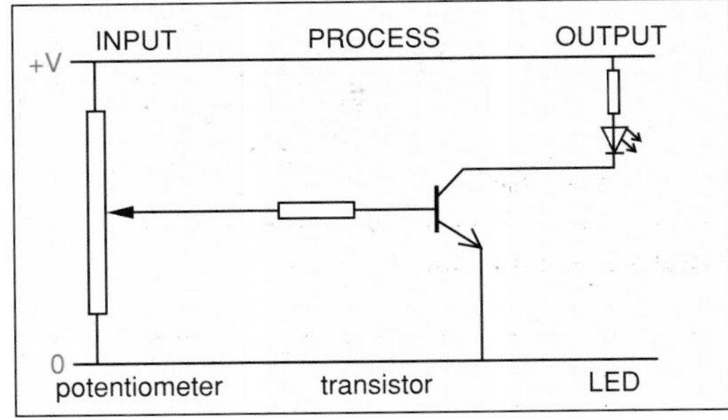

Picture 8 The transistor processes an input.

The history of the transistor

The transistor was developed during the 1940s at the Bell Telephone Laboratories in the United States, where research was being carried out into the properties of semiconductors.

It had long been known that certain crystals would only allow a current to flow in one direction, and such crystals were used in early radios. This is why the first radios were sometimes known as 'crystal sets'. Crystals were eventually replaced by the much more efficient vacuum tubes, or 'valves'.

William Shockley, Walter Brittain, and John Bardeen found that germanium crystals containing certain impurities were far more reliable than the early crystals, and had many advantages over fragile glass valves.

By combining different layers of material, it was possible to *trans*fer a signal across the re*sistor* formed by the germanium crystals – hence the name *transistor*. Unlike valves, these components were completely solid, and so the term *solid-state electronics* came in to use. Further advantages were that there could be extremely small and did not need time to warm up before beginning operation.

In 1948, Shockley and his co-workers produced a transistor which could act as an amplifier. The techniques for manufacturing semiconductor crystals quickly improved, and by 1953 tiny transistors were being used in hearing aids which could fit inside the ear.

Shockley, Brittain and Bardeen received the Nobel Prize for Physics in 1956.

D5 Transistor switches

Using the transistor for simple processing.

Keeping warm

Tropical fish come originally from warmer climates, so the water in their aquarium must be kept at a suitable temperature, especially during cold winter nights. If we include a thermistor in a voltage divider, then we can design a circuit that will operate when the temperature drops below a certain level.

In picture 2, as the temperature falls, the resistance of the thermistor *increases* and so the voltage across it *rises*. At a certain point, the transistor will operate a relay, switching on a heater. When the temperature of the water has risen to an acceptable level, the voltage across the thermistor drops, which causes the transistor to switch off the relay and the heater.

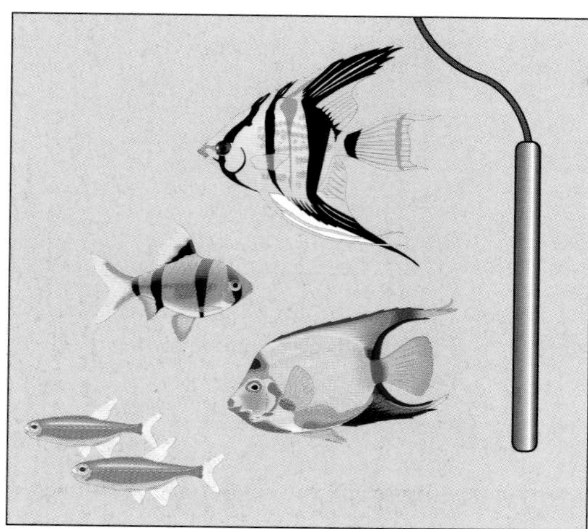

Picture 1 Controlling an aquarium heater.

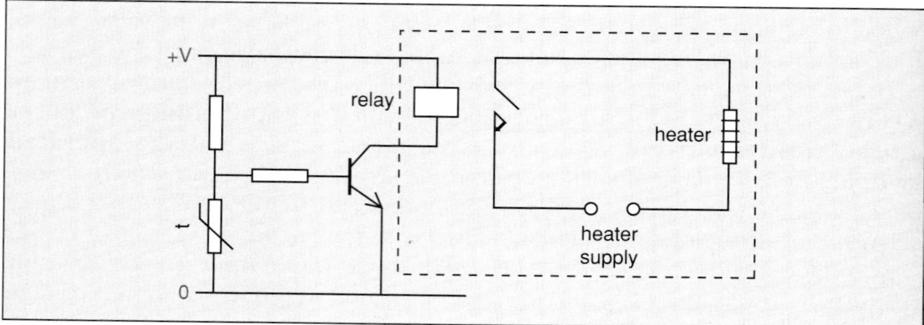

Picture 2

Staying healthy

Many people use microwave ovens to defrost food from the freezer. If a chicken has not been properly defrosted, it may not cook properly when placed in a normal oven. This could result in food poisoning. As part of a science project, some students designed a device, using a thermistor near the tip of a spiked metal probe (picture 3). This checks the temperature of the inside of the chicken. When the probe is pushed into the centre of the chicken, the LED will light if the temperature of the meat is at least several degrees above zero.

The thermistor and fixed resistor are connected as shown in part (a) of picture 4. As the temperature rises, the thermistor resistance *decreases*. The voltage across the fixed resistor *increases* until the transistor switches on. When the transistor conducts, it causes the LED to light.

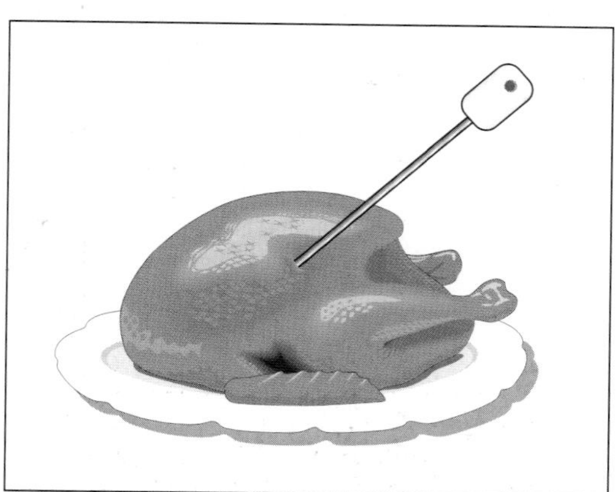

Picture 3 Checking temperature with a thermistor device.

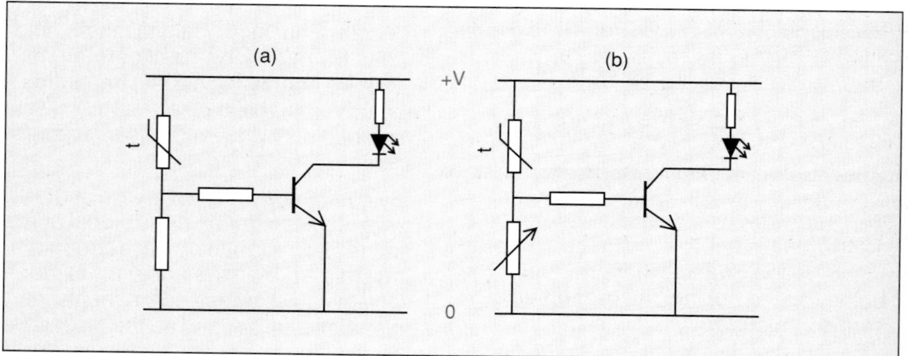

Picture 4

If we replace the fixed resistor with a **variable** resistor, as in part (b) we can alter the voltage ratios. This would alter the temperature at which the transistor switched on. The device could now also be used to check the internal temperature of the **cooked** chicken. Using a variable resistor in this way makes potential divider circuits more flexible.

Getting dry

A restaurant owner installs a hot-air dryer in the toilet (picture 5). Customers can push a button on the machine and dry their hands in the stream of warm air.

When the machine is off, as in picture 6, the capacitor is fully *charged*, so the voltage across it is equal to the supply voltage. The transistor is *on*, and operates a relay which holds the dryer switch *open*.

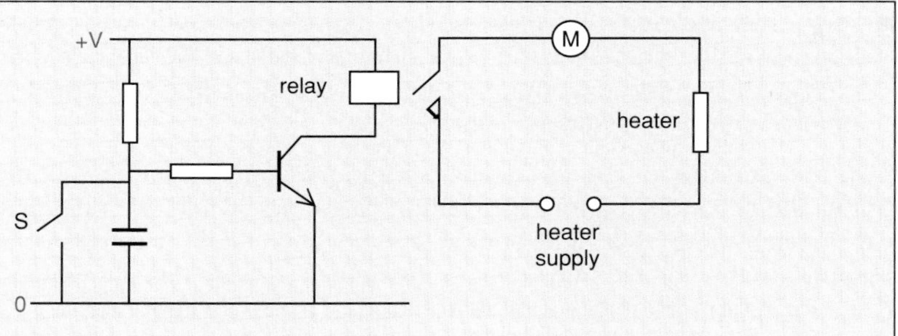

Picture 5

When the button switch **S** is pushed, the capacitor is *discharged*, the transistor switches *off*, and the relay *closes*, starting the blower. As soon as the button is released, the capacitor starts to charge up. The customer dries his hands until the capacitor has reached a voltage which activates the transistor, opening the relay switch and stopping the blower.

The owner finds that the blower is staying on long after the customers have dried their hands, and so adding to his electricity bill. He calls the company which supplied the dryer, and they send a technician. What *two* alterations could the technician make to the circuit?

Staying bright

The owner of a house wishes his front room curtains to close automatically when it becomes dark outside. When he is on holiday, it will not be obvious to burglars that the house is empty. He designs a circuit as shown in picture 7. The LDR is fitted to the outside wall of the house, as a light sensor. When the light outside the window falls to a certain level, the voltage across the LDR has increased sufficiently to switch the transistor on. The small motor turns a pulley that draws the curtain cords, moving the curtains across.

When he first assembles the system there is a problem: the curtains shut during the day every time a dark cloud crosses the Sun. He adjusts the variable resistor until the circuit only operates when the light level outside is very low.

In real life, of course, things would not be as simple as our example suggests. For example, how would you switch the motor off when the curtains had closed fully? How do you make the circuit reverse the motor to open the curtains in the morning? To produce systems that deal with complicated situations, where events depend on combinations of circumstances, we need more sophisticated processing devices. This is examined in the next topic.

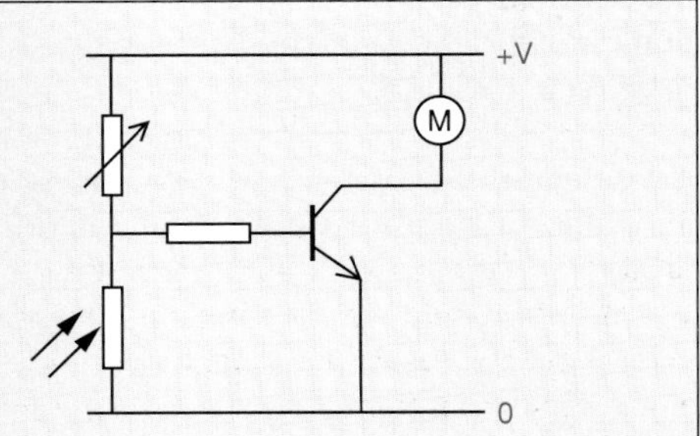

Picture 6 A light sensor circuit.

Questions

1 The diagram below shows an automatic hand washing unit in a restaurant.

Inserting the hands into the unit breaks a light beam and causes a stream of water to be turned on for ten seconds.

a The light beam is directed at a light dependent resistor (LDR) which is part of the circuit shown below.

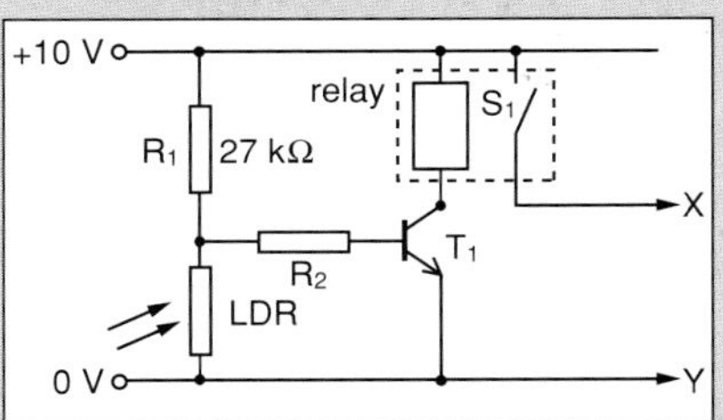

i) When hands are inserted into the unit, the circuit causes the switch S_1 in the relay to close. Explain why this happens.

ii) Calculate the voltage across the LDR when its resistance is 9.0 kΩ.

b When the relay switch in the figure above is closed, another circuit connected to X and Y as shown in the figure below opens a water valve for ten seconds.

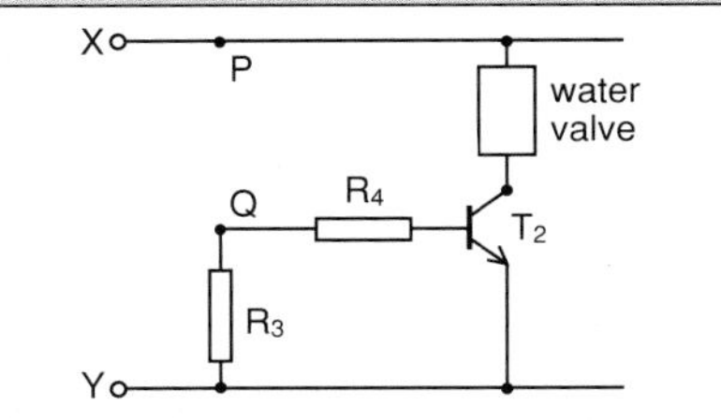

Complete the diagram to show the component which should be connected between P and Q so that the water is turned on for ten seconds.

D6 Gates

Gates allow us to make decisions about what happens in a system.

We have explored the ways in which electronic systems can use sensors to respond to events. Life can be rather complicated, however, and we may wish to design a system which will react when different combinations of conditions occur. Consider the following examples:

- We may wish the courtesy light in a car to come on when either the passenger *or* the driver door is opened.
- At home we may have a garden light which we wish to switch on automatically, whenever the back door is opened. We do not want to waste energy during the daytime, so the light should come on only if the door is opened *and* it is also dark outside.

In the example of the car doors, simple mechanical switches could be used but in the second situation, in addition to a door switch, we need a switch that can be activated by a light sensor. As we have seen, a transistor switch can respond to the voltage output from a variety of sensors. Finally, we need to relate the information from the door switch to that from the light sensor to so that our system can **make a decision**.

This can be done by connecting transistors to produce an output when they receive a particular *combination* of signals. Such arrangements of transistors are known as **gates**. A gate is something that lets you through or keeps you out depending on whether it is open or shut. Electronic systems use gates which 'open' or 'close' depending on what their inputs tell them. This means they can be used to send signals to other circuits.

Using logic

Logic is a way of thinking and making decisions based on clear rules. Logic words are short and simple, like AND, OR, or NOT. Let us think about using logic to make decisions.

AND decisions

Decision needed: Do I have to carry an umbrella?
Input facts: **A** it is raining. **B** I have to go out.
Decision (output): **Yes**, this means I have to carry an umbrella.

This decision is correct only if *both* the input facts are correct. There is no law against carrying an umbrella on a fine day, but you would look a bit silly. The same is true if it *is* raining, but you are carrying one around while staying indoors.

OR decisions

Decision needed: Shall I go to the school disco?
Input conditions: I will go *if* either: **A** Jane invites me,
or **B** Tracy invites me.
Decision (output): Jane has invited me. **Yes**, I will go.

NOT decisions

Decision needed: Shall I go to the school disco?
Input conditions: I don't like Sheila. I will NOT go if she is going.
Decision (output): Sheila isn't going. **Yes**, I will go.

Picture 1 shows how we can summarise each of these decisions by using **truth tables**. These show at a glance the different decisions arrived at for different situations.

AND truth table

A	B	output
NO	NO	NO
NO	YES	NO
YES	NO	NO
YES	YES	YES

OR truth table

A	B	output
NO	NO	NO
NO	YES	YES
YES	NO	YES

NOT truth table

A	output
NO	YES
YES	NO

Picture 1

The AND gate

Picture 2 shows a simple circuit where the lamp will light only if switch S_1 *and* switch S_2 are closed. Picture 3(a) shows transistors connected in a similar way.

Transistor T_A conducts when it receives a high (logic 1) input signal. If only input A receives a signal, no current flows, as T_B is *off*. Similarly, if T_B is on but T_A is *not*, there will still be no current. Only if a signal is received at both inputs A *and* B will a current flow through the transistors. This produces an output voltage across the resistor R, switching on the output transistor T_Z and lighting the LED. This arrangement is known as an **AND gate**, and its symbol is shown in picture 3(b). The behaviour of this gate can also be summarised in a truth table, which shows the output produced by different input conditions.

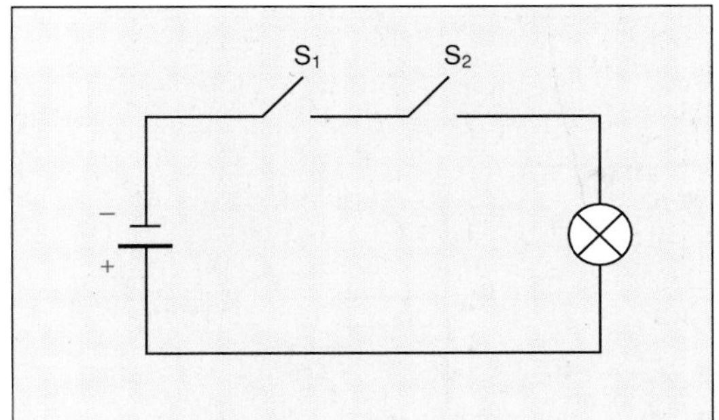

Picture 2

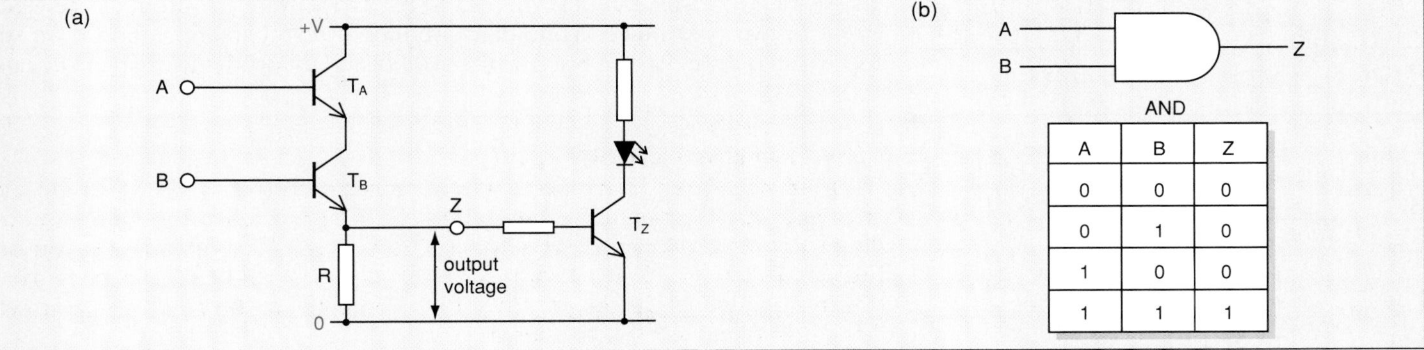

A	B	Z
0	0	0
0	1	0
1	0	0
1	1	1

Picture 3 An AND gate circuit.

Sensors plus AND gates

The fan in a car cooling system (picture 4) switches on only when the engine gets too hot and the car is running. This means that it must be controlled by an AND gate. One input to the gate is from the car ignition switch, and the other is from a temperature sensor. The output from the AND gate makes the fan switch on when the engine is running *and* the temperature gets too high. The car manufacturer has to set the temperature sensor to the right value to give a 1 when the engine is too hot.

Picture 5 shows a simple circuit for doing this. It uses a thermistor as part of a voltage divider. The resistor R is chosen so that at the 'danger temperature' the voltage input to B is high enough to give a 1.

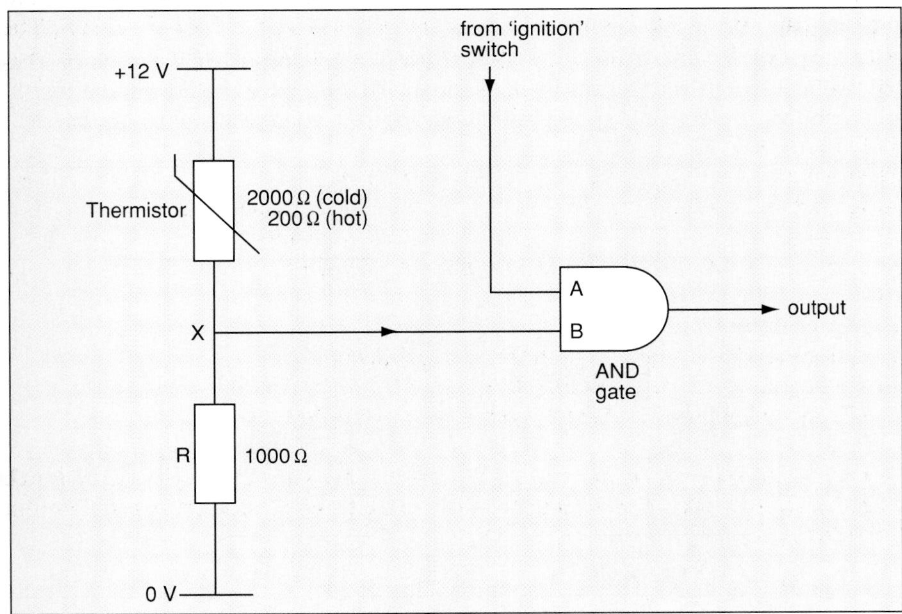

Picture 5 A control system for the cooling fan.

Picture 4 A car cooling system. A sensor turns on the air fan.

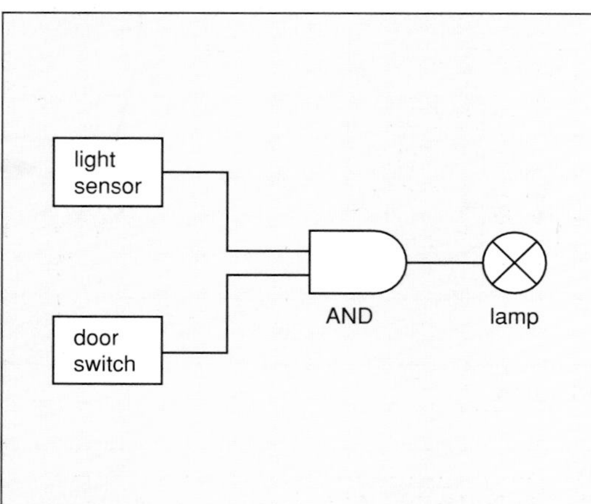

Picture 6 Solving the garden light problem.

When drawing diagrams of gates, to keep matters simple we do not usually show the details of the sensor circuit. Instead we represent the various input devices on a block diagram. Picture 6 illustrates this and shows how we can use the AND gate to provide a solution to the garden light problem, mentioned in the introduction to this section. The picture shows a simplified block diagram for the system. The door switch produces a 1 when open, and the light sensor does the same when light levels fall. The lamp lights only when the door is opened *and* it is dark outside.

The OR gate

In this arrangement, (picture 7) an output signal is achieved when Transistor A *or* Transistor B receives an input. This can be used to activate an output device when *either* of two prearranged conditions are met. If *both* conditions occur, we still receive an output. Picture 8 shows the symbol and the truth table for an OR gate.

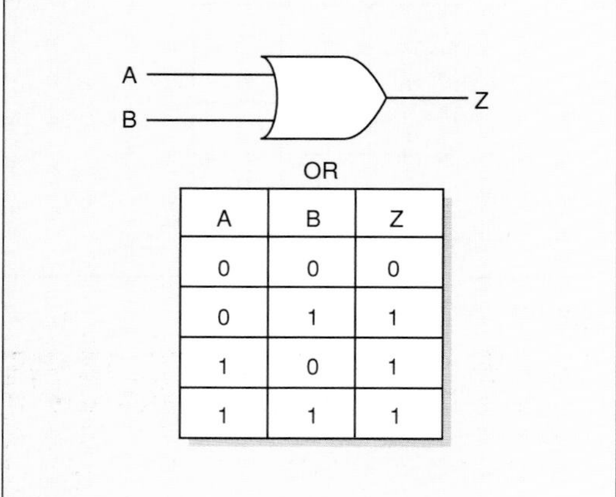

A	B	Z
0	0	0
0	1	1
1	0	1
1	1	1

Picture 8 An OR gate and truth table.

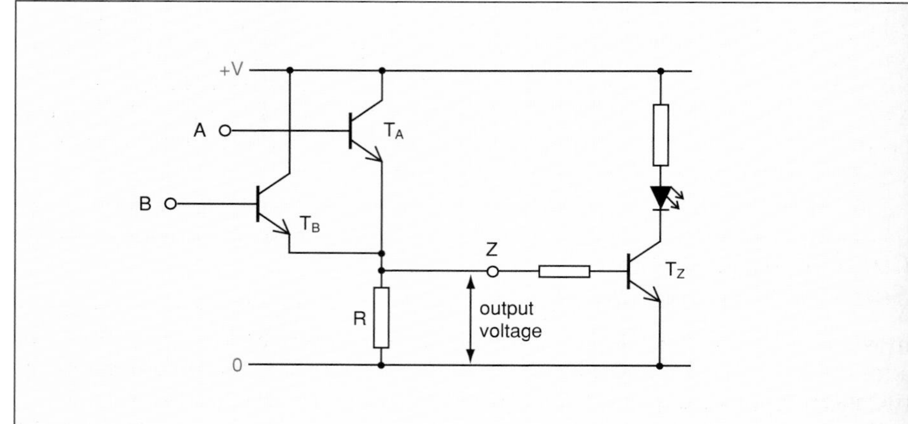

Picture 7 An OR gate circuit.

The NOT gate

We saw in the section on input devices that a switch can be used to provide a voltage signal. In part (a) of picture 9, we see that if switch S is closed, there will be zero volts across it. In other words, when the switch is *on* ('1'), it gives an *off* ('0') signal.

The reverse is also true: a '0' input gives a '1' output. If we replace the mechanical switch with a transistor, as in part (b), we have the advantage that it will respond at electronic speeds, and we can use a voltage signal to operate it.

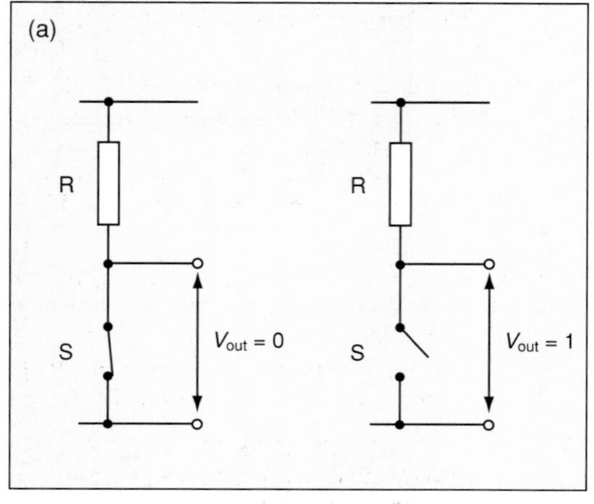

Picture 9(a) Switches producing different voltage signals.

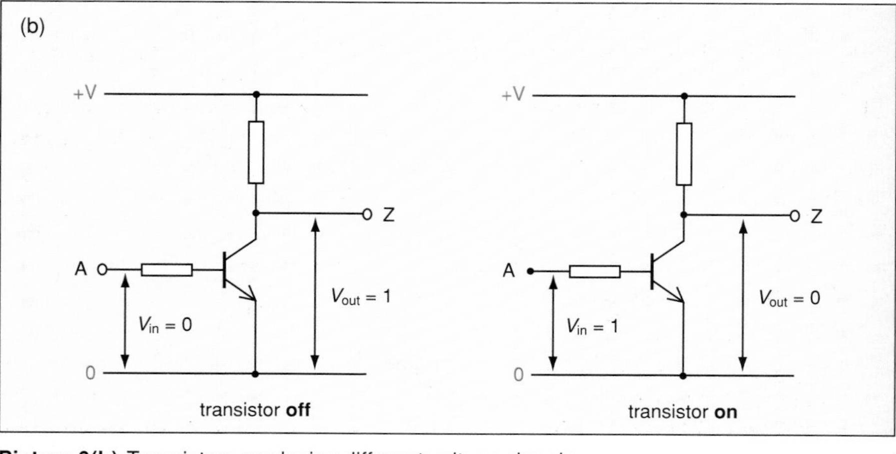

Picture 9(b) Transistors producing different voltage signals.

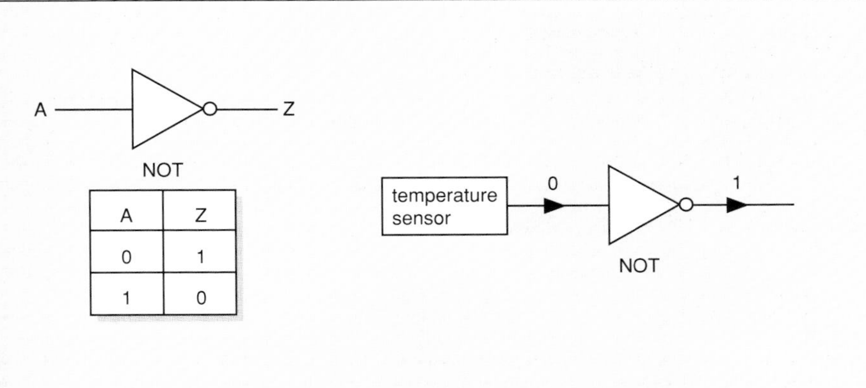

Picture 10 Using a NOT gate to produce the required signal.

door switch
A
vibration sensor
B
OR
buzzer
Z
AND
alarm switch
C

Picture 11 A car alarm system.

Suppose we need an output signal that is the opposite of the input. For example, we may only have available a sensor which produces a '1' when the temperature rises, but we require this output when the temperature *falls*. For this we can use our transistor switch as an INVERTER or **NOT gate** (picture 10). As we can see from the truth table, a NOT gate produces an output which is the opposite or *inverse* of the signal it receives. Combining it with our temperature sensor allows us to produce the desired effect.

Combining gates

A car alarm must work if the door is opened, or a vibration sensor detects a movement of the vehicle. This could be inconvenient when driving! The additional condition that must be met, of course, is that the driver has activated the alarm *after* parking and leaving the vehicle.

The block diagram in picture 11 shows how to achieve this by combining an AND gate with an OR gate. Unless the alarm switch has been set by the driver, the AND gate will not function at all, regardless of the signals produced by the sensors. When the switch has been closed, if a '1' is received from either of the sensors, the OR gate will send a '1' to the other AND gate input. With both inputs receiving a '1', it activates the alarm buzzer.

The truth table for this combination is quite complicated, see table 1.

In the next topic, we have an example of how to solve problems using different combinations of gates.

Table 1

A	B	C	D
0	0	0	0
1	0	0	0
0	1	0	0
1	1	0	0
0	0	1	0
0	1	1	1
1	0	1	1
1	1	1	1

Questions

1 The diagram for an alarm system is shown below.

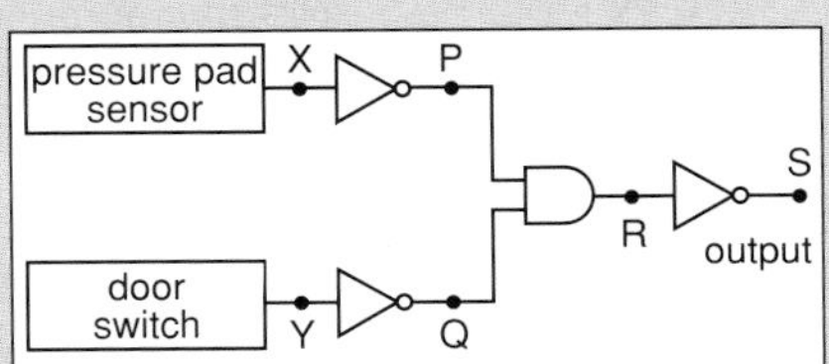

The alarm system is designed to operate if someone steps on a pressure pad or opens a door.

When someone stands on the pressure pad sensor, the logic level at X changes from 0 to 1.

When the door is opened, the logic level at Y changes form 0 to 1.

a Copy and complete the table below to show the logic levels at P, Q, R and S when the logic levels at X and Y are as indicated.

X	Y	P	Q	R	S
0	0				
0	1				
1	0				
1	1				

b The pupil could have designed the alarm system using only one logic gate. Name the gate he could have used.

c Two possible circuits for the door switch are shown below. When the door closes, the switch closes.

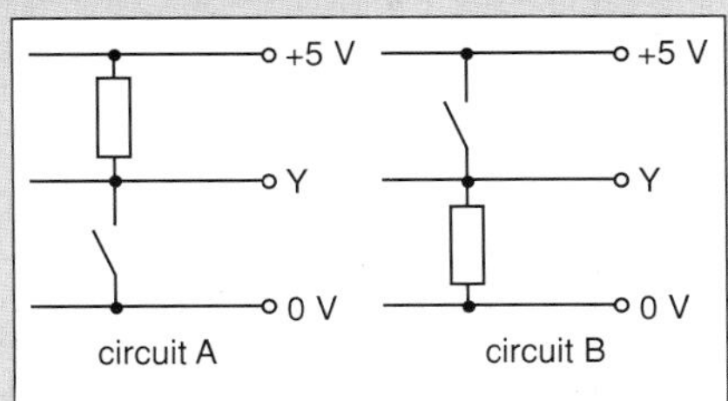

Explain which circuit should be used in the above system.

D7
Solving problems with electronics

To solve problems with electronics, you have to be quite logical.

Picture 1 Cats like cat flaps.

The cat flap problem

Suppose we want to design an automatic 'cat flap'. This is a small wooden flap cut into the back door. It can be pushed open by the cat (see picture 1). But you can lock it shut, if you want to.

To do this we want to use an electrically operated lock that is opened and closed by a small electric motor. This motor can be switched on or off.

Keep the cat out at night!

At first you decide that the cat can only come in during the day time, so the lock can be controlled by a simple sensor. You make a circuit as shown in picture 2. The light sensor can be a light-dependent resistor (LDR). It makes a 1 output when it is light. This lets the door open.

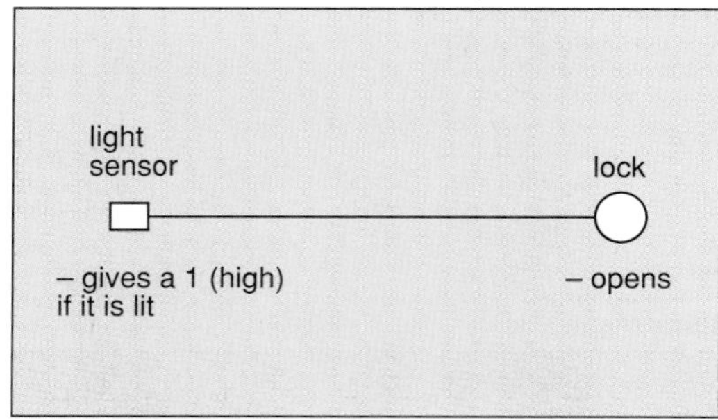

Picture 2 A first attempt.

—unless it is raining!
Then you take pity on the poor animal and agree to let it in at night, *provided it is raining*. So we need a 'wet sensor'. The wet sensor can be two bare wires very nearly touching. A current flows to give a 1 when they get wet.

Picture 3 shows how these two sensors might be fitted to an OR gate. The cat can get in if it is light OR if it is wet. But not if it is dark and dry.

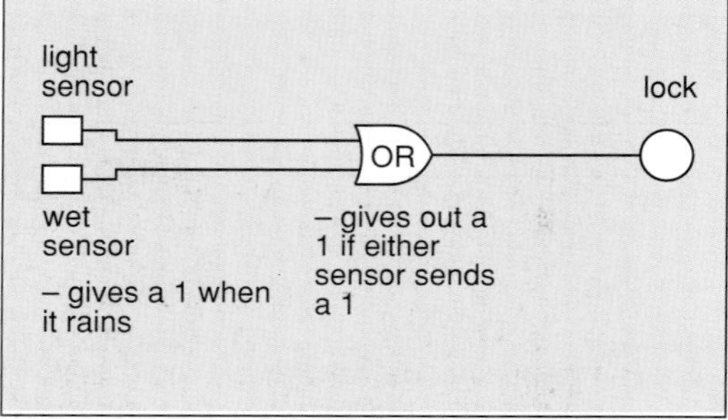

Picture 3 Cats don't like to get wet.

—or very cold!
Then you are persuaded that the cat ought to be let in if it is *cold* at night. This needs a temperature sensor. It is connected to another OR gate as shown in picture 4. Now the flap will open if it gets a 1 either from the first OR gate or from the temperature sensor.

But there is something wrong with this! When it is cold the sensor you happen to have sends a 0, and this would not open the flap. Both you and the cat want it to send a 1 when it is cold. This can be done by putting a NOT gate between the temperature sensor and the input (picture 5).

A 0 signal from the temperature sensor is changed by the NOT gate to a 1. The cat is happy because a low temperature sends a 1 to the lock, to open it. Thus the flap will now open on a cold, dry night, as well as on a wet night.

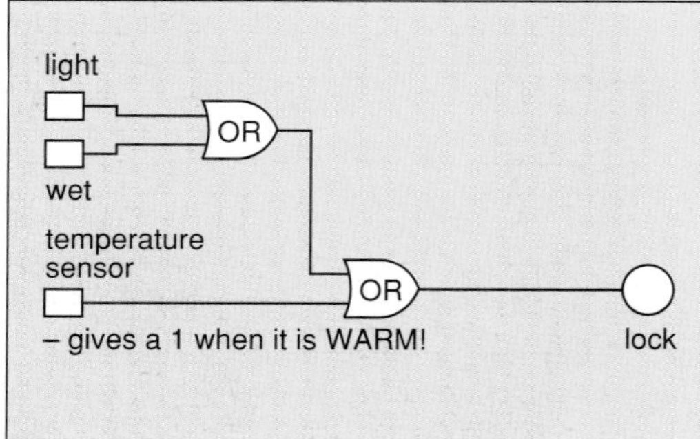

Picture 4 – or to get cold!

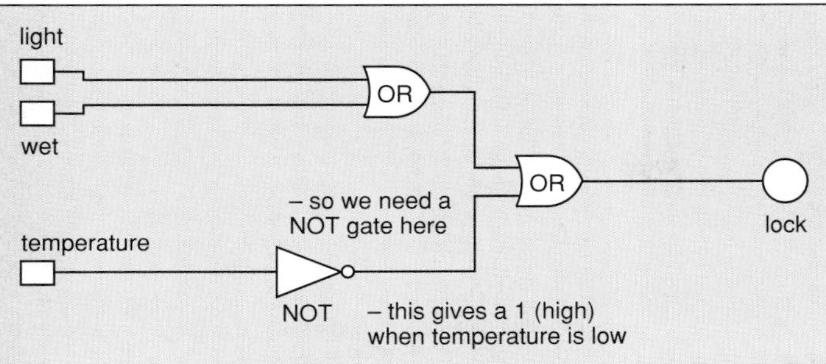

Picture 5 This is better!

light
wet
temperature
OR
OR
NOT
AND
reed
switch
lock

Picture 6 The final solution (but see if you can do better).

Oh no!

One cold night you wake up to a terrible noise and find that the kitchen is full of cats. What can you do now?

Invest in a magnet collar, and add a reed switch to the system. A **reed switch** will close when a magnet is brought near, giving a **'1'**. If the reed switch is positioned at the entrance to the cat flap, then the magnet on your cat's collar will close the switch as it attempts to get in, sending a '1' to an AND gate (picture 6). The flap will now open if it is cold, or wet, or daylight *and* it is *your* cat, with its sophisticated collar, waiting at the entrance.

One final thought – you may wish to add a time delay circuit to give your cat a few seconds to get through before the flap starts to close on it!

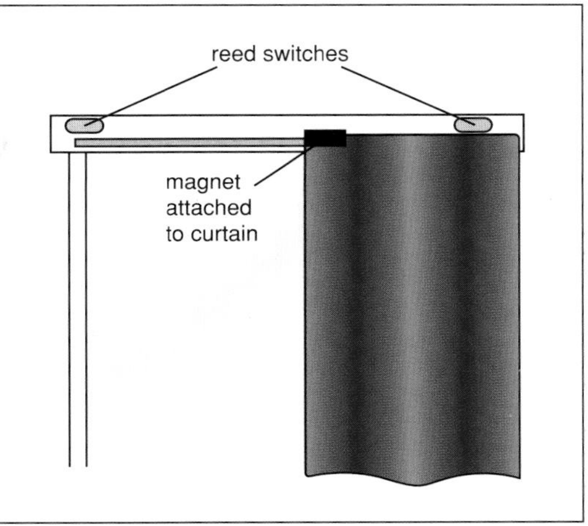

Picture 7 Can you make the curtains open and close?

Curtain call

Let's return to the problem of the curtains on page 109. You are now given a magnet and a couple of reed switches, as shown in picture 7. You are also given a switch which will reverse the direction of the motor. By using a selection of gates, can you construct a system which will stop the motor when the curtains close, and open the curtains as soon as it gets light in the morning?

Draw a logic circuit diagram, showing your arrangement, and have it checked by your teacher. Good luck!

Questions

1 In the washing machine shown below, an electric motor is used to turn the drum. Before the clothes are washed, the machine fills with water which is then heated to the correct temperature. (b) shows part of the control circuit for the washing machine.

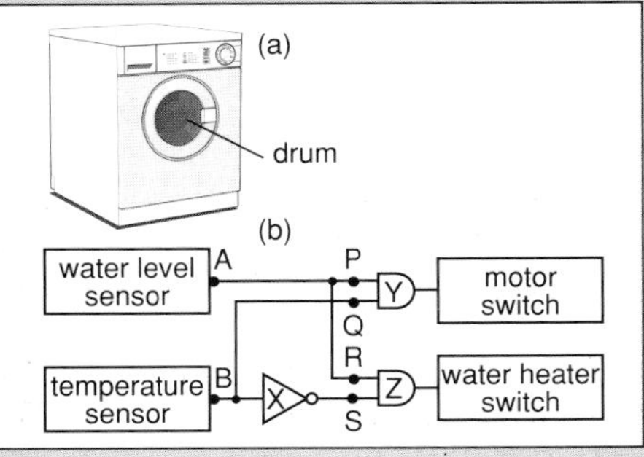

When the machine fills to the correct water level, A changes from logic 0 to logic 1.

When the water reaches the correct temperature, B changes from logic 0 to logic 1.

When the output from gate Y is at logic 1, the motor is ON.

When the output from gate Z is at logic 1, the heater is ON.

a What type of gate is X?

b Give an example of:

i) an input device which could be used as a temperature sensor;

ii) an output device which could be used as the motor switch.

c A table may be constructed to show the logic levels at P, Q, R and S and to show whether the heater and motor are switched on or off in a number of cases.

Case 1: just after the machine is switched on and begins to fill with cold water.

Case 2: just after the water reaches the correct level.

Case 3: just after the water reaches the correct temperature.

Copy and complete the table for case 2 and case 3.

	P	Q	R	S	Motor	Heater
Case 1	0	0	0	0	OFF	OFF
Case 2					OFF	ON
Case 3					ON	OFF

D8
Perfect timing

Things must happen at the correct time to produce the desired result.

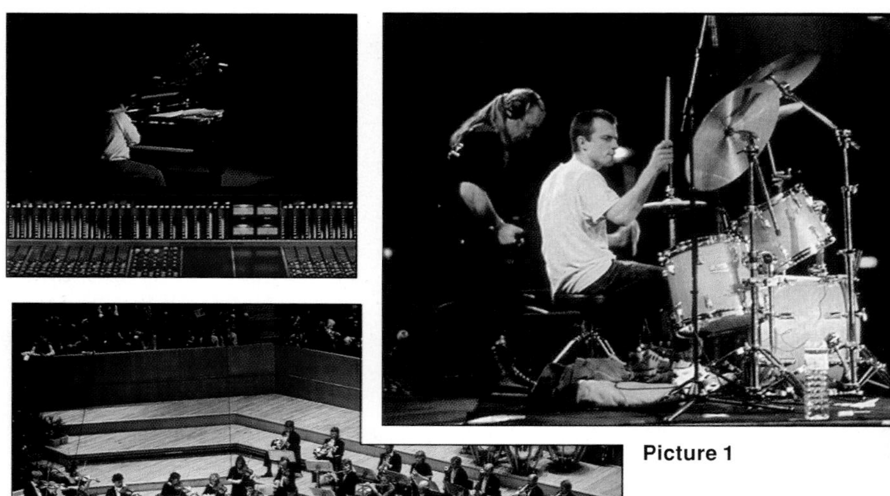
Picture 1

Timing is very important in music. Piano students use a metronome to keep time as they practice. In recording studios, a drummer can hear a regular 'click' in his headphones, helping him to keep to the beat. An orchestra needs a conductor to keep time and to direct the musicians. They must not only play in time, but various combinations of instruments must play together, at exactly the right moment, at different stages of the performance.

In electronic systems, such as a computer, many different signals need to be brought together at the correct time and in the correct order. The computer needs an internal 'clock' which makes sure all the different parts of the system keep step with each other. How could such a clock be built?

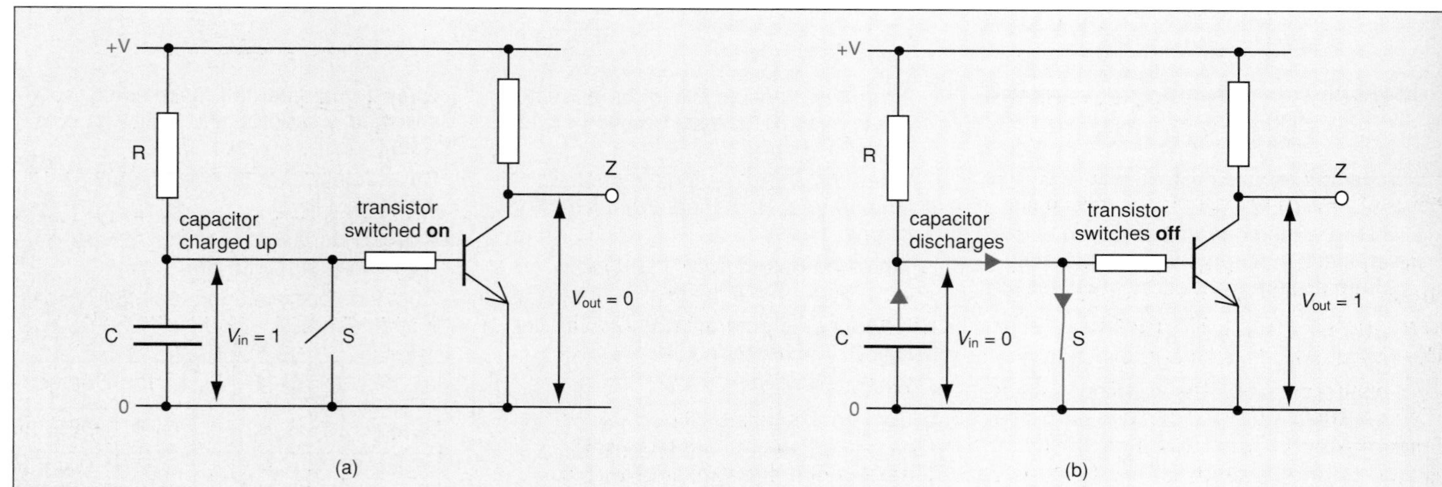

Picture 2 A timing circuit.

In the section on input devices, we saw that a capacitor in a time delay circuit will charge up until it reaches the maximum voltage. In the circuit in picture 2, before the capacitor has charged up, the voltage across it is *zero* and the transistor is *off*. When the capacitor has reached a high enough voltage level, as in part (a), it switches the transistor on. In part (b), when switch S is closed, the capacitor discharges, and the transistor switches *off* again.

Notice that the transistor is acting as a NOT gate: when the input from the capacitor is *high* or 1, the voltage at output Z is *low*, giving a 0.

Let us imagine we could connect a NOT gate to a capacitor so that it would *automatically* charge and discharge according to the voltage output from the gate. What would happen?

The Schmitt–input inverter

Look at the NOT gate in picture 3. It is receiving input from a potentiometer. If we move the contact upward until the NOT gate *just* receives a 1, the gate will give us an output at Z of 0. If the slider is moved slightly down, the input drops to 0 and the output changes to a 1. The potentiometer is an **analogue** input device. So is a capacitor; its voltage increases smoothly as it charges.

A **Schmitt-input** inverter is a special type of NOT gate. As its input signal falls below 1, it *continues* to give a 0 output. Only when the input voltage has dropped to a particular value does its output change to 1. The output stays there until the input voltage has climbed back to a set level. When the input reaches a 1, the gate changes back to 0.

By using it with a capacitor, we can electronically produce regular on/off voltage signals or **pulses**. Because they are produced with a regular frequency, we call them 'clock' pulses.

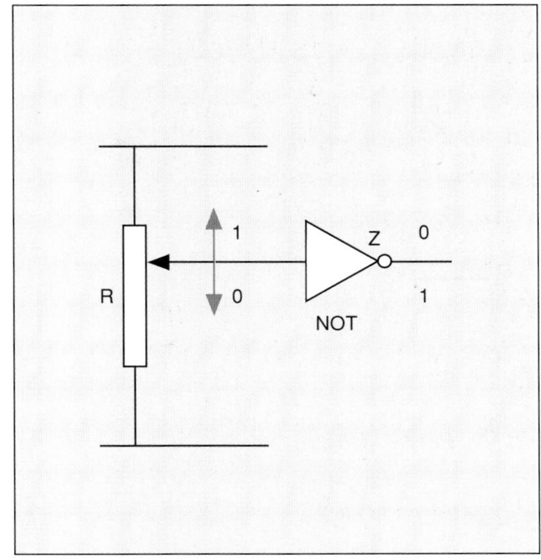

Picture 3 Changing a NOT gate output.

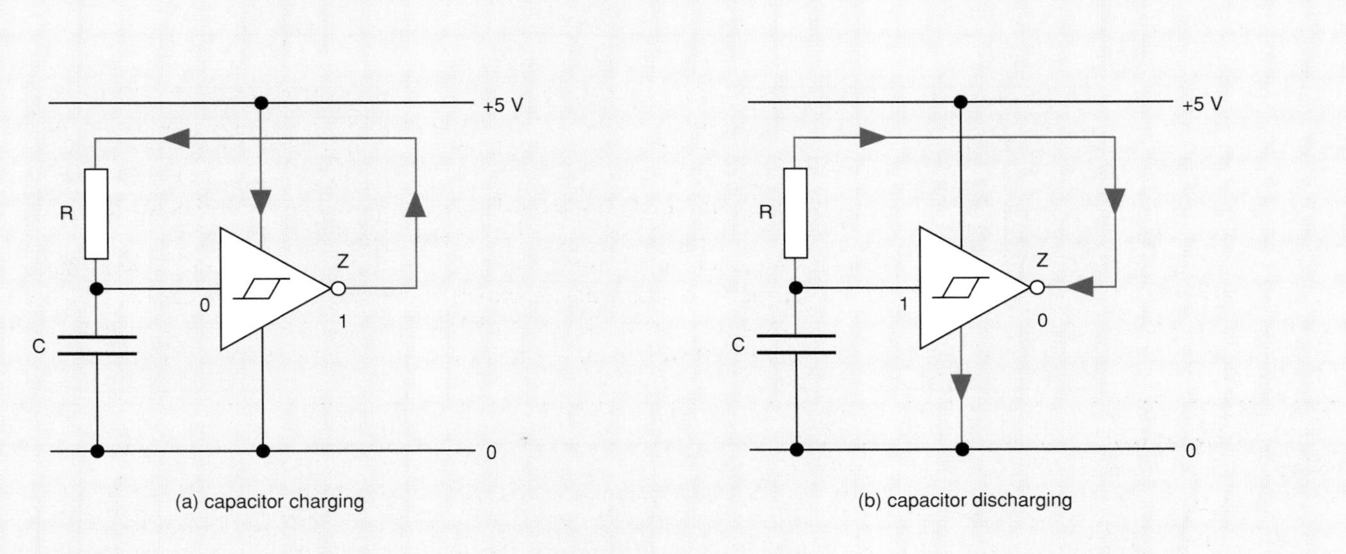

Picture 4 How a Schmitt-input inverter produces pulses.

Picture 4 shows a Schmitt–input inverter as part of a clock-pulse generator circuit. To avoid confusion, we do not usually show the connections from a gate to the power supply. We are normally only interested in the path of the signals. The power supply connections have been included in picture 4 to illustrate how the current flows as the capacitor charges and discharges.

When the NOT gate output at Z is 1, it is at a high voltage (usually 5 V). Current flows from this high voltage through the resistor to charge the capacitor, until it sends a 1 to the NOT gate. This changes the output at Z to 0. The capacitor is now at a higher voltage than Z, and so current flows from it through Z as it discharges.

In picture 5 the LED is connected between the 5 V supply and the low voltage level at Z. It will conduct and light when output is 0.

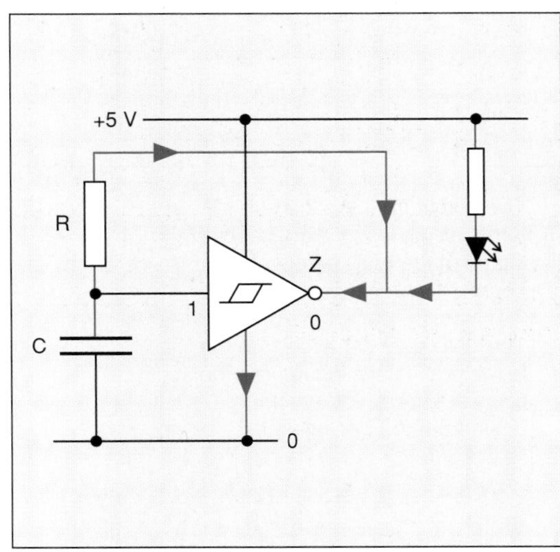

Picture 5 Using an LED to indicate pulses.

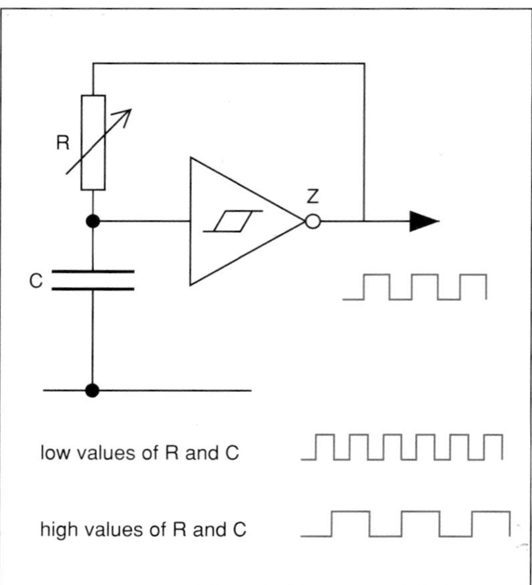

Picture 6 Changing pulse frequency.

We now have a device which will produce a regular series of clock pulses, a shown in picture 6. If we replace C with a smaller capacitor, the charging tim is reduced, and the frequency of the pulses will increase. Similarly a larg capacitor would give lower frequencies. If we replace R with a variable resisto we can increase or decrease the frequency by adjusting the resistance.

If we alter the frequency to produce clock pulses of one second, then we hav a timing circuit. Greater accuracy may be required; in which case we woul adjust the pulse generator to produce pulses of 0.1 or 0.01 seconds. This give us frequencies of 10 Hz or 100 Hz. Home computers now have chips tha produce timing pulses at MHz frequencies – millions of pulses per second.

Counting the pulses

Now that we are producing our pulses, we need a device to count them, suc as the board in picture 7. The integrated circuit chips mounted on it display number in binary, using the LEDs mounted in the output section. When receives a pulse from the pulse generator circuit, it converts this into a binar signal. One pulse causes the first LED to light. Two pulses switch on LED 2. Fiv pulses would light LED 4 and LED 1. This is the same binary counter that wa discussed when studying LEDs and the seven-segment display in topic D2.

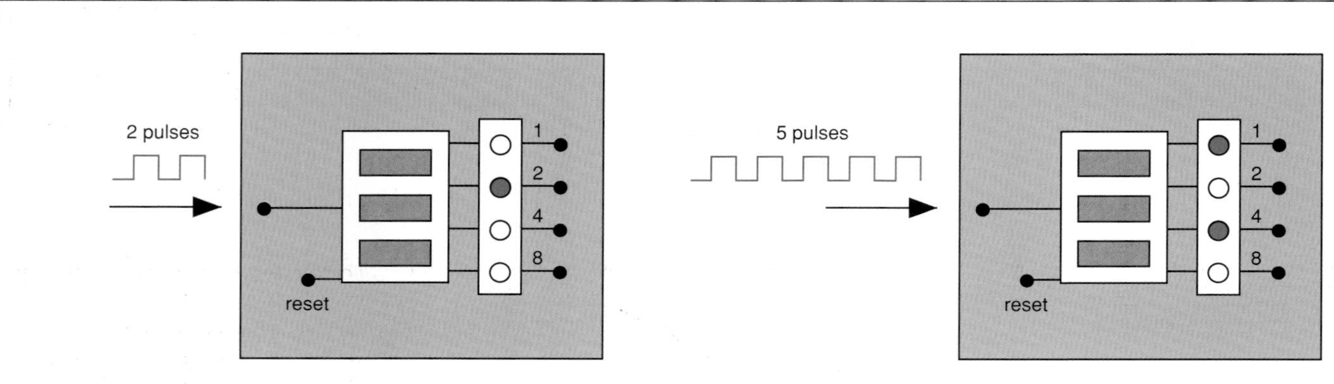

Picture 7 Counting pulses in binary.

The biggest number the counter can register is 1 1 1 1 = 8 + 4 + 2 + 1 = 1 After 15, it resets to 0 0 0 0 and begins again. The board has an external rese terminal that will return the counter to zero if it receives a pulse. We find convenient to count in 'tens', so we would like the counter to reset when receives 10, that is 8 + 2.

If we connect the 2 and the 8 output to an AND gate, and then connect it output to the reset terminal, the counter will count up to 9 and then return t zero.

The output from the 2 and 8 terminals give a '1' signal at both inputs of the AND gate when the counter has reached 10.

The AND gate sends a '1' to the reset terminal, which returns the counter to zero. It then starts again from the beginning.

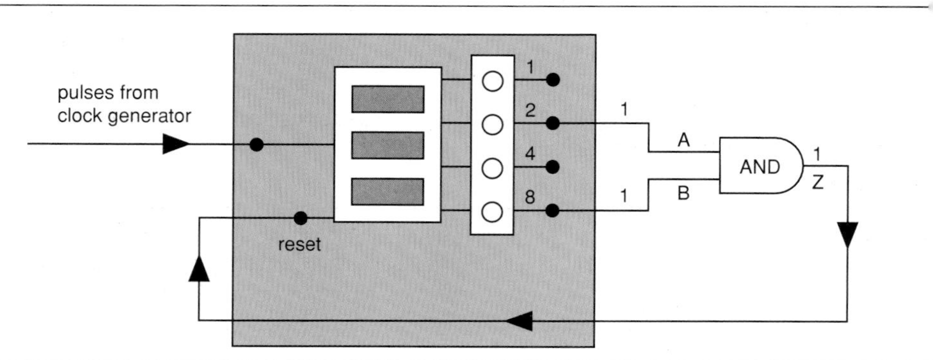

Picture 8 Automatic reset of the counter.

Counting in decimal

As we saw in topic D2, the binary counter can be connected to a decoder and seven-segment display, to give us a decimal output. If we need to display numbers greater than 9, (for example, 11, 37, 92), we can connect the AND gate output to a second counter (picture 9). Every time the first counter resets, a pulse will go to the second counter. In other words, each time the first counter reaches '10', the second counter will count the pulse and display it.

If 25 pulses have been sent to the first counter, it will have reset twice and be displaying the number '5'. The second counter will be displaying '2'. It can be used as the 'tens' display, and the first can be used as the 'units' display.

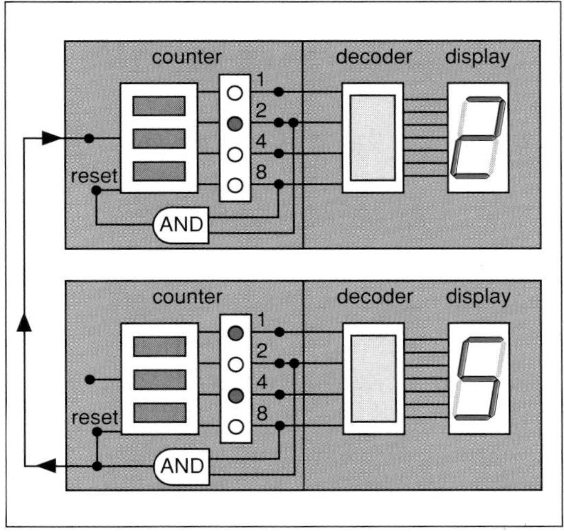

Picture 9 Counting in decimal.

Questions

1 Figure 1 shows an electronic system which can be used as a timer.

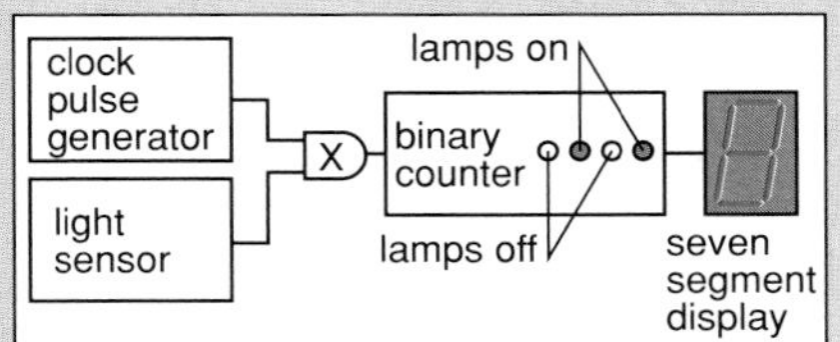

Figure 1

The timer is switched on and off using a beam of light and a light sensor.

The logic level at the output from the light sensor is shown in table 1 below.

The clock pulse generator produces an output voltage which changes with time as shown in the graph below. The logic levels are indicated on the graph.

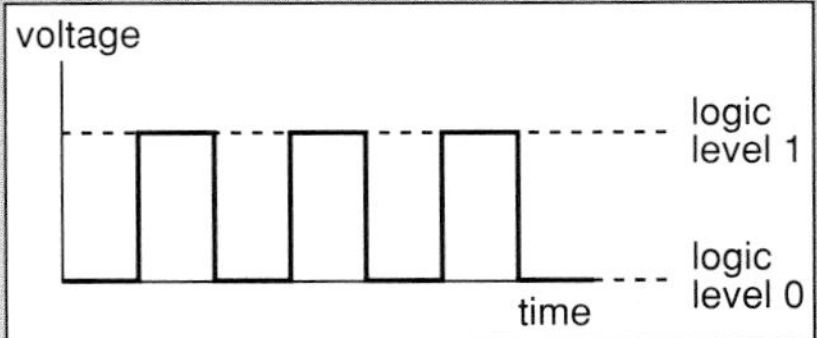

a i) What name is given to logic gate X?

Table 1

Lighting condition at light sensor	Logic level at output from light sensor
dark	1
light	0

ii) Explain why no counts are recorded on the binary counter when the light beam shines on the light sensor.

iii) What number appears on the seven-segment display when the binary counter displays 0101 as shown in figure 1?

b Saeed makes use of the electronic system in figure 1 to help him measure the speed of a toy car. He sets up the apparatus as shown in figure 2 below and resets the binary counter and seven-segment display to zero.

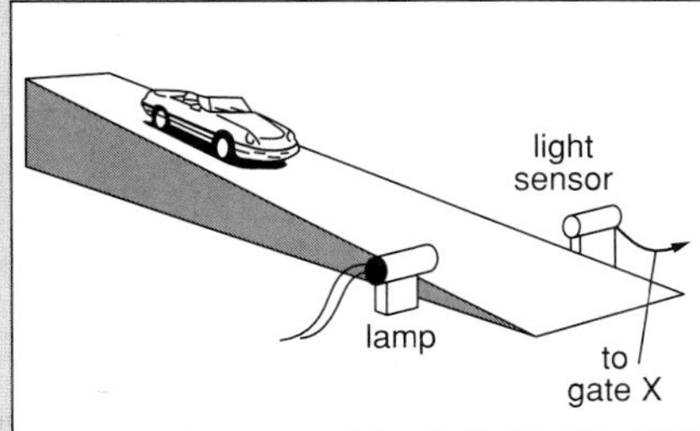

Figure 2

When the car has passed through the light beam between the lamp and the light sensor, the seven-segment display shows the number eight. The time for each clock pulse is shown in figure 3.

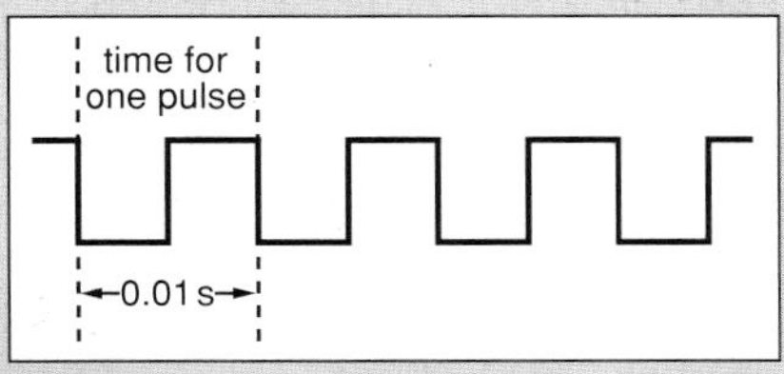

Figure 3

i) Calculate the time taken for the car to pass the light beam.

ii) What other measurement is required so that Saeed can calculate the speed of the car as it passes through the light beam?

iii) How would Saeed use his measurements to calculate this speed?

c The electronic circuit which produces the clock pulses is shown in figure 4.

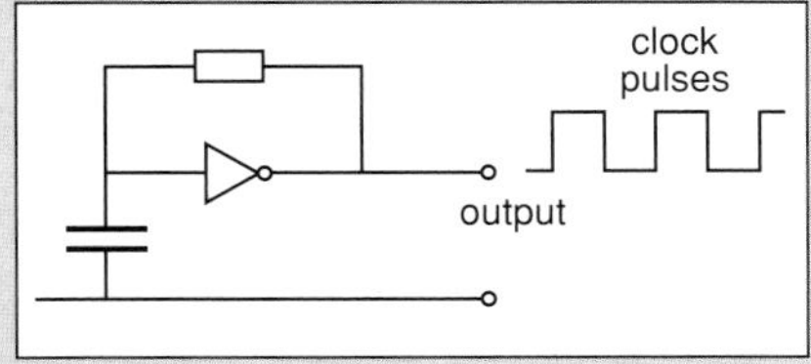

Figure 4

i) Speed increases the value of the capacitor.

What effect does this have on the frequency of the clock pulses?

ii) What effect should this have on the accuracy of Saeed's time measurement?

D9 Analogue processes

Not all signals are digital.

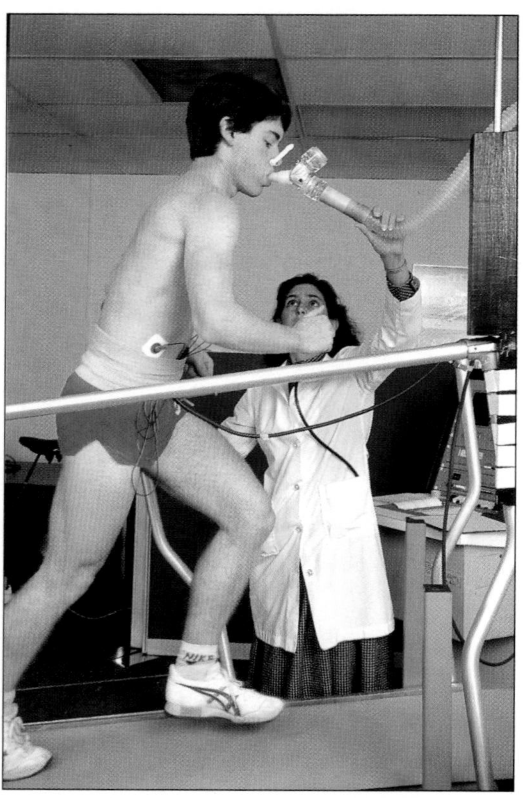

Picture 1 The body of this athlete is being monitored by electric sensors.

Strengthening the signal

We have seen that electronic systems obtain information by the use of input devices. The man in picture 1 is undergoing exercise, while information is collected by sensors that detect tiny electrical changes in his skin and muscles. The signals produced by the sensors are so weak that they cannot be used unless they are made stronger by **amplification**. Most people are familiar with amplification in audio devices, such as hi-fi systems in the home or PA equipment used by musical performers.

In the Communications section, we saw that the signals received and decoded by a radio must be amplified before being sent to the final output stage of the loudspeaker. Signals transmitted over long distances through telephone wires lose energy, so the weakened signal must be restored to its original strength at regular stages. Repeaters containing amplifiers boost the energy of the signal before sending it on the next stage of the journey.

In these systems, we are usually dealing with an **analogue** process. Picture 2 shows the typical arrangement of a sound system. The input and output devices are both analogue, as are the signals *processed* by the amplifier. Of course, an amplifier should not change the signal in any way other than increasing it. Sometimes, however we may wish deliberately to alter the input signal, before boosting it. In a guitar amplifier, the tone is altered by boosting the bass or treble frequencies in a pre-amplifier stage. This final signal is then fed into the main amplifier.

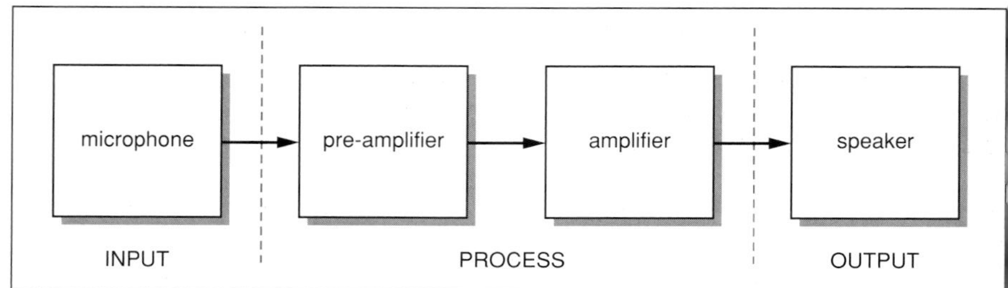

Picture 2 A typical sound system.

Occasionally when someone uses a microphone in public, their voice sounds 'tinny' or 'fuzzy' as it comes out of the speakers. A poor amplifier **distorts** the original signal. This can be irritating when listening to a favourite song, but could be very serious if we are transmitting an emergency message. The output of an amplifier should be an *exact* but *stronger* copy of the input signal.

The transistor as an amplifier

So far we have dealt with the use of the transistor as a switch. We have been concerned only with whether the transistor is on or off, that is we have used it as a **digital** component. To see how an analogue signal might be amplified by a transistor circuit, it would be helpful to use pictures 3 and 4 to remind ourselves of how the transistor works.

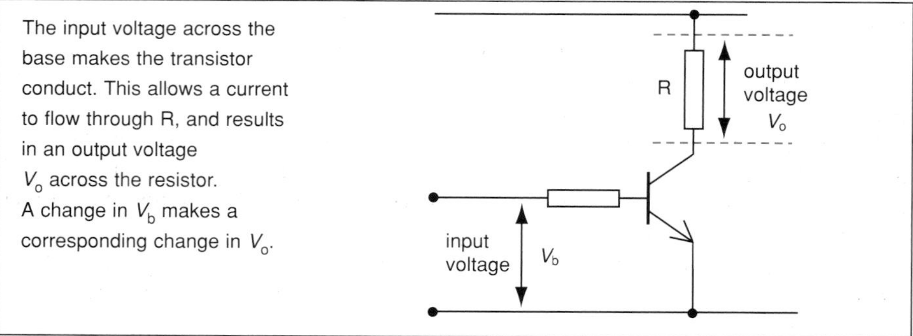

Picture 3 Output changes with input.

Average speed

What we have worked out for the sprinter was the *average* speed over the distance. The runner wouldn't have travelled at this speed steadily for all of the 13 seconds of the race.

A runner starts slowly then accelerates to her fastest speed. She might slow down near the end when her legs get tired. A graph would show this (see picture 2).

In the same way, a car might take four hours to travel a distance of 200 km. Unless it was on a very clear motorway it isn't likely that it would have travelled at the same speed of 50 km/h all the time. It's useful to know the *average* speed of a car on different kinds of roads. When you are planning a journey you can use it to work out how long the journey is likely to take.

We can work out average speeds using a formula:

$$\text{average speed} = \frac{\text{total distance covered}}{\text{time taken for journey}}$$

Written as a formula: $\bar{v} = \frac{d}{t}$

Picture 3 Police can measure the speed of a car using radar.

Instantaneous speed

Sometimes we need to know more about what happens when moving things are changing speed. To do this we need to be able to measure the speed at any given instant. This is not so easy to do. It means that we have to measure the distance an object travels in a very small interval of time, usually much less than a second.

This can be done by using **radar**, as the police are doing in picture 3. The radar 'speed gun' measures the distance the car moves in a time of less than a millionth of a second! A built-in computer works out the result. In school laboratories a useful device called a ticker-timer used to do the same job (picture 4). It used a time interval of a fiftieth of a second.

Nowadays, your school lab will have electronic speed measuring devices using interrupted light beams (see picture 5). All these things might look quite complicated, but all they do is what you do with a stop watch and measuring tape. They measure time and distance covered.

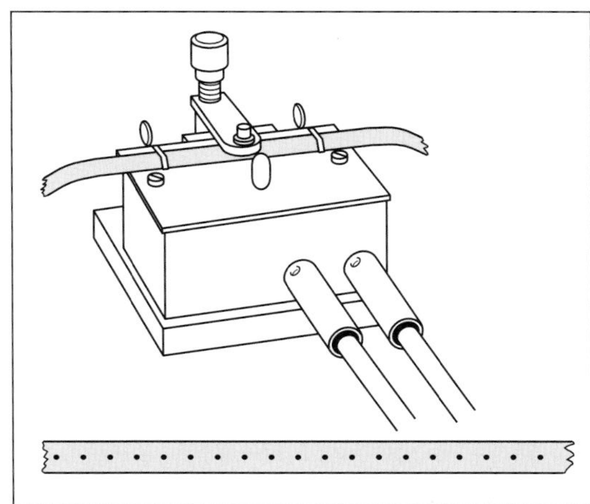
Picture 4 A ticker-timer and a sample of tape: the object was moving with a constant speed. Each length shows how far the object travelled in a fifth of a second. A 'ten-tick' length has 10 spaces.

Movement formulae

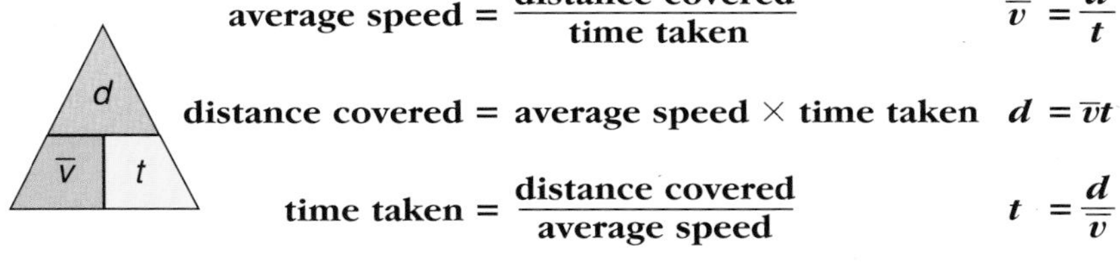

$$\textbf{average speed} = \frac{\textbf{distance covered}}{\textbf{time taken}} \qquad \bar{v} = \frac{d}{t}$$

$$\textbf{distance covered} = \textbf{average speed} \times \textbf{time taken} \qquad d = \bar{v}t$$

$$\textbf{time taken} = \frac{\textbf{distance covered}}{\textbf{average speed}} \qquad t = \frac{d}{\bar{v}}$$

Picture 5 These students are using a computer-assisted speed measuring device.

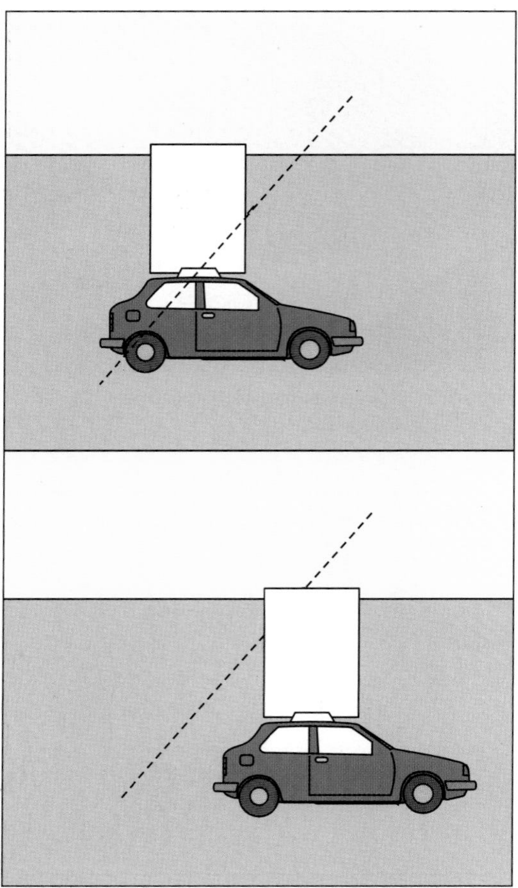

Picture 6

Measuring instantaneous speed

To find speed, we have to measure a distance and a time *interval*. Therefore we can never actually measure a truly *instantaneous* speed. We must start timing at one instant, and stop timing at another. As we have seen, the police radar gun measures the distance travelled by a car during a millionth of a second. This time interval is so short that we can regard the result as an instantaneous speed.

In the school laboratory, we must try to make our measurements over the shortest time and distance possible. For example, to measure the speed of a toy car we can fix a small piece of card, with a set length of say 10 cm, to the car roof (see picture 6). By timing how long it takes for the piece of card to pass a certain point, we can calculate the speed of the car.

Measuring time accurately

In Physics, it is always important to obtain measurements that are as accurate as possible. If we use a stopwatch, the experimenter never starts or stops the clock *exactly* as the car passes a set point. There is a delay known as **reaction time**.

When measuring **average** speed, over a larger distance, this is not a great problem. We could time the car as it travelled between two chalk marks on a bench. Suppose that the error due to reaction time in starting and stopping a watch is 0.1 seconds. If the car travels 1 metre in a real time of 4 seconds, then its *average* speed is

$$\bar{v} = \frac{d}{t} = \frac{1.0}{4.0} = 0.25 \text{ m/s}$$

Due to reaction time, our *measured* time is 4.1 seconds, which gives a calculated speed of 0.244 m/s. This is not a serious level of error.

Imagine we are trying to measure the instantaneous speed of the toy car. We time the 10 cm (0.1 m) card as it passes a marker. If the car is travelling at 0.25 m/s, the actual time for it to pass the marker will be 0.4 seconds. Due to reaction time, our result might be 0.5 seconds. When we do our calculation, we get

$$v = \frac{d}{t} = \frac{0.1}{0.5} = 0.2 \text{ m/s}$$

This time, our result is only 4/5 of the actual speed. The reaction time is a larger fraction of the actual time measurement, so our calculation has a bigger error.

For experimental work, we must use timing devices which eliminate this kind of error. A **light gate** can be used to automatically start or stop a timer. When an object passes through the gate, this breaks the beam of light, and the timer starts. As soon as the object has passed, the timer stops. By using a computer interface, as in picture 7, the speed calculations can be done automatically.

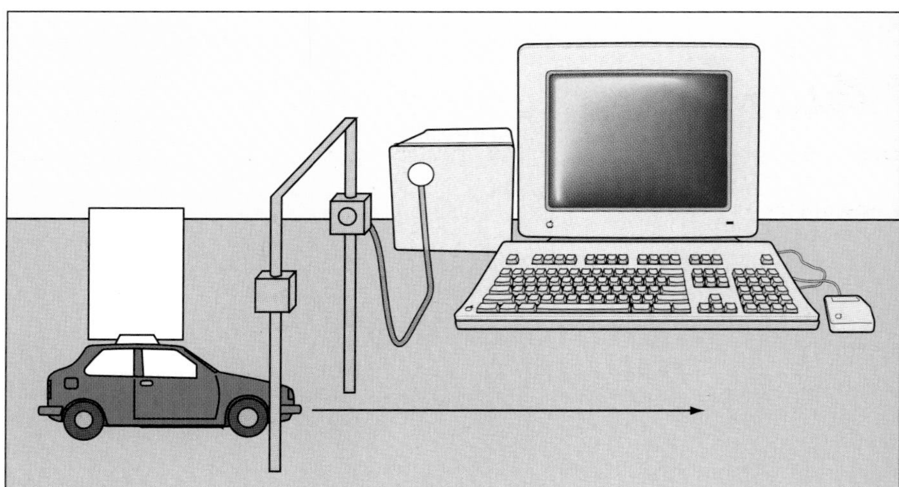

Picture 7 Using a computer to measure the speed of a toy car.

Putting the foot down

We use average speed in many situations because the speed of a moving object rarely remains perfectly constant – in real life, vehicles speed up and slow down all the time. Car manufacturers advertise the performance of their cars by timing how long it takes them to reach a speed of 60 mph from a standing start – the **acceleration** of the car.

The car manufacturers use a *fixed* change of speed: 0–60 mph. They then compare the different times taken by different cars. In Physics, we need a general rule to deal with a situation where speed is changing. We say that the acceleration is given by:

$$\textbf{acceleration} = \frac{\textbf{change in speed}}{\textbf{time taken for change}}$$

This means we must know the the speed at the start and finish of the interval of time in which we are interested, as in picture 8. The final speed is represented by v, and the starting or *initial* speed is written as u. The symbol for time is t. This gives us the formula:

$$a = \frac{v - u}{t}$$

The change in speed is measured in metres per second (m/s). The acceleration will be the change in speed *per second*. We therefore measure acceleration in metres per second *per second*, or metres per second *squared* (m/s^2). Picture 9 shows the triangle rule and the different versions of the formula.

To measure acceleration in the laboratory, we must use two light gates, as shown in picture 10. As the card passes through the first gate, a time is measured and the initial speed u is calculated. Final speed v is calculated after the card has passed through the second gate. The computer also times the interval between the card passing through each gate, to give us t. The results can be displayed on the screen, so that we can calculate the acceleration, or we can get the computer to do it for us.

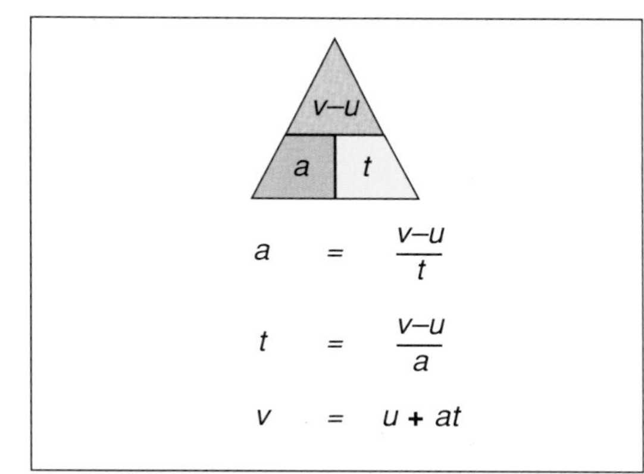

Picture 9

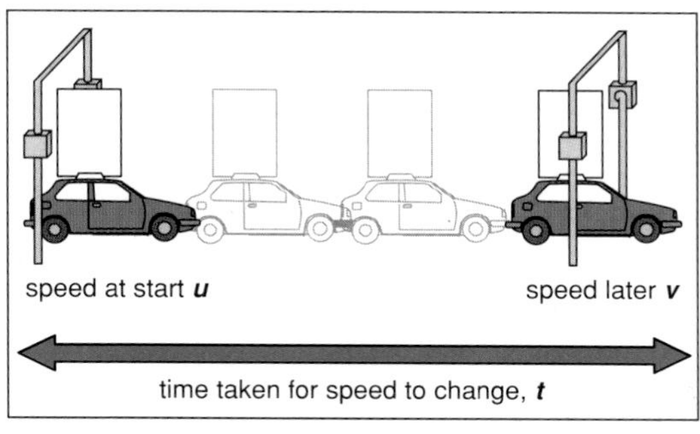

Picture 10

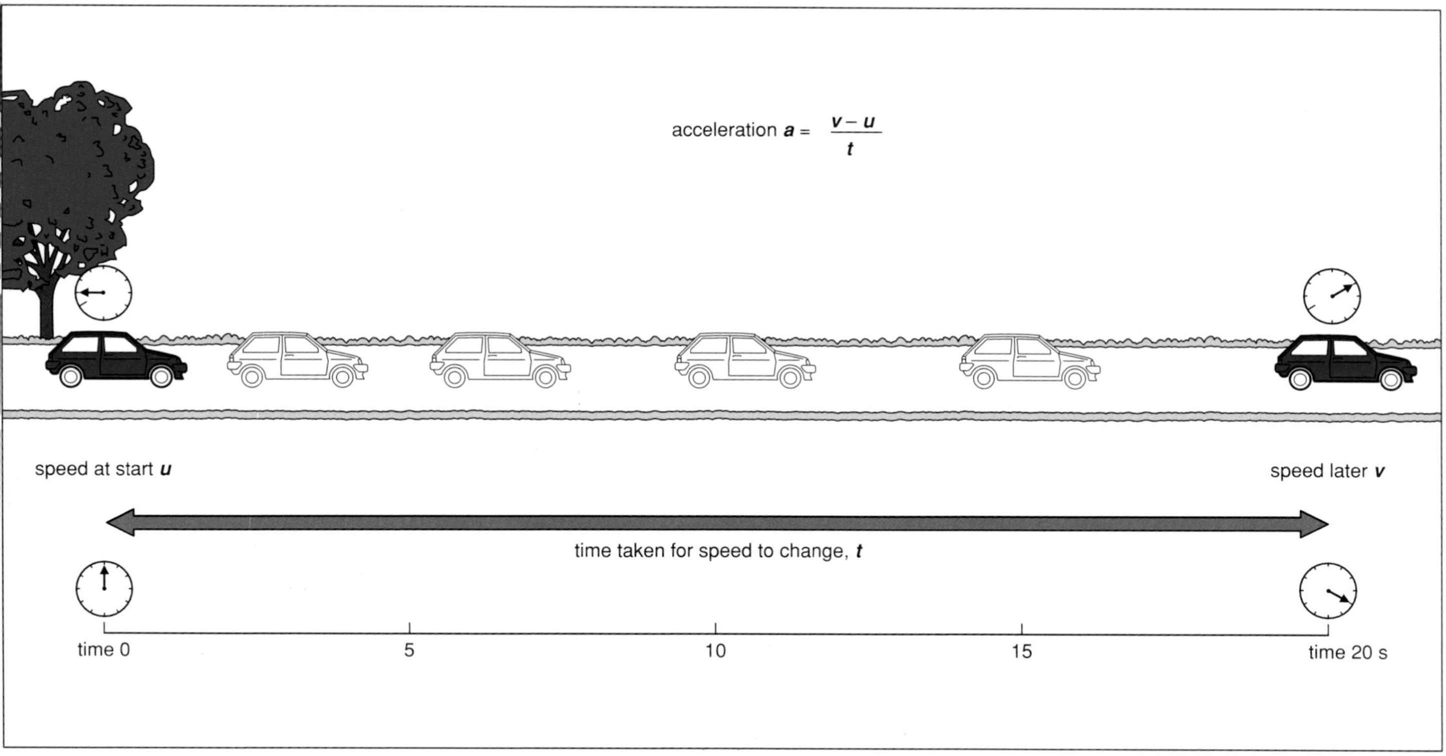

Picture 8 How acceleration is calculated.

Equations and formulae of motion

$$\text{average speed} = \frac{\text{distance covered}}{\text{time taken}}$$

$$\bar{v} = \frac{d}{t}$$

$$a = \frac{v-u}{t}$$

$$v = u + at$$

distance = area under a speed–time graph.

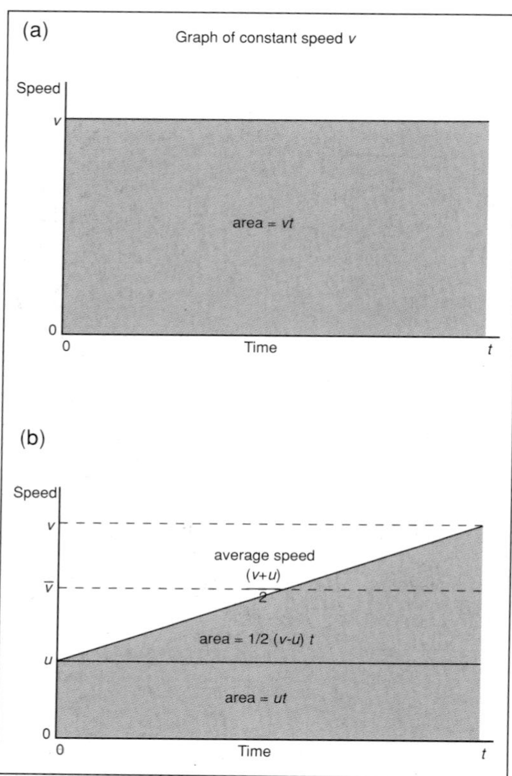

Picture 11 Graphs of motion.

Finding the distance travelled

If we know the average speed of an object, or if it has been moving at a constant speed, we can calculate the distance travelled. We multiply the constant speed by the time taken:

$$d = vt$$

What can we do if the object has been accelerating? A solution to the problem is to use **speed–time graphs**. Picture 11(a) shows a graph of constant speed, v plotted against time t. If we multiply vt, we are multiplying the sides of the shaded rectangle – we have found the **area** under the line of the graph.

On a speed–time graph, the ***distance*** *travelled is represented by the* ***area*** *under the graph. This is true* ***whatever*** *the shape of the graph.*

Picture 11(b) shows the speed–time graph of an object that is already moving at a speed u when timing starts. Because it is accelerating steadily, the speed is increasing at a constant rate. This gives us an upward sloping straight line, which reaches a final speed of v after a time t.

To find the total area under this graph, we must calculate the area of the rectangle with sides u and t, and add the area of the triangle above it.

This method can be used for any speed–time graph, even those with a complicated shape. The different sections of the graph must be broken up into rectangles and triangles, and their areas calculated (see picture 12). Adding all the areas together gives us the **total** distance. We can then calculate the **average speed**.

Finding a formula

What if we are given u, v, and t, instead of a graph? We could take the time to draw one, but it would be more convenient if we could work out the average speed, and then use it to calculate distance. Look again at picture 11(b).

Area of rectangle = length × breadth = ut

Area of triangle = $\frac{1}{2}$ × base × height = $\frac{1}{2} \times t \times (v-u) = \frac{1}{2}(v-u)t$

Total distance travelled $d = ut + \frac{1}{2}(v-u)t$

$$d = \frac{1}{2}(v+u)t$$

We already know that $d = \bar{v}t$

This means that average speed $\bar{v} = \frac{1}{2}(v+u)$ or $\frac{(v+u)}{2}$

Using information

Graphs can be used to obtain information needed to calculate acceleration. Picture 13 shows the motion of a car. We can see that its initial speed is 6 m/s and its final speed is 12 m/s. The time interval is 4 seconds, thus

$$a = \frac{v-u}{t} = \frac{12-6}{4} = 1.5\ \text{m/s}^2$$

In picture 14, we obtain

$$a = \frac{v-u}{t} = \frac{2-12}{5} = -2\ \text{m/s}^2$$

The negative sign shows that the vehicle has **decelerated**. A deceleration is a **negative** acceleration.

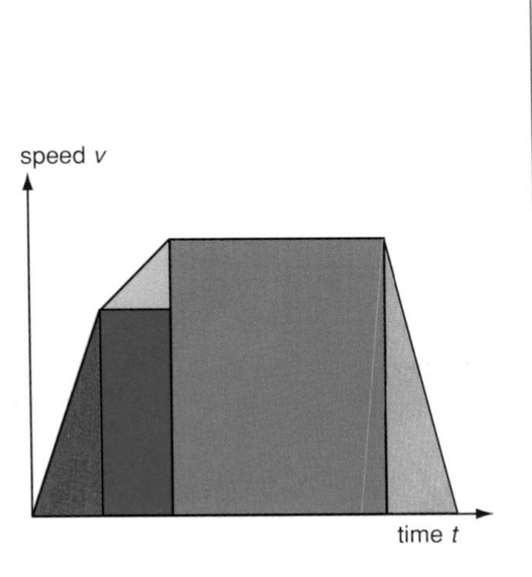

Picture 12 Adding the areas gives the total distance.

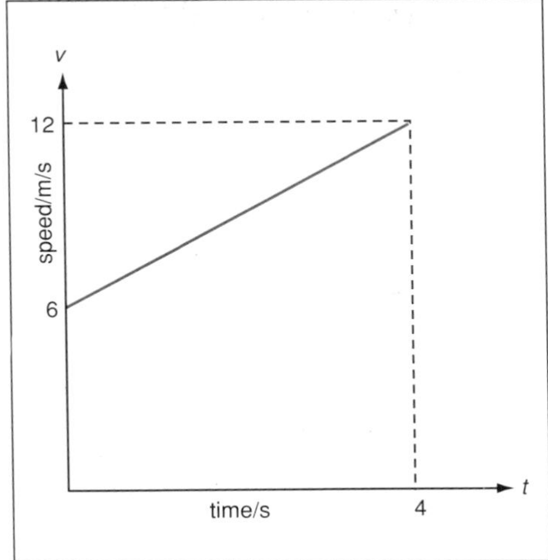

Picture 13 Calculating acceleration from a graph.

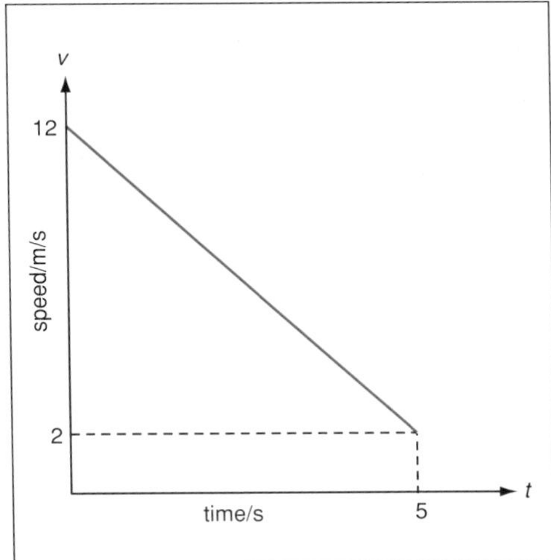

Picture 14 Deceleration is negative acceleration.

Questions

1 A competitor takes part in a speed skating race. The competitor takes 50 seconds to complete the race. The graph below shows how the competitor's speed changes with time during the race.

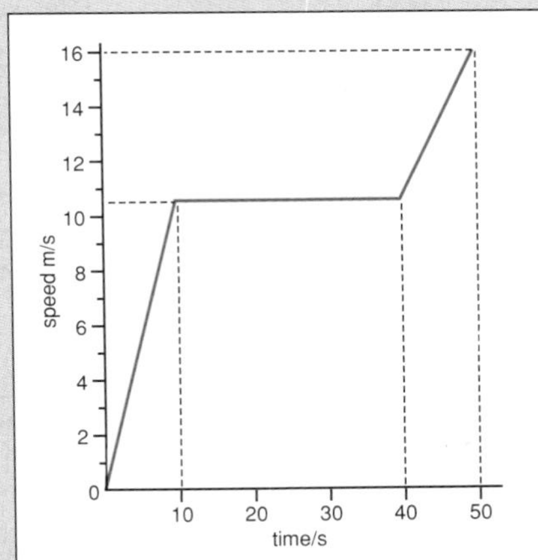

a Calculate the acceleration of the skater at the start of the race.

b Calculate the distance over which the skater raced.

2 The driver of a car, travelling along a motorway, sees a speed limit of 20 m/s (45 mph) flashing on an overhead gantry in front of him and decides to brake. The graph shows the speed of the car from the instant the driver sees the sign.

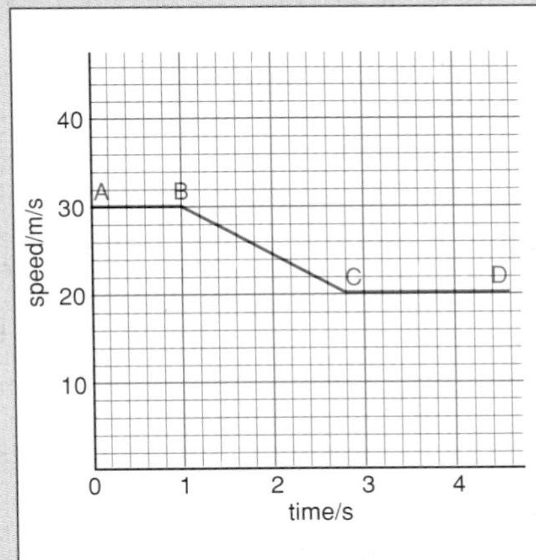

a How long did it take the driver to react by applying the brakes of his car after seeing the sign?

c Describe the motion of the car between:

i) B and C;

ii) C and D

c The driver was 100 m from the gantry when he saw the sign.

Was the car travelling at the required speed when it passed the gantry? You **must** clearly show your working which leads you to your answer.

d Calculate the deceleration of the car.

3 A class has been asked to find the average speed of a toy car as it rolls along the horizontal part XY of a track.

Iain's method and Jill's method are shown below.

Iain starts his stopclock when the car passes the first mark X and stops the clock when the car passes the second mark Y.

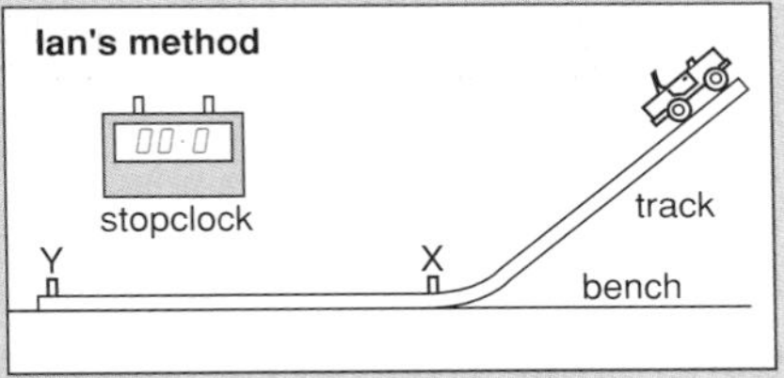

Jill uses a light-gate placed at X. This is connected to an electric timer which records the time taken for the car to cut the beam.

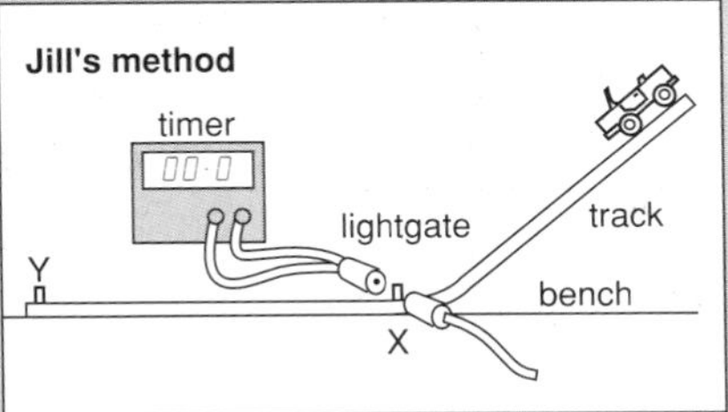

a How would Iain find the average speed?

b The teacher tells Jill that her method does not measure the average speed of the car over the section XY.

i) What speed could be found using Jill's timing method?

ii) Jill's method could be changed to allow the measurement of the average speed by adding a second light gate.

How could Jill use the two light gates and the timer to find the average speed?

E2 Forces

We recognise a force by its effects.

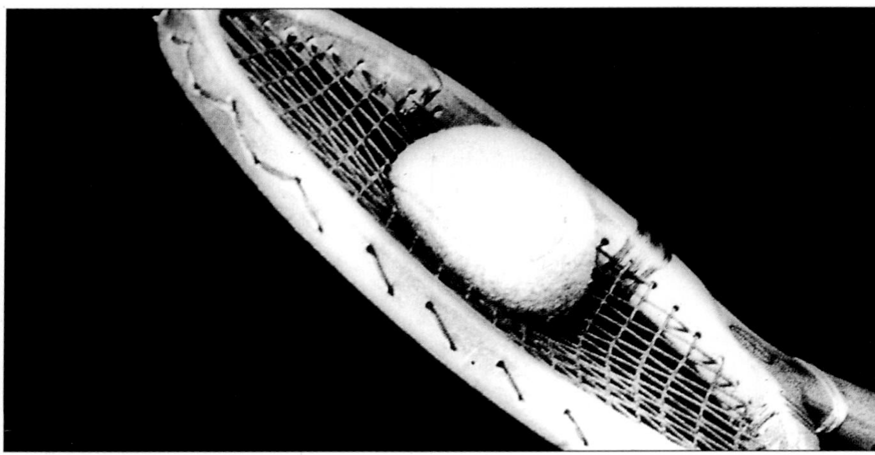

Picture 1 Hitting a tennis ball.

Changing shape

The photograph in picture 1 shows a tennis ball just as it is being hit by the racket. You can see why they change the balls so often, and why the rackets have to be made very strong. The forces on both are very large.

Both the racket and the ball are *distorted* by the force of the impact. The ball is squashed almost flat, and the racket strings are stretched. This is a good example of how a force can change the *shape* of an object.

In a collision, forces act for a very short time. The forces are often quite large and the objects that collide run a risk of being damaged. This is what happens in traffic accidents.

In ball games, the equipment is designed to avoid damage. The ball, for example, will spring back into shape after hitting the racket. Unfortunately, most cars are not built of elastic materials, and usually have their shape permanently altered when they collide!

Picture 2 Forces can accelerate objects.

Changing speed

Apart from any damage that might happen in a collision, there is also a change in movement. The forces involved make objects speed up or slow down. Picture 2 shows a spacecraft being speeded up by the force from the rocket motors. To place it in orbit, they must accelerate the craft to a speed of almost 40 000 kilometres per hour. The force produced by its engine accelerates a car to high speed on the motorway, but the car must be able to stop quickly in an emergency. The force of friction in the brakes will produce a rapid deceleration.

Forces can change the *speed* of an object.

Changing direction

A footballer jumps to meet a ball and exerts a force on it with his head. This changes the *direction* of the ball, hopefully into the back of the net! In ball games the players use forces to change the direction of the ball. The force of friction between the road and the front tyres of a car enables a driver to steer the car in the right direction.

Picture 3 shows all three effects of a force occurring as a tennis player hits a ball with a racket. First the ball and the racket change shape, at the same time as the ball changes speed. For an instant it has stopped completely, then it accelerates away from the racket. The player strikes the ball to send it back towards the opponent's side of the court, changing its direction.

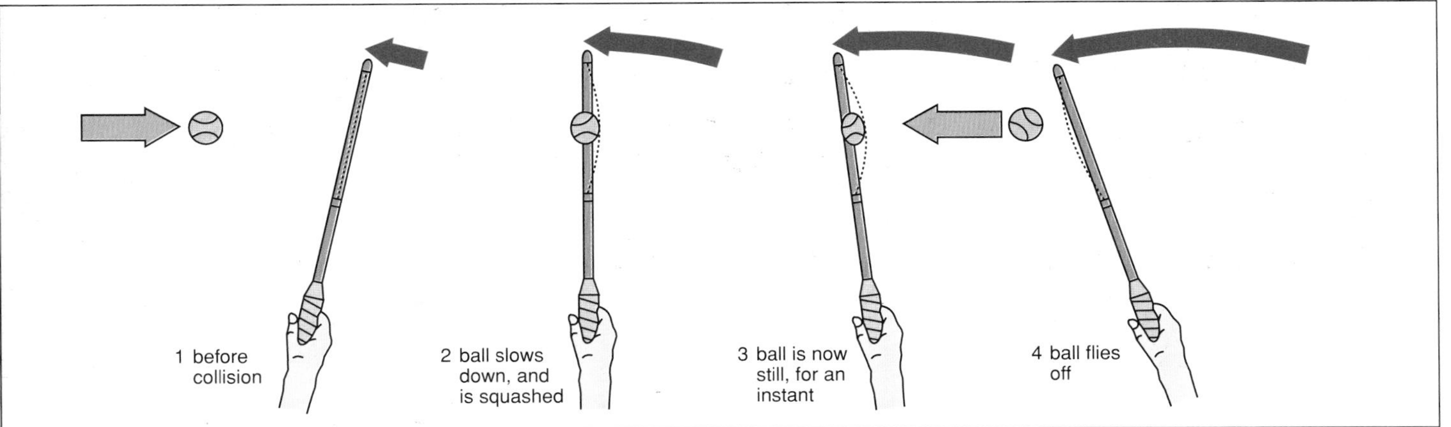

Picture 3 Forces and movements in tennis.

Measuring forces

We can find the size of a force by measuring the effect it has on an object. A force can change the shape of a spring by increasing its length, and the increase is **proportional** to the size of the force. If we double or treble the force, this produces twice or three times the extension of the spring.

Picture 4 shows a simple experiment which demonstrates this. As masses are added to the holder, the elastic material stretches. The distance from the starting point is read off from the position of the pointer against the ruler.

A spring balance uses this principle. As the spring stretches, a small marker moves down a scale. The force being exerted can be read off from the scale. Spring balances are commonly used for weighing things, that is, measuring the force of gravity acting on an object, but they can also be used to measure forces acting in other directions.

Sir Isaac Newton was the famous scientist who first developed a theory explaining the principles of gravity. He also produced a set of laws describing how objects moved when forces acted on them. For this reason, we measure force in **newtons** (N), and a spring balance is often referred to as a **newton balance**.

Picture 5 shows different examples of newton balances being used to measure forces.

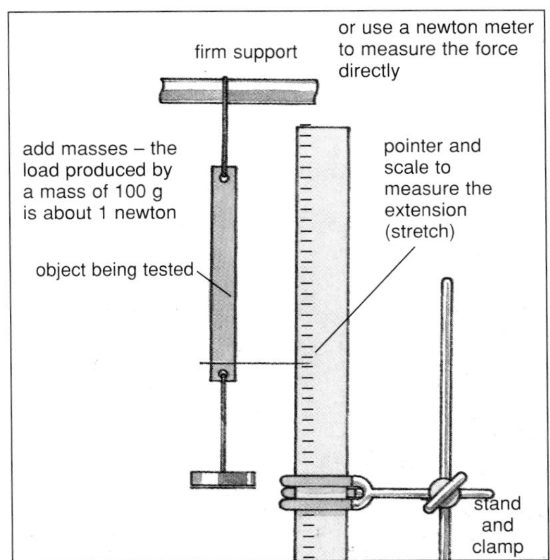

Picture 4

Picture 5

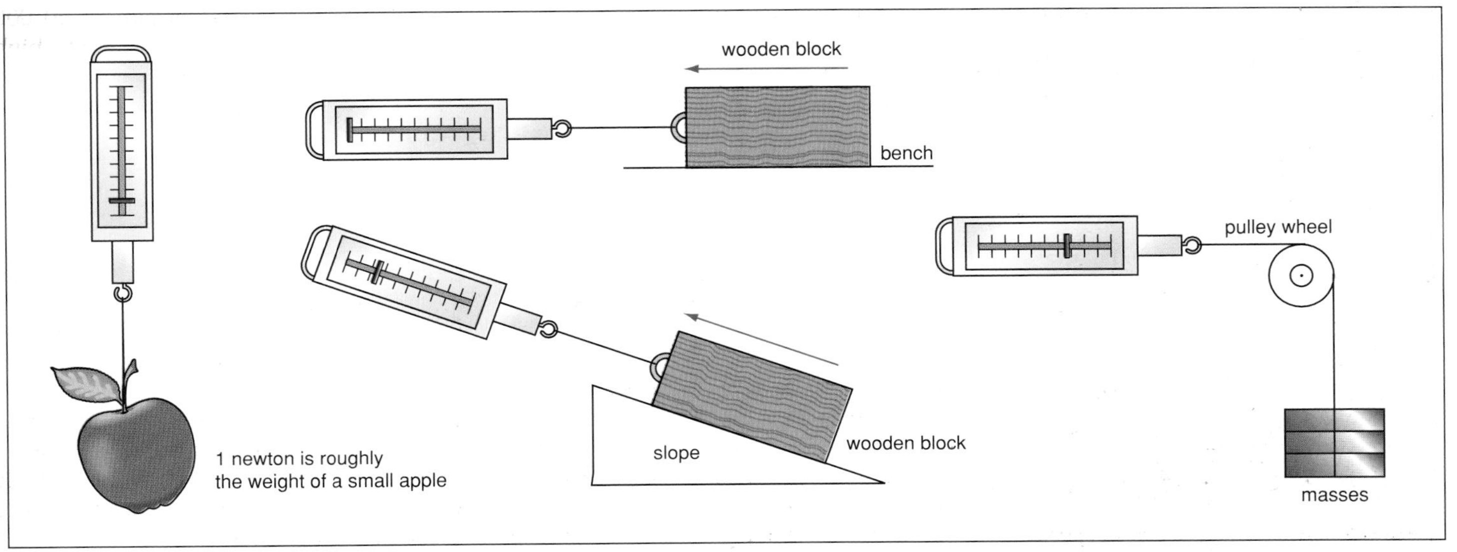

E3 Gravity

Gravity is one of the great forces of nature. It makes things fall, and keeps the planets in their orbits.

Gravity is everywhere

Everything we do is affected by gravity. Running, jumping, swimming or just standing still, our bodies are affected by the force that pulls us towards the centre of the Earth. We are so used to it that our very bones grow weaker without it. This happens to astronauts who spend a long time in 'free-fall' (see below).

We can't switch gravity off, the way we can switch off an electromagnet. We can't neutralise it, like we can the forces of static electricity. We have to live with the fact that everything on the surface of the Earth is in a strong gravity field.

The design of roads, railways, buildings, aircraft and even the bodies of living things has to take gravity into account. The study of movement under gravity is vital in physics and engineering, as well as in ball games like tennis and football.

The gravity force field

Every object attracts every other object with a gravity force. The gravity force between you and the person sitting next to you is very small. You attract each other with a force of about a millionth of a newton. You will not notice this.

Gravity forces become important when at least one of the objects is very massive. The Earth has a mass of about six million million million million kilograms, so its gravity field is quite strong.

The Earth's gravity field

The strength of a gravity field is measured in terms of how much force it exerts on a 1 kilogram mass.

On Earth, the force of gravity on an object of mass of 1 kilogram is about 10 newtons – or 9.8 newtons to be more exact. So the strength of the Earth's gravity field, $\boldsymbol{g}$, is **9.8 N per kg**.

If we put a more massive object in the gravity field it will have a bigger gravity force acting on it. A piece of iron with mass 2 kg has twice as much iron in it as a piece of iron with a mass of only 1 kilogram, so it will be pulled towards the Earth with twice the force.

A 2 kg mass feels heavier than a 1 kg mass because it is being pulled down by a force of about 20 N, compared with only about 10 N for the 1 kg mass. The force caused by gravity on a mass is called its **weight**.

We can get a rough measure of weight by just holding the object up. To measure it more accurately we need a newton meter.

The weight of an object of mass m – the force F due to gravity on it – is given by the formula $\boldsymbol{F = mg}$.

gravity force (weight) = mass × field strength

Picture 1 Playing with gravity.

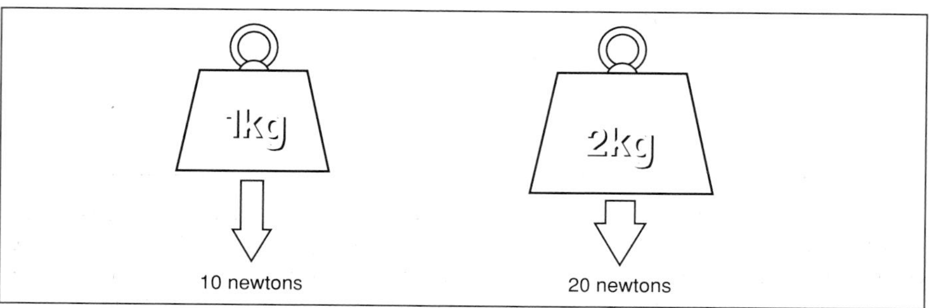

Picture 2 Gravity fields pull harder on a greater mass.

What decides the strength of a gravity field?

Gravity is a force between two or more objects. The size of this force depends on two things:

- how massive the objects are,
- how far apart they are.

Like all forces, gravity forces occur in pairs: both objects pull equally on each other.

This means that you pull on the Earth with just as much gravity force as the Earth pulls on you. Of course, when you jump off a diving board into a swimming pool you do the moving, not the Earth. This is because the Earth has so much more mass than you have, and so doesn't move so easily.

When we look at objects on Earth, the Earth is so massive that it alone decides the strength of the field. By comparison, a tennis ball, an aeroplane or even a continent is too small to make much difference to the main field.

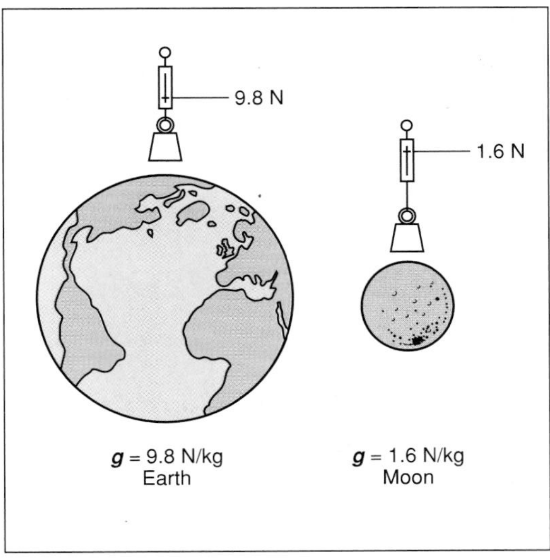

Picture 3 The Earth's gravity field is 6 times stronger than the Moon's.

The Sun

The Sun is very much larger than the Earth and its field is so strong that it affects the Earth. The Sun is a long way away, but it is the Sun's gravity that makes the Earth travel in an orbit around the Sun. It also helps to make the tides of the sea.

The Moon

On the Moon, the gravity field is smaller than on the Earth, because the Moon is so much less massive (picture 3). Its field strength is only 1.6 N per kg – about a sixth of that on Earth. So on the Moon you weigh only one-sixth of your weight on Earth.

Gravity and distance

But distance also comes into it. The further away you get from a massive object the smaller is the strength of its gravity field (picture 4).

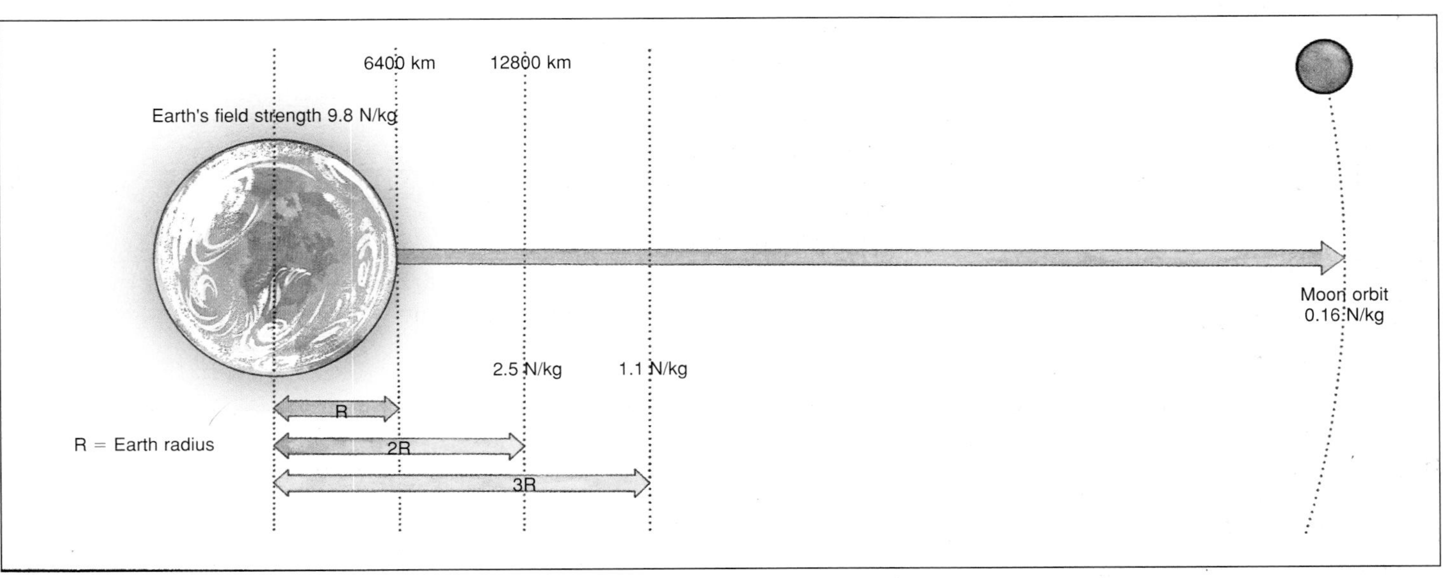

Picture 4 The gravity field grows weaker with distance – doubling the distance cuts the field to a quarter.

If the Earth was compressed to the size of the Moon the gravity field on its surface would be a lot bigger – about 14 times bigger. This is because you would be much closer to the centre of the Earth. You would weigh 14 times as much and need much stronger bones to be able to stand up and move about. Life on Earth would be very different.

E4 Friction, force and acceleration

Force speed things up and slow them down.

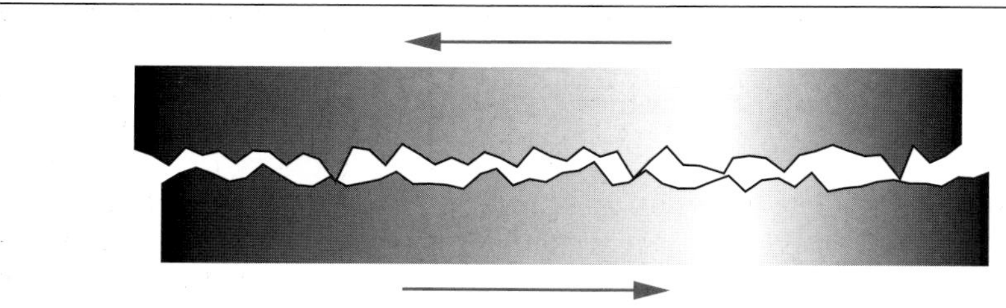

Picture 1 Two jagged surfaces sliding against each other.

If you were to look through a microscope at a smooth, shiny surface such as stainless steel or glass, you would be amazed to see a mountainous landscape. Materials which appear flat and smooth to the naked eye are really very uneven. If two surfaces are placed together, as in picture 1, and we try to slide them in different directions, the points that jut out catch against each other. This produces **friction**.

Picture 2 On an icy road, there is no friction to provides a force, so there will be no turn.

Using friction

Anyone who has ever stepped on a patch of ice will know that friction is important, particularly when there is none! When you walk, your foot exerts a force on the ground. The surface of your shoe and the surface of the ground rub against each other and provide grip. If they slid easily against each other, you would not get very far. Friction produces the force that moves you forward. It is also extremely important if you try to slow down or change direction (picture 2).

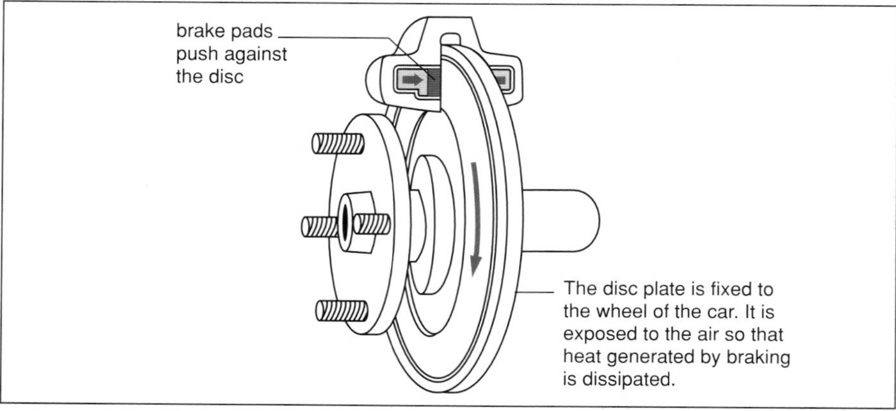

Picture 3 Friction can be used to stop vehicles safely.

The braking systems of cars and bikes are good examples of using friction to provide a resistive force (picture 3). The brake pads rub against the metal of the wheel, and the harder the two surfaces are pressed together, the greater the braking effect.

Whenever we get a frictional force being exerted as two surfaces rub together, **energy** is transferred. The simplest example of this is when you rub your finger on a desk, or rub your hands together to warm them. Kinetic (movement) energy is transferred to your hands as heat energy. The brakes on a car sometimes glow red if the car accelerates and decelerates repeatedly.

Friction welding is a way of joining metals by rubbing them together! A piece of metal is rotated while in contact with another. The two surfaces become so hot that the metals melt and join.

Friction can occur when a gas or a liquid move over a surface. As a boat hull moves through the water, or a car drives along a road, they experience a force which resists their movement. Air resistance or 'drag' can be reduced by designing shapes which allow the stream of air to flow smoothly around and over the vehicle. Picture 4 shows a car being tested in a wind tunnel. The 'stream

Picture 4 Cars are tested for air resistance in a wind tunnel.

lines' of smoke can be clearly seen. Picture 5 shows the **streamlined** shape of a locomotive.

Friction between two surfaces can only be effectively reduced if we *separate* the surfaces. When we lubricate machinery, we provide a very thin layer of oil which 'floats' the surfaces apart. If the tread on a car tyre is worn, then in rainy conditions a layer of water can build up between the tyre and the road. Frictional grip is reduced, and the car may become uncontrollable. When you step on a patch of ice, your weight causes a small layer of the ice to melt, reducing friction. When you slip on ice, you are really 'floating' on water.

Air can also be used to separate surfaces and reduce friction. In the Physics laboratory you may use a linear air track for experiments on motion. The vehicles 'float' on a layer of air, so that there is no contact between them and the track. A hovercraft uses a similar effect.

Picture 5

How do things move?

A famous scientist called Galileo performed some of the first experiments on motion. One of his most important experiments did not actually happen! As he was unable to eliminate friction from his work, he performed a 'thought experiment' – he imagined what would happen to a moving object if friction did not exist. His reasoning is illustrated in picture 6 and went as follows:

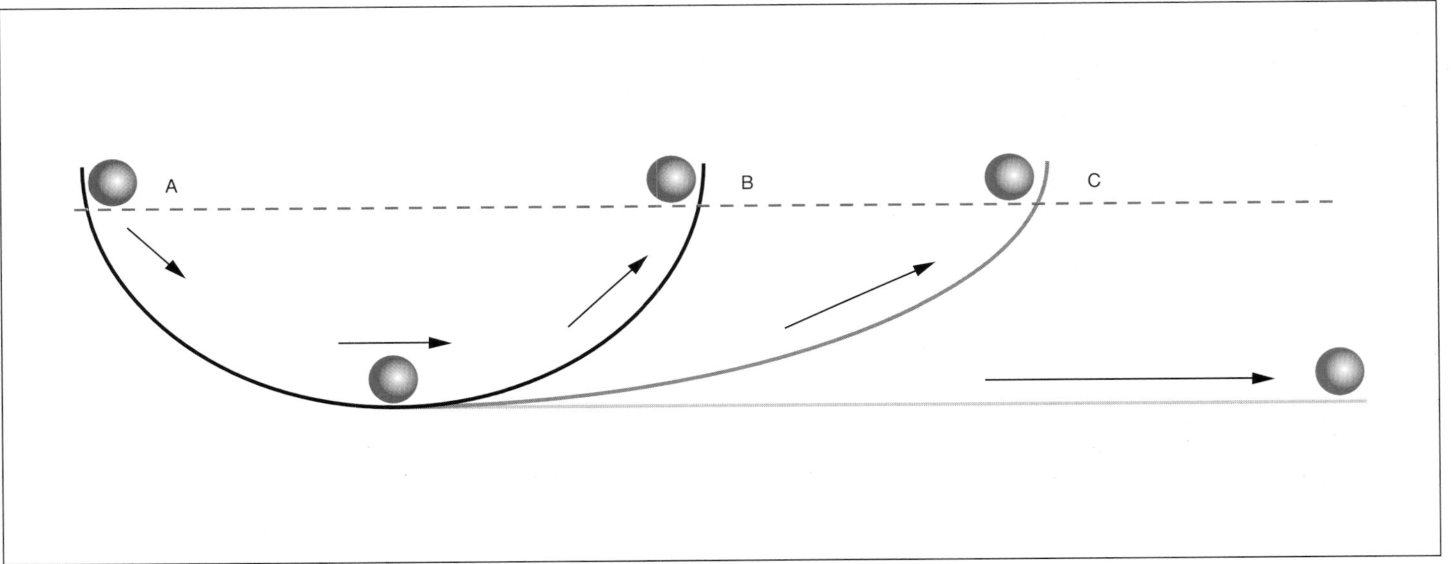

Picture 6 Galileo's thought experiment.

- A ball is allowed to run down an incline and up a similar slope on the opposite side. At the start, it has **potential energy**, due to its height. The potential energy changes to **kinetic energy** as it rolls down. As there is no friction, it will not lose any energy. It should keep going until it reaches point **B**. It now has the same amount of potential energy as it had at the starting height at **A**.
- If we alter the slope of the second part of the track, this should make no difference to the ball. It will still reach the same height, but this time at **C**.
- If the slope is made totally flat, then the ball will keep the same amount of energy and go on forever, as there is no frictional force to oppose it.

In everyday life, we are used to situations where we have to push things to keep them moving. In Galileo's time, most transport was by horse and cart, and so friction was always present. Galileo's work suggested that objects only changed their motion if a force acted on them, and if the force of friction could be removed, we would reach a better understanding of the laws that govern moving objects.

Sir Isaac Newton used Galileo's work to develop his **First Law of motion**: *objects remain stationary, or keep moving at a constant speed in a straight line, unless an* ***unbalanced*** *force acts on them.*

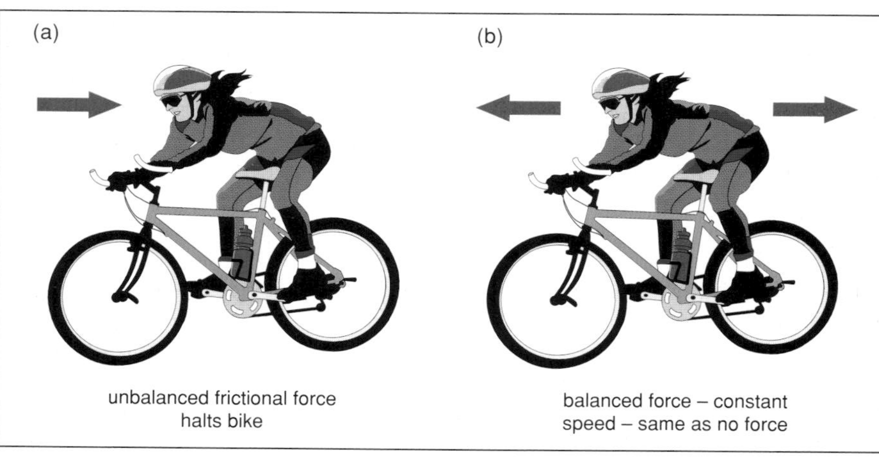

Picture 7 A balanced force is the same as no force at all.

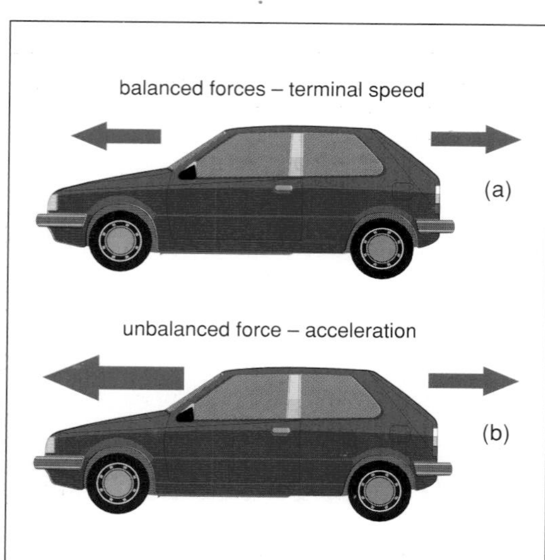

Picture 8 An unbalanced force produces an acceleration.

Balancing forces

According to Newton, a moving object should simply keep on moving in a straight line at a constant speed, if there is no unbalanced force acting on it. In the real world, we frequently travel at constant speed in a car, bus train or plane. Yet we know that the force of friction is constantly resisting this movement. What keeps things moving?

The important word is *unbalanced*. If you are riding your bike over level ground, and you stop pedalling, as in picture 7(a), the only forces acting on you are the frictional forces. Eventually you come to a halt because of air resistance, friction in the bearings of the wheels, and between the tyres and the ground.

If you resume pedalling, and manage to keep your speed constant, the frictional forces are *exactly balanced* by the driving force from the pedals. When forces are **balanced**, as in picture 7(b), the effect is the same as if there were **no forces** at all.

When a car starts from rest and accelerates, the force of the engine is much greater than the frictional forces. As the speed of the car increases, the air flows faster over the car body, and friction in the wheels becomes greater. There comes a point where the frictional forces balance the driving force (picture 8(a)), and the car moves at a steady or **terminal speed** (see page 141). If the driver wishes to overtake, he must press the accelerator to increase the force from the engine. There is now an *unbalanced* force in the forward direction (picture 8(b)). The car speeds up.

Newton again

We have seen that an unbalanced force produces an acceleration, but we do not know how the *size* of the force will affect that acceleration. What effect will the *mass* of an object have on its acceleration? The answer to these questions are important in everyday life. For example, what acceleration will a car have if we use a certain size of engine? Would a car manufacturer use the same size of engine for a small family model and a large estate car? To stop them both safely, would you use the same type of brakes?

Commonsense and experience tell us that if we push something harder, it goes faster. We also know that the larger an object is, the greater the push required to make it reach a certain speed. To get precise answers, what we need is a formula with which to do calculations.

Sir Isaac Newton carried out experiments which enabled him to describe how an acceleration depends on

- the size of the unbalanced force,
- the mass of the object it acts on.

Using equipment similar to that shown in picture 9, you can repeat these experiments in the laboratory.

Newton showed that the acceleration, a, was *directly proportional* to the force, F. This means that twice the force doubles the acceleration, with six times F we get six times a, and so on. Picture 10(a) shows a graph of this relationship.

If the *force* is kept constant, and the mass m is altered, we get a graph as shown in picture 10(b). This shows that acceleration is *inversely proportional* to mass, or we say that a is proportional to $\frac{1}{m}$. If we plot this on a graph, we get a straight line.

So we have a is proportional to F

and a is proportional to $\frac{1}{m}$

If we measure F in newtons, m in kilograms, and a in metres per second squared, we can write:

$$\boldsymbol{a = \frac{F}{m}}$$

or as it is more usually written:

$$\boldsymbol{F = ma}$$

This formula represents **Newton's Second Law**, which states that: *the acceleration of a body is* ***directly proportional*** *to the* ***unbalanced force*** *acting on it, and* ***inversely proportional*** *to the* ***mass*** *of the body.*

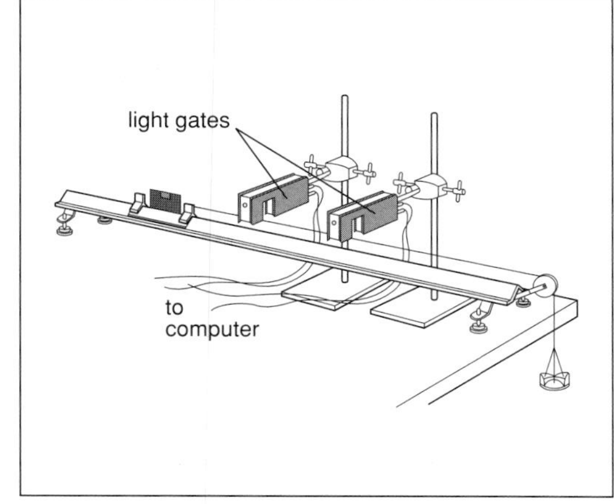

Picture 9 Finding the relationship between force, mass and acceleration.

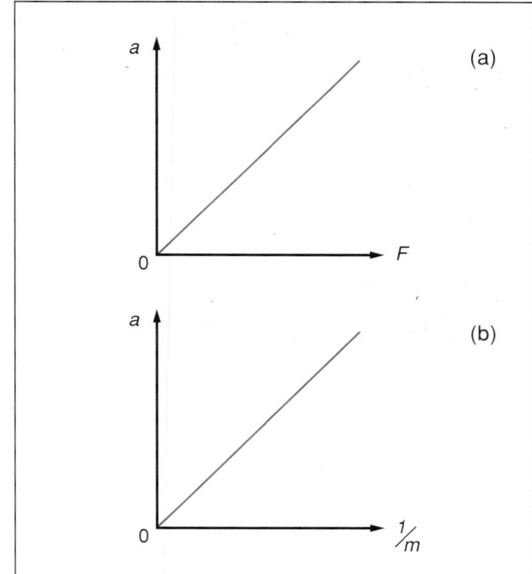

Picture 10

$F = ma$

$a = \frac{F}{m}$

$m = \frac{F}{a}$

F
m a

Picture 11

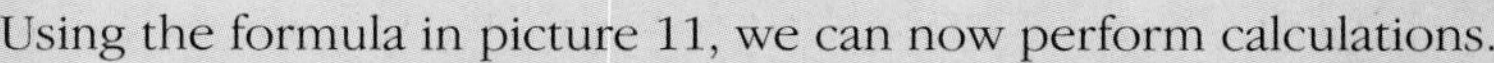

Using the formula in picture 11, we can now perform calculations.

For example, what will be the acceleration of the car in picture 12?

Unbalanced force $F = 1200\text{ N} - 400\text{ N} = 800\text{ N}$

mass $m = 600\text{ kg}$

$$a = \frac{F}{m} = \frac{800\text{ N}}{600\text{ kg}} = 1.33\text{ m/s}^2$$

Several passengers enter the car, increasing the mass to 900 kg. It accelerates away at 1.2 m/s². What unbalanced force does the engine exert on it?

$$F = ma = 900 \times 1.2 = 1080\text{ N}$$

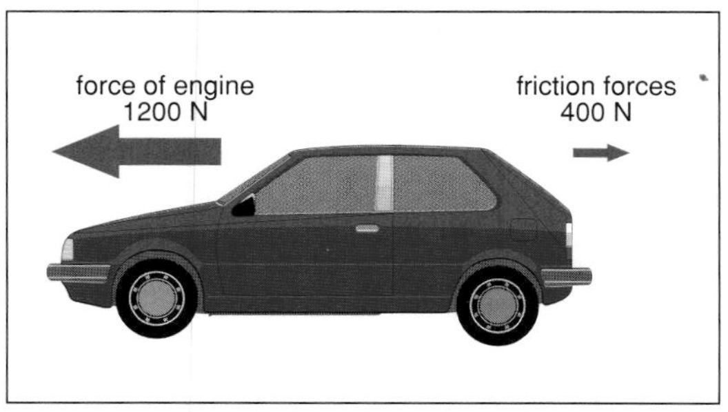

Picture 12

Picture 13 Why safety belts and crumple zones are helping to save lives.

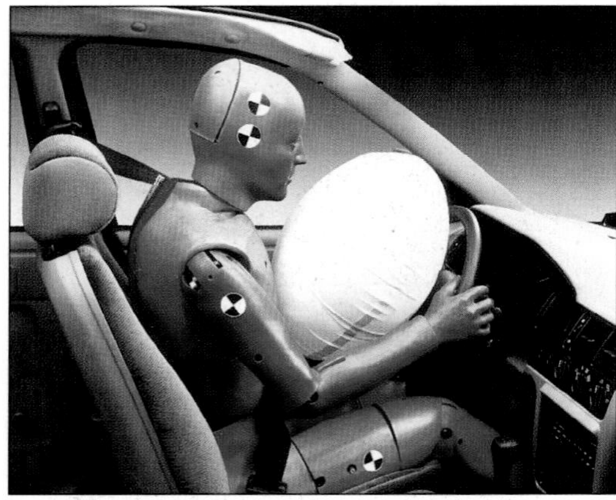

Picture 14 A car air bag in action.

Picture 15 Do posters help to save lives?

Stopping safely

To stop a moving object, you have to apply an unbalanced force. If a car stops slowly, so do the people in it. The frictional force between them and the seat is enough to slow them down. According to Newton's Laws, in a collision or even very sharp braking, *they will carry on moving* unless they are strapped in. Picture 13 illustrates this in a forceful way.

In a crash at 100 km/h, the driver or passengers will hit the windscreen or steering wheel at this very high speed. Very serious injuries are caused in this way. This is because when you hit something rigid, you stop in a very short time. **Seat belts** are designed to 'give' a little, so that the driver and passenger take a little longer to stop than the car does.

A passenger hitting the steering wheel and one wearing a seat belt are both slowing down from 100 km/h to 0 km/h. The *change in speed* is the same, but the *time taken* is different. The shorter the time, the greater the deceleration or *negative* acceleration. As we know from Newton's Second Law, the greater the acceleration, the bigger the force acting on the person.

Car designers now build cars with a central solid 'cage' surrounded by a much weaker **crumple zone**. The front or back of the car will be weak enough to collapse, but strong enough to do so slowly. This again increases the stopping time, reducing the forces involved. Similarly, many steering wheels now collapse slowly in a collision, reducing chest injury.

Air bags (picture 14) are triggered by a sudden deceleration, and can inflate in a few microseconds. The driver's head and chest are prevented from striking the windscreen or steering wheel.

Stopping in time

The chart shows the official stopping distances for cars with good tyres and brakes. It has been worked out by the Department of Transport. When a car has its brakes 'full on', it will be decelerating at its maximum rate. The faster the car is going, the longer it will take to come to a halt. The **braking distance** is how far the car will travel in this time.

If we *double* the speed, we need *four* times the braking distance to stop the car. *Trebling* the speed multiplies the braking distance by *nine*.

The chart also shows the **thinking distance**. It takes time for a driver to react to an emergency. The thinking distance can be found by multiplying the driver's **reaction time** by the speed of the car. The **overall stopping distance** is the thinking distance *plus* the braking distance.

Table 1 Official stopping distances.

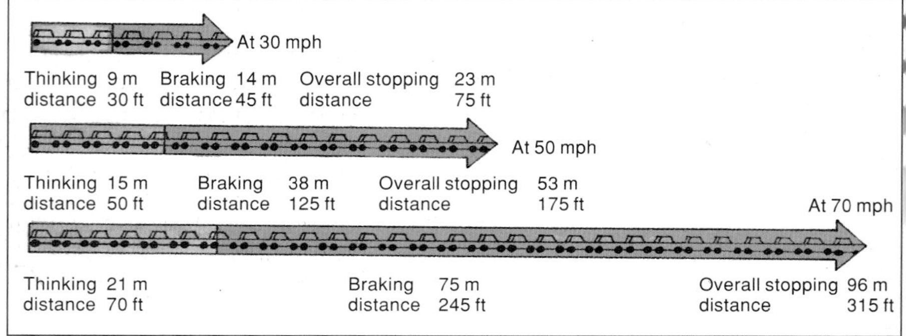

Questions

1 During the Apollo space programme, an astronaut of mass 80 kg travelled to the Moon. The gravitational field strength did not remain the same throughout the journey.

a What is meant by *gravitational field strength*?

b Copy and complete the **last two columns** of table 1 (top right) to show the astronaut's mass and his weight in different situations.

2 The diagram below shows the forces acting on an aeroplane which is flying at a constant height.

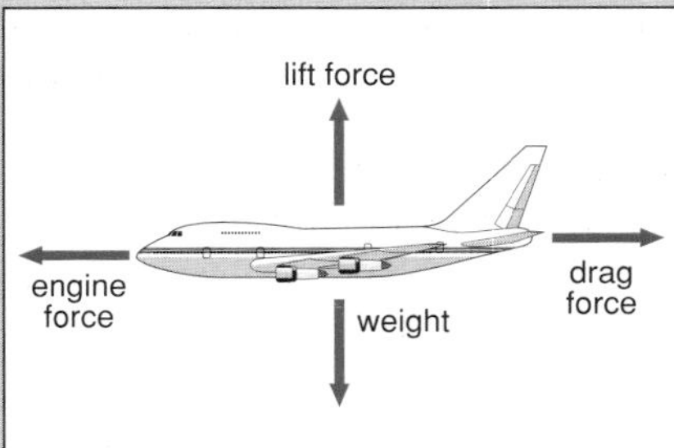

a How do the engine force and the drag force compare when the aeroplane is travelling at a steady speed?

b The aeroplane has a mass of 62 000 kilograms.

i) What is the weight of the aeroplane?

ii) What will be the lift force when the aeroplane is flying at a constant height?

3 A spacecraft is far out in space. An astronaut leaves the spacecraft to go to a small artificial satellite nearby. She has a jet pack strapped to her back.

The astronaut and her equipment have a mass of 70 kilograms and the jets can exert a constant thrust of 14 newtons when switched on.

a Calculate the acceleration of the astronaut when she switches on the jets.

b Describe the motion of the astronaut if the jets are now switched off. Explain your answer.

Table 1

Situation	Gravitational field strength	Mass	Weight
On the Earth	10 N/kg		
At a point in the journey	negligible		
On the Moon	1.6 N/kg		

4 During space missions, crews experience the effect known as weightlessness. Weightlessness can be demonstrated on Earth. Figure (a) shows a person holding a newton balance from which a 2 kilogram mass is suspended. Figure (b) shows the person shortly after stepping off a diving board.

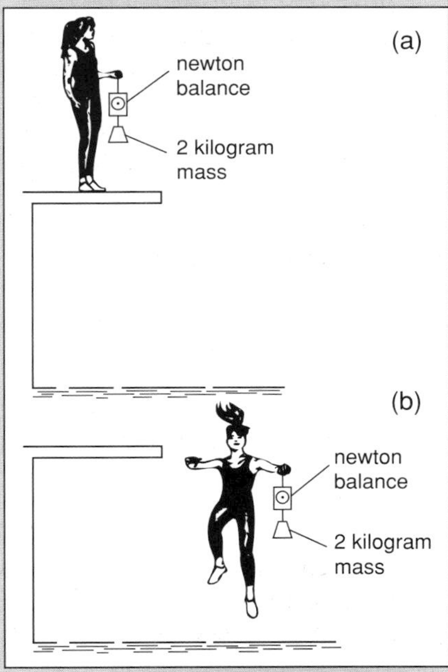

a What is the reading on the newton balance while the person is standing still on the board as shown in the figure above?

b What happens to the reading on the newton balance as the person is falling towards the water?

5a A car of mass 1200 kg is being towed at a constant speed of 5 m/s by a breakdown lorry. The force of friction on the car at this speed is 400 N.

What size of force is exerted by the tow rope on the car?

b The force exerted by the tow rope on the car is increased to 2000 N. Assuming that the force of friction on the car remains constant at 400 N, find the acceleration of the car.

6 A skateboarder starts from rest at the top and skates down a slope.

a After 2.5 seconds, the skateboarder has reached a speed of 10 metres per second.

Calculate the acceleration of the skateboarder.

b The skateboarder has a mass of 60 kilograms.

Calculate the unbalanced force causing the skateboarder's acceleration.

7 A car, travelling at 20 metres per second, accelerates to 30 metres per second, along a straight section of motorway, in a time of 5 seconds.

a Calculate the acceleration of the car.

b The mass of the car and passengers is 1200 kilograms.

What size of force is required to give the acceleration?

c The Highway Code suggests that a car travelling at 30 metres per second needs a distance of 70 metres to stop from the instant the brakes are applied.

Why will a distance greater than this be required when the driver of a car, travelling at 30 metres per second, has to make an emergency stop?

E5 Gravity, movement and energy

Whenever something happens, energy is transferred.

Picture 1(a) shows a ball falling freely towards the Earth. It has been taken using a flashing light that lit the ball every tenth of a second. As you can see, the ball travels a greater and greater distance in each tenth of a second. It is *accelerating*.

This is because it is being pulled down with a steady force, and this produces a constant acceleration (see topic E4). It is called the **acceleration of free fall**.

Picture 1(b) shows the ball again. This time it has been thrown sideways. But gravity still acts, and the ball is pulled downwards exactly as before. This will happen however fast the ball is thrown sideways.

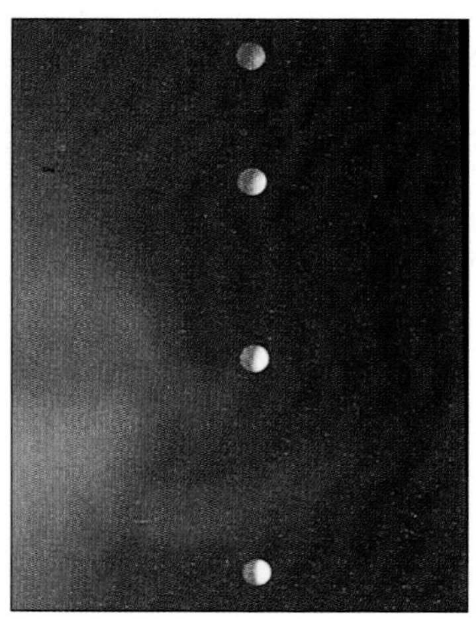

Picture 1 A freely falling object accelerates.

Do heavy objects fall faster than light ones?

No – but keep on reading.

An object is **heavy**, and feels heavy, because gravity is pulling on it with large force. This is because a heavy object has more mass than a light object.

But because it has more mass it is harder to accelerate! The extra gravity force on the heavy object exactly compensates for the extra mass. So the acceleration of free fall is exactly the same, whatever the mass of the object – see picture 2. This is shown below mathematically.

We have seen that a force causes an acceleration according to the rule

force = mass × acceleration

$$\text{or } F = ma \qquad (1)$$

The gravity force on an object in a field of strength g is

force = mass × field strength

$$\text{or } F = mg \qquad (2)$$

Putting these two ideas together (1) and (2) tell us that if the accelerating force is gravity, then

$$F = ma = mg$$

and this can only be true if $a = g$.

The size of the acceleration of free fall in a gravity field is equal to the size of the field strength.

Picture 2 Freely falling objects accelerate at the same rate.

How free is free fall?

There is another force that acts on a falling object, on Earth at least. This is the force of friction caused by the object moving through the air. This force depends on the size and shape of the falling object. People falling from an aeroplane accelerate quite rapidly to a high speed – unless they are using a parachute. The shape of the parachute increases the air friction, so they slow down once the parachute is opened.

But whether they wear a parachute or not the falling people eventually reach a steady speed, when they are not accelerating any more. This happens because the force of air resistance acts on them in the opposite direction to the gravity force – see picture 3.

The force caused by air resistance gets bigger the faster you go. (You can feel this when you travel fast on a bicycle.) When the air resistance becomes equal to the gravity force a falling object stops accelerating (picture 4). It has reached its final speed or **terminal velocity**.

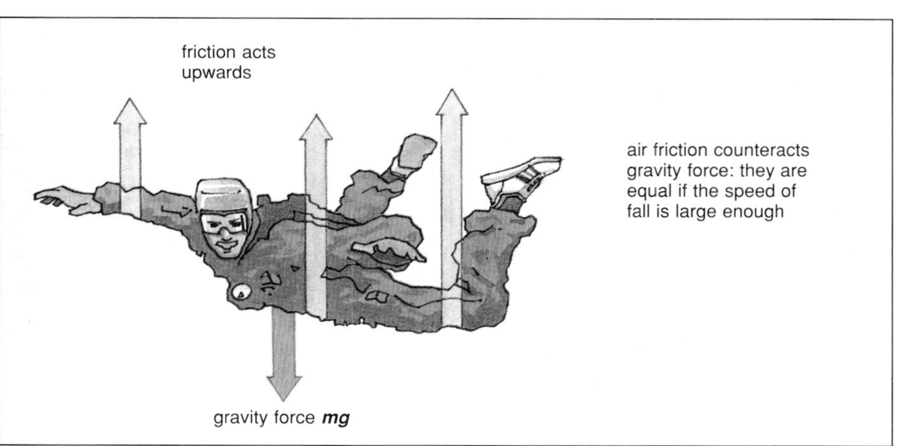

Picture 3 A free-fall parachutist – but they don't fall freely!

friction force *F*

when the parachute opens, the friction force is great enough to equal the gravity force at a much lower speed

gravity force *mg*

Picture 4 Parachutes greatly increase the force of air resistance.

Working against gravity

Climbing up a hill is usually hard work, whether we walk or ride a bicycle. We are doing work by using muscular force to lift ourselves against the force of gravity. Mountain roads and paths are built in zig–zags to make this job easier (see picture 5).

We can do this work by using part of the 'energy store' in our bodies, obtained from combining chemicals from the food we eat with the oxygen we breathe in. A car climbing up this same mountain road uses the energy obtained from burning petrol in oxygen. Food and fuel are sometimes called sources of **chemical energy**, because the energy is released (made useful) via chemical reactions. In both the car engine and our bodies, some is given off as heat. Thankfully, quite a lot of the work hasn't been wasted. It has been transferred into a mysterious kind of energy called **gravitational potential energy**.

Energy change

Potential energy can be a rather dangerous energy for someone high up on a mountain. The reason for this is that potential energy can be changed to movement energy, which is usually called **kinetic energy**. If you fall off a mountain, the force of gravity pulls you down and you move faster. A car reaching the top of the the mountain road could switch off its engine, and as it freewheels down the slope, the potential energy will change to kinetic energy.

When it reaches the foot of the mountain, all the potential energy will have been changed to kinetic energy, plus heat due to braking at the corners.

Picture 5 An Alpine road.

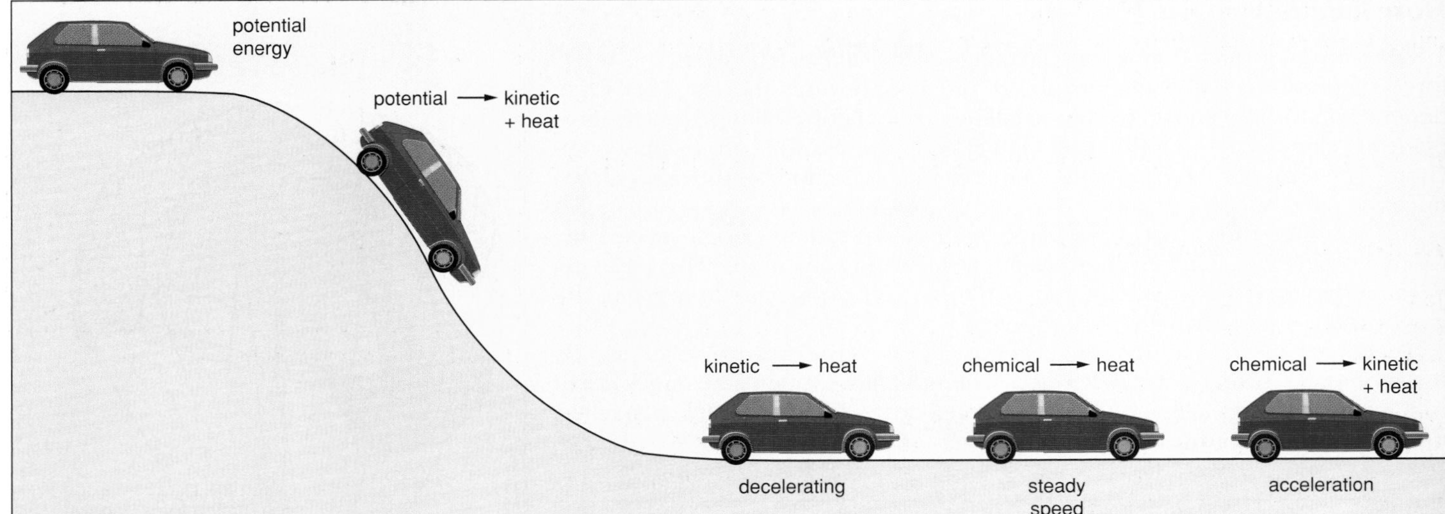

Picture 6

As it coasts along the level road, frictional forces will cause it to slow down. Its kinetic energy is being transferred to the surroundings, heating them.

The driver switches on the engine, and proceeds at a steady speed. The engine force is balancing frictional forces. Now all the energy obtained by burning the petrol is transferred as heat.

The driver accelerates. Chemical energy is changed to heat but also to kinetic energy as the car speeds up.

Picture 6 shows all these stages. There will be other types of energy involved, for example sound from the car engine, but we have concentrated on the main energy transfers.

We can calculate energy transfers using a lot of different techniques once we realise that moving energy from one form to another doesn't alter the fact that it is still **energy**. We can lift a can of beans up on to a shelf in all sorts of ways. But whatever source the energy comes from, the same **quantity** of energy has to be transferred, whether it is done by an electric robot, a conveyer belt or a human being.

NUTRITION INFORMATION

Typical composition by weight

	per 100 g	per 45 g serving
Energy	1410 kJ 330 kcal	635 kJ 150 kcal
Protein	9.8 g	4.4 g
Carbohydrate	72.8 g	32.8 g
Fat	2.1 g	1.0 g
Dietary Fibre	10.5 g	4.7 g

Picture 7 Breakfast energy!

Look at the packet

Energy is measured in **joules**. Picture 7 shows the label on a packet of cereal. Amongst other things it tells you that when you eat one serving (45 g) it could supply 635 kJ (635 000 joules) of energy. This is a lot of joules – more than half a million! It is roughly the same as the amount of movement energy you would gain if you fell off a cliff 1000 metres high. It is 20 times the energy carried by a high-velocity rifle bullet.

An average 16-year-old boy needs about 12 million joules a day. This is enough to lift a 60 kg person a height of 20 km. Mount Everest is less than 9 km high!

Working

One way that scientists measure energy is by seeing how much **work** it can do. In Physics, the term work has a very clear scientific meaning:

work is a measure of the amount of energy transferred when a force is applied.

Forces do work when they move something. First we need to measure the size of the **force** (in newtons). Then we measure the **distance** (in metres) that the object moves *in the direction the force is acting*. Then we can calculate:

work done = force × distance moved

W (joules) = ***F*** (newtons) × ***d*** (metres)

Suppose it takes a force of 25 N to move a saw when you cut a piece of wood, and you move it 0.2 metre each time. Then one cutting movement needs:

$$W = F \times d$$
$$= 25\ \text{N} \times 0.2\ \text{m} = 5\ \text{J of energy.}$$

If it takes 20 sawcuts to get through the wood, you do 100 J of work (picture 8).

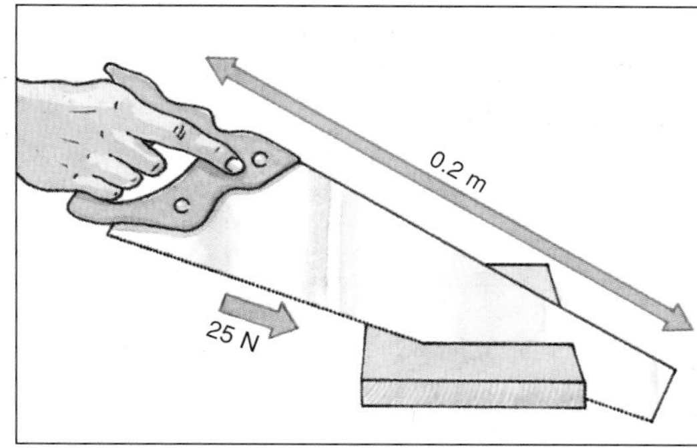

Picture 8 Work and energy.

James Joule – heating with energy

James Joule lived over 150 years ago. He was one of the first scientists to do experiments which actually measured how much energy was needed to *heat* something.

James Joule did experiments to show that when you do work, by moving a paddle wheel against the friction of water in a container, the water gets hot (picture 9). More importantly, he showed that the more work he did the hotter the water got. He demonstrated that *movement* energy and *heat* energy were just different versions of the same thing.

We now know that energy can appear in all kinds of different ways, doing different jobs.

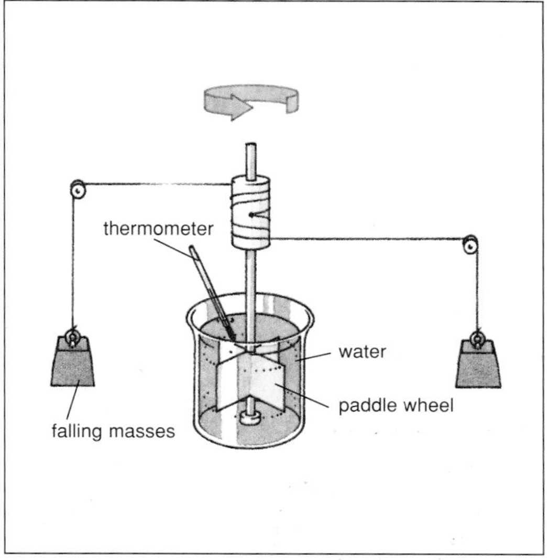

Picture 9 Joule's Paddle Wheel Apparatus showed that 'heat is a form of energy'.

Measuring potential energy

Lifting an object to give it potential energy is simply a special case of doing work in the *vertical* direction. The potential energy gained is equal to the work done. The vertical force is equal to the *weight* of the object. As we saw on page 140, if it has a mass m it will have a force F on it of mg.

When you move it a through a *vertical distance*, you are moving it through a height h.

$$\text{potential energy } E_p = \text{work done}$$
$$= F \times d$$
$$= mg \times h$$
$$\boldsymbol{E_p = mgh}$$

You can get this potential energy 'back' by allowing the object to fall. All the potential energy will be changed into kinetic energy. In picture 10, we can see the basic plan for a hydroelectric power station. Water behind a dam flows down a pipe to a turbine. The kinetic energy of the water does work to drive the turbine and produce electricity. The dam is a height of h metres above the turbine. The kinetic energy gained by a mass of water, m, is equal to the potential energy it had in the dam:

$$\boldsymbol{E_k = E_p = mgh}$$

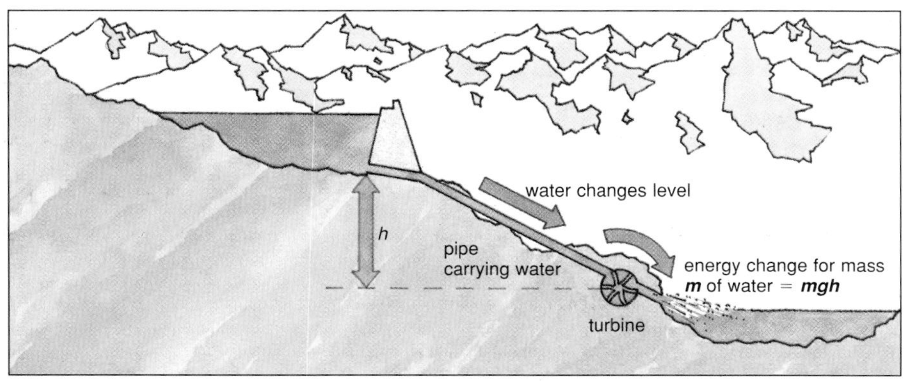

Picture 10 Energy transfers in a hydroelectric power station.

E6
Work, kinetic energy and power

How much energy does a moving object have?

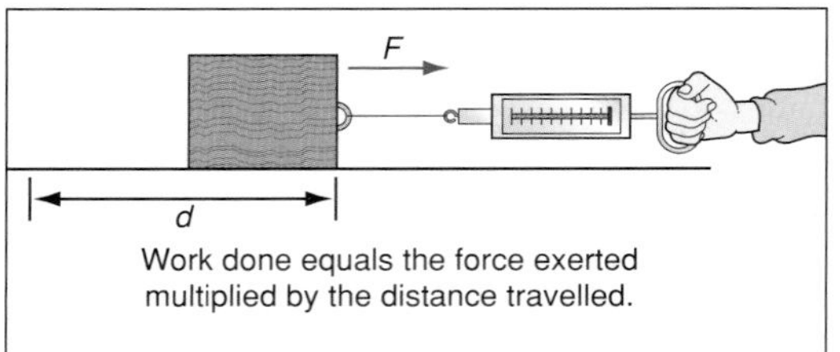

Picture 1

We have seen that **work** is a measure of the amount of energy transferred by a force. A simple experiment is shown in picture 1, where a block of wood is being pulled along a bench at a steady speed. The amount of force being used can be found from the reading on the newton balance. The distance the block is pulled can be measured with a metre stick. We can calculate the work done using:

$$\text{work done} = \text{force} \times \text{distance}$$
$$W = F \times d$$

After the block has stopped moving, we could ask the question: where is the energy that has been transferred? The block of wood was pulled at a steady speed and is now stationary. It has not gained any kinetic energy. The force that was exerted was just large enough to balance the forces of friction and keep the block moving. The energy that was transferred has made the block (and the table) hotter!

Picture 2(a) shows exactly the same process. The car is moving at a steady speed, and the force produced by the engine is doing work against friction as it moves the car through a distance. Once again, the final form of the energy is heat.

In picture 2(b) we have a different situation. The car is now *accelerating*, because there is an *unbalanced* force. This time, some of the work done by the engine force is being transferred as **kinetic** energy. The greater the amount of kinetic energy, the faster the car travels. We can write:

$$\text{kinetic energy gained} = \text{work done} = \text{unbalanced force} \times \text{distance}$$
$$E_k = W = F \times d$$

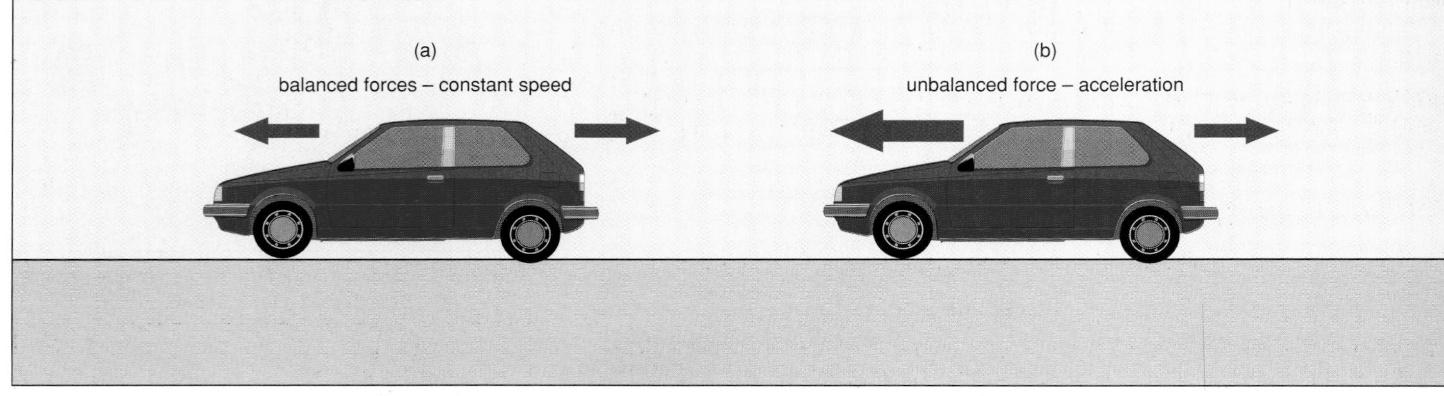

Picture 2 Work done by an unbalanced force is transferred as kinetic energy.

Anyone who has pushed cars which have failed to start knows that the bigger the car, the greater the effort required. We would expect that, to accelerate a more massive object to the same speed as a smaller one, we would have to do more work and the object gain more kinetic energy. Most of us would also jump to the conclusion that if we *double* the speed of an object then we *double* its kinetic energy.

When we perform a simple experiment, such as that shown in picture 3, we get a very different result. The potential energy in one elastic band is transferred as kinetic energy to the air-track vehicle. When two and three elastic bands are used, we double and triple the amount of energy. The speed is measured using light gates, and when we plot E_k against v we do *not* get a straight line. In fact, we find that kinetic energy is proportional to the *square* of the speed.

In other words, to *double* the speed requires *four* times the kinetic energy. This explains why, as stated on page 138, the stopping distance of a car increases by a factor of four when the speed doubles. The brakes must do four times the work to transform the kinetic energy of the car into heat. The force must be exerted by the brakes through four times the distance.

The kinetic energy of a car is transferred from the chemical energy in the petrol. Imagine accelerating your car from zero to 40 kilometres per hour.

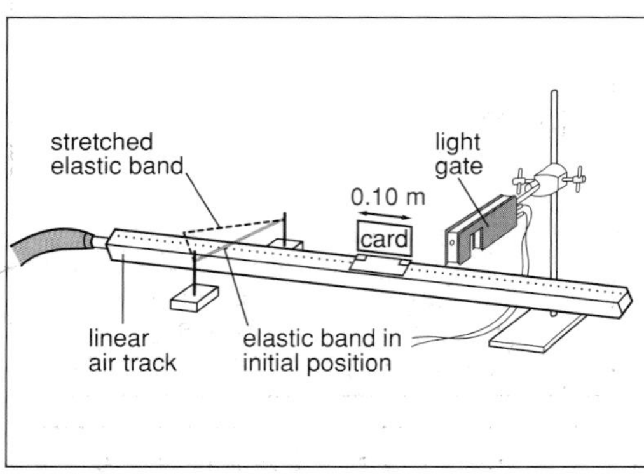

Picture 3

Treble the speed, to 120 kilometres per hour, and the car has nine times the original kinetic energy. You have used *nine* times the amount of fuel.

Calculating kinetic energy

We find that the relationship between **mass** and kinetic energy is directly proportional for the same speed – double the mass requires double the kinetic energy, and so on.

If we know the mass m and the speed v of an object, we can calculate its kinetic energy using the formula:

$$\boldsymbol{E_k = \frac{1}{2} mv^2}$$

At the scene of an accident, the police make careful measurements of the distance travelled by a car before stopping. They know the force exerted by the brakes. The work done by the brakes in stopping the car is equal to the amount of kinetic energy the car had before the brakes were applied. The police know the mass of the car, and can therefore say that:

$$\begin{aligned} \text{work done by brakes} &= \text{kinetic energy of the car} \\ W &= E_k \\ F \times d &= \tfrac{1}{2} mv^2 \\ 7500\ \text{N} \times 15\ \text{m} &= \tfrac{1}{2} mv^2 \\ 112\ 500\ \text{J} &= \tfrac{1}{2} mv^2 \end{aligned}$$

If the mass of the car is 1000 kg, then we arrive at:

$$\begin{aligned} v^2 &= 225 \\ v &= 15\ \text{m/s} \end{aligned}$$

A speed of 13 m/s is equivalent to 30 mph, so the driver was above the speed limit for that stretch of road and will be prosecuted.

Potential energy to kinetic energy

We have seen that the formula for the potential energy of an object is:

$$\boldsymbol{E_p = mgh}$$

where m is the mass of an object, g the strength of the gravity field and h the height through which the object has been lifted, or can fall.

When you lift a can of baked beans on to a shelf a metre above the ground you have given it some extra potential energy. If the can weighs 0.5 kg you increase its potential energy by

$$\begin{aligned} mgh &= 0.5\ \text{kg} \times 10\ \text{N/kg} \times 1\ \text{metre} \\ &= 5\ \text{J} \end{aligned}$$

As stated above the energy in a moving object depends on how massive it is and how fast it is going. It is calculated using the formula:

$$E_k = \tfrac{1}{2} mv^2$$

When an object falls freely in a gravity field, its *loss* in potential energy equals its *gain* in kinetic energy. So if our can of beans fell off the shelf (picture 4), how fast would it be going just before it hit the ground? We can use these two formulae to work this out:

$$\begin{aligned} \text{kinetic energy gained} &= \text{potential energy lost} \\ \tfrac{1}{2} mv^2 &= mgh \end{aligned}$$

which gives

$$\begin{aligned} \tfrac{1}{2} v^2 &= gh \\ \boldsymbol{v^2} &= \boldsymbol{2gh} \end{aligned}$$

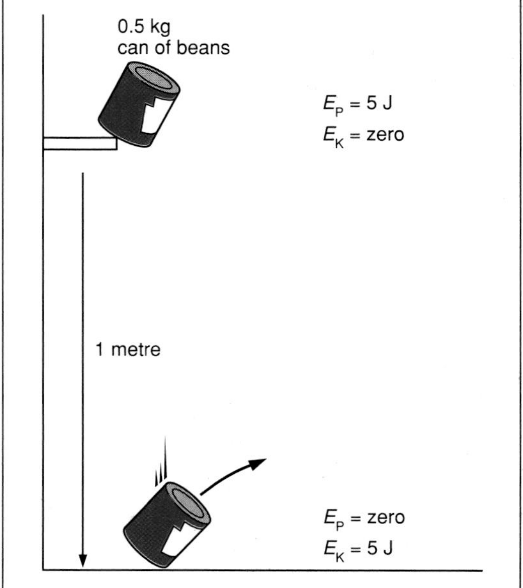

Picture 4 Potential energy changing to kinetic energy.

In other words, to find the speed of an object as it hits the ground, we do not need to know the mass, *only the height*. We take g as constant.

$$v^2 = 2gh$$

$$v^2 = 2 \times 10 \times 1$$

This gives

$$v = \sqrt{20}$$

$$v = 4.5 \text{ m/s}$$

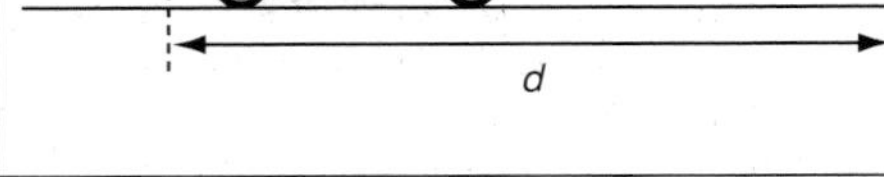

Picture 5

Power

In scientific terms **power is the rate of transfer of energy**. This means that power is a measure of the rate at which we can do work. It is measured in **joules per second** or **watts**.

A more powerful engine can do work more quickly than a less powerful one. The engine of a sports car may transfer energy at a rate of about 200 000 J per second, while a small car may have a rate of about 40 000 J per second.

Their power ratings are 200 000 W (200 kW) and 40 000 W (40 kW).

Calculating power

When calculating a power rating, we can use the definition:

$$\text{power} = \frac{\text{work done}}{\text{time taken}} = \frac{\text{energy transferred}}{\text{time taken}}$$

As a formula:

$$\boldsymbol{P} = \frac{\boldsymbol{W}}{\boldsymbol{t}} = \frac{\boldsymbol{E}}{\boldsymbol{t}}$$

We can adapt these to the particular situation we are dealing with. For example, a car is driving down the road at a constant speed (picture 5). It has an engine which is producing a force F as it moves the car through a distance d.

$$P = \frac{W}{t} = \frac{F \times d}{t}$$

We know that:

$$\text{speed} = \frac{\text{distance}}{\text{time}} \quad \text{or} \quad v = \frac{d}{t}$$

so we can say:

$$P = Fv$$

Consider a situation as shown in picture 6. The motor of the winch takes seconds to lift the miners up to the surface through a height h. How powerful is the motor? The work done is equal to the amount of potential energy gained by the cage and miners, which has a total mass of m.

$$\text{power} = \frac{\text{work done}}{\text{time taken}} = \frac{\text{energy transferred}}{\text{time taken}}$$

$$P = \frac{W}{t} = \frac{E_p}{t} = \frac{mgh}{t}$$

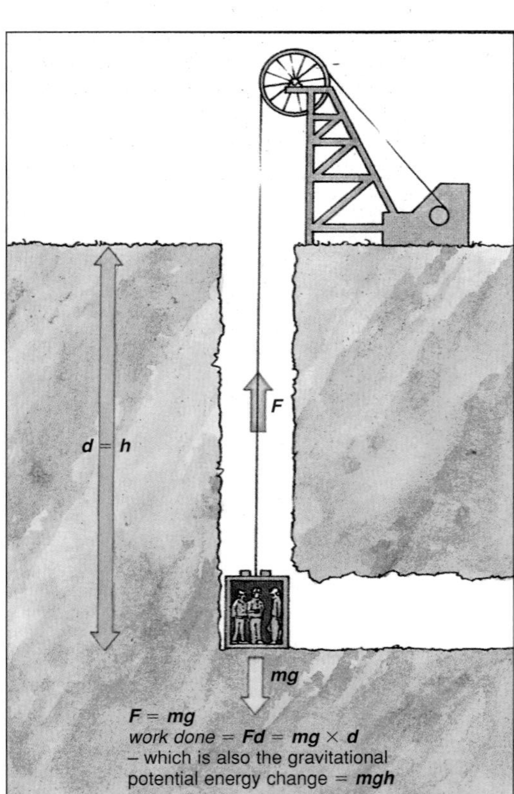

Picture 6 Doing work against gravity: ***E*** = ***Fd***

Questions

1 A cyclist travels a distance of 400 metres at constant speed. A constant frictional force of 70 newtons acts on the cyclist.

Calculate the work done by the cyclist against friction.

2 A mountaineer of mass 70 kilograms climbs through a height of 900 metres. Calculate the gain in the mountaineer's potential energy.

3 Jack uses 3600 joules of energy running up a hill in 12 seconds.

What is the average power developed by Jack?

4 The engines of European Space Agency rocket Arianne produced 8 000 000 000 joules of energy during the first 5 seconds after take off.

Calculate the average power of the engines during the first 5 seconds after take off.

5 A boy pushes a bale of straw of mass 45 kilograms up a ramp on to a trailer by applying a force of 250 newtons as shown. The length of the ramp is 5 metres and the height of the trailer above the ground is 1.2 metres.

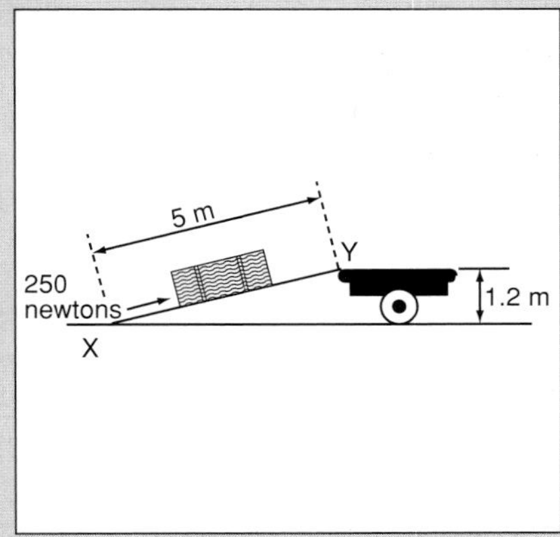

a How much work does the boy do pushing the bale up the ramp from X to Y?

b What is the weight of the bale of straw?

c How much work does a man do in lifting an identical bale vertically from the ground on to the trailer?

d Why does it take more work to push the bale up the ramp than to lift the bale vertically on to the trailer?

6 The diagram shows a water chute at a leisure pool. The top of the chute is 11.25 m above the edge of the pool. A girl, of mass 50 kg, climbs from the edge of the pool to the top of the water chute.

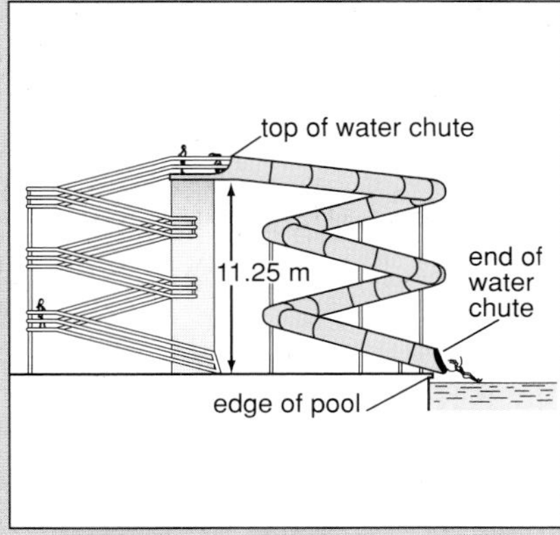

a Calculate the potential energy gained by the girl in climbing from the edge of the pool to the top of the chute.

b The girl slides from rest to the bottom of the chute. Assuming that her potential energy is all transferred to kinetic energy, show how the girl's speed at the bottom of the chute is 15 m/s.

c Frictional forces act on the girl so that her actual speed at the bottom of the chute is 12 m/s. The graph below shows how the girl's speed varies with time as she slides down the chute.

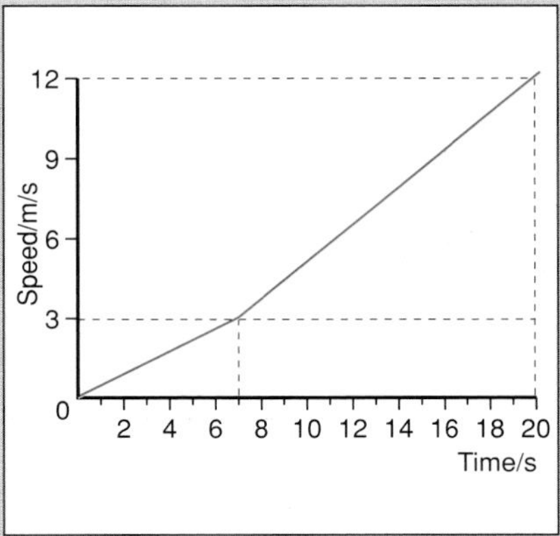

i) Calculate the distance travelled by the girl in sliding from the top to the bottom of the chute.

ii) The energy transferred as heat in her journey down the chute is 2025 J. Calculate the average frictional force acting on the girl.

7 The NASA space shuttle has a mass of 68 500 kg. After re-entry, it has a touchdown speed of 93.0 m/s and travels 2 km along the runway before stopping.

a Calculate the kinetic energy of the shuttle at the instant of touchdown.

b What is the size of the force necessary to stop the shuttle in the 2 kilometre distance?

c During re-entry, the orbital speed of 7800 m/s is reduced to the touchdown speed of 93 m/s. The shuttle experiences a large reduction in its kinetic energy when this happens.

Explain what happens to this 'lost' kinetic energy.

F1
Where does energy come from?

All life on Earth needs energy; we can control it, but cannot create it. Are we using it wisely? Is the world going to run out of energy?

Where does the energy we use actually come from? We usually take it for granted. Just press the switch and electrical machines start to work, or the heating comes on. We stop at a garage and fill up with petrol, or someone comes and delivers oil, coal or coke to our homes. The gas supply is always there when we want it.

The pie chart (picture 1) shows where we use energy. Most of it is fairly evenly shared out between home, industry and moving things about. A smaller amount is used for what are called 'services', which means things like schools, hospitals, town halls, shops, etc.

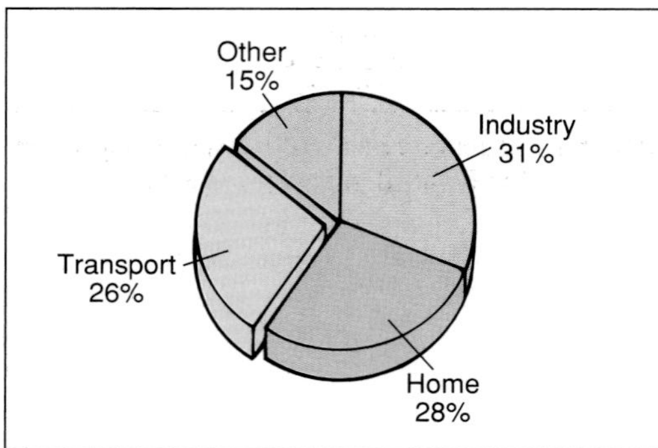

Picture 1 What do we use energy for?

How much energy do you use?

One way or another every person in this country uses, each year, the energy that could be got from burning 3.5 tonnes of oil. North Americans use more than twice as much, and the average for the world is 1.5 tonnes per person.

Of course, the energy you use is not all supplied from oil. One of the great things about energy is that it can be changed into various 'forms', and can be moved about in so many different ways. What is really happening is that the energy is being transferred from one 'system' to another.

A system can be something quite simple, like a spinning wheel. It can also be something very complicated, like a human cell or a power station. Let's take a look at how the energy you get from an electric fire actually got there. It took a longer time than you might think!

Moving along the energy trail

Think of sitting in front of an electric fire. The energy has moved along quite a long trail before it reached you.

The start of the trail – the Sun

The Sun is millions of kilometres away, and the energy from the fire that warms you started just there, millions of years ago. **Nuclear fusion** is the process that makes the Sun very hot (picture 2). This makes the Sun send out energy as various kinds of **radiation**. A very small fraction of this gets to the Earth and keeps the Earth warm.

Some of the radiation energy, visible light, is used by plants to make the chemicals they need through a process called **photosynthesis**. In photosynthesis, the simple molecules of carbon dioxide and water are turned into new, more complicated molecules of sugar and starches. These are **carbohydrates**. Animals use the carbohydrates from the plants they eat, so the energy which came from the Sun is also stored in the chemicals in their bodies.

Picture 2 Nuclear fusion changes mass to energy.

Forming fossil fuels

Fossil fuels are so called because they are the remains of plants and animals that died a very long time ago. Under certain conditions, these remains were not broken down and recycled in the usual way. Over millions of years, the carbohydrates in ancient plants and animals have been converted to fossil fuels: oil, coal and natural gas. Fossil fuels contain many different chemical compounds, but the most important ones are **hydrocarbons**.

Energy from fossil fuels

Fossil fuels are now our major source of energy. The energy is released by burning with oxygen. The waste products are oxides, mostly of carbon (carbon dioxide) and hydrogen (hydrogen oxide – water).

This is the reverse of the process which formed the hydrocarbons in plants. olar energy was used to convert carbon dioxide and water into sugars with the elease of oxygen into the atmosphere.

The main hydrocarbon fossil fuels are: **coal**, **crude oil** and **gas**. Crude oil is mixture of oils from which useful fuels such as diesel, petrol and paraffin can e extracted. Gas is mainly **methane**, one of the simplest hydrocarbons.

'he fuel–oxygen system

'he chemicals in fossil fuels can only release their energy when they change nto other chemicals. The most common way is by combustion (burning). They ombine with oxygen and heat up their surroundings, producing the waste ases steam and carbon dioxide. The energy cycle has brought us back to where started all those millions of years ago, as shown in picture 3.

'rom coal to electric fire

Aost of our electricity is generated in power stations that burn coal. As the lectricity flows through the resistance wire in the bars of our fire, it delivers nergy and the wire glows red hot. It is not as hot as the Sun, but it gives out nergy in the same way, as radiation. Our skins absorb this radiation, warming p as they do so. It has been a long trail from the Sun to the electric fire, and icture 4 sums up the changes.

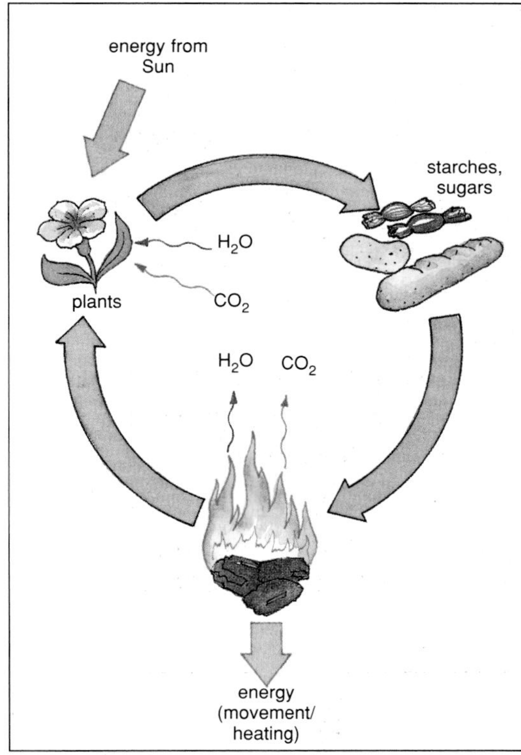

Picture 3 Water and carbon dioxide are recycled in the Earth–Sun energy system.

The problem with fossil fuels

'he main problem with fossil fuels is that we are using them up far more quickly han they were made. For example, by the year 2040 there will be no more oil eft. Britain's North Sea oil wells will be pumped dry by the time you are settling own to raise a family, but coal will last longer because there is much more of t. The reserves of fossil fuels could last longer, or be used up sooner. This lepends how sensibly we use them. A great deal of the energy we obtain is vasted because we don't manage it sensibly.

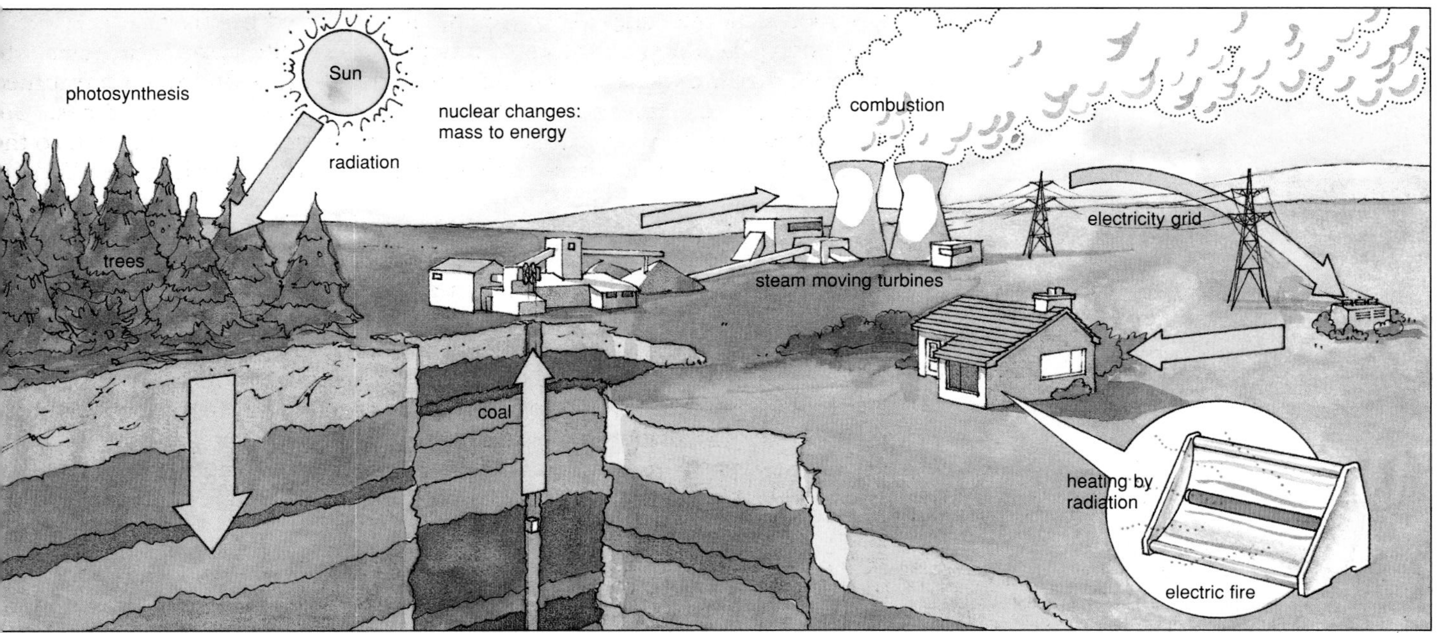

'icture 4 The Sun is our main energy source – but it might take a long time to become useful.

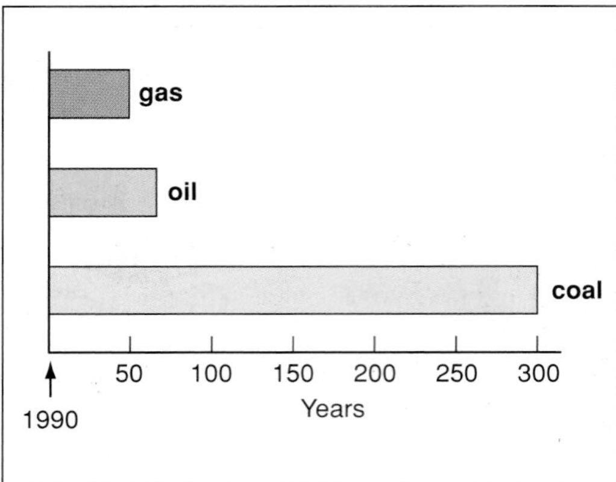

Picture 5 These are estimates of how long world supplies of fossil fuels will last – if we go on using them at the present rate.

We might also begin to make use of **alternative** sources of energy. These could be renewable sources such as wind, Sun, tides and waves. We can make use of the energy of 'biomass' from plants and from animal wastes. These sources of energy are dealt with in the next topic. We might also make more use of **nuclear energy** – see page 160.

Energy supplies

Most of the energy that we use on Earth comes from fossil fuels – at present this is almost 90% of the total. Picture 5 tells you how long we expect the reserves of fossil fuels to last. The pie chart in picture 6 shows the main sources of energy that the people of the world use. But it does not show all of it. It shows only the 'artificial' energy that we buy in the form of fuels and electricity.

The chart does not show the energy that we get 'free', for example, the energy coming from the Sun. All the crops on Earth rely on this solar energy to keep them warm enough to grow, and to give the light they need to photosynthesise. It warms up sea and land, and keeps people warm in summer, so that they don't need to buy so much fuel. We should remember that for most of human history energy from the Sun was the only energy we were able to use.

Neither does the chart show the energy used by millions of people all over the world that they collect for themselves. It might surprise you to learn that most people on Earth rely on **wood** for their heating and cooking. These people live in Africa, and much of Asia. Picture 7 shows the simple type of wood-burning stove that is widely used. The advantage of wood is that it is a **renewable** energy source – provided people keep on planting trees to replace the ones they cut down for fuel.

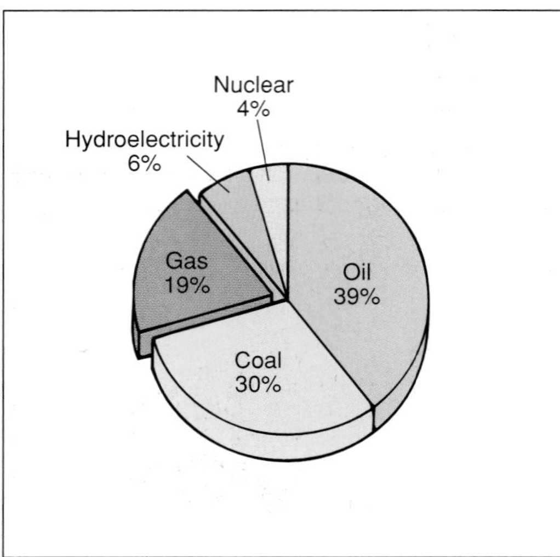

Picture 6 The world's main energy sources.

Are we using too much energy?

Fifty years ago most people travelled long distances by bus or train. Now we tend to go by car. Then, people washed clothes by hand, instead of using a washing machine. Men shaved with razor blades fitted into a holder, instead of using an electric razor. Not many people had central heating. They just wore more clothes in winter!

We now expect to find fruit and vegetables in the shops at all times of the year not just in their 'natural season'. This is because we can freeze them and keep them for years, if necessary.

All this makes life a lot more comfortable, but it does take a lot of energy. There was a time when people were very worried that the world was 'running out of energy'. There was an 'energy crisis'. The price of energy went up. Oil coal and electricity cost more. This made people try to use less energy.

In the 1990s energy has become slightly cheaper. In the UK we have been able to use gas and oil from the North Sea. People have become more careless in their energy use. Now, the problem that is worrying people is the polluting *effect* of energy use. Burning fuels produce carbon dioxide, which increases the greenhouse effect. They often give off gases which make rain more acid.

Do we need to use as much energy as we do? Do North Americans need to use twice as much energy as Britons? What changes would there be in your life if you had to cut your personal energy use by half, and what will happen when everybody in the world wants to use energy at the rate that Western countries do? Of course, fossil fuels will not last for ever. British oil and gas will run out by early in the 21st century. Would it be wise to make it last longer by using it more carefully? Page 151 shows some examples of how we could conserve energy at home, in industry, and for transport.

Picture 7 Most people on Earth use wood as their main fuel.

Energy saving

Energy saving in industry

Factories and industrial plants often use processes that produce hot gases and fumes. For health and safety reasons, the factory must be well ventilated. This means the waste heat is also lost.

The **heat wheel** shown in picture 1 uses the outgoing air or fumes to heat fresh, incoming air. It can recover up to 80% of the waste heat, saving a lot of energy.

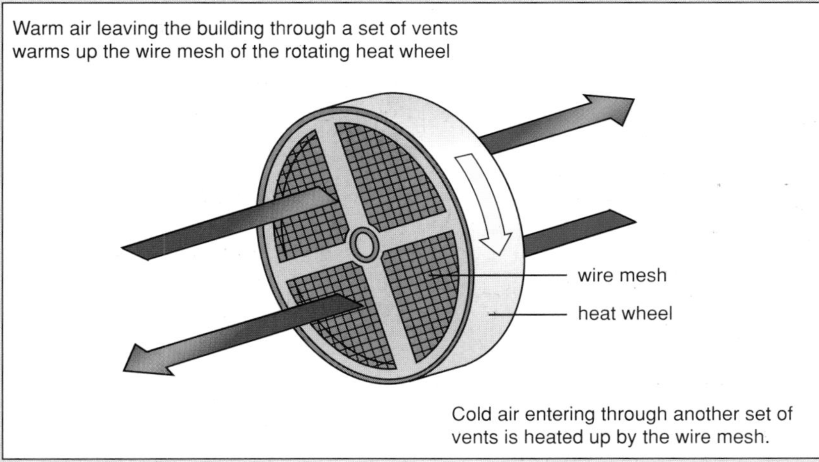

Picture 1

Energy saving in the home

An ordinary light bulb gives out most of its energy as heat. **'Low-energy'** bulbs (which are fluorescent lamps) are more expensive to buy, but they last longer and use less electricity. More of the energy appears as light, rather than heat. They therefore save money in the end and also save energy. It has been calculated that if every house in Britain used low-energy bulbs, we could do without three large power stations.

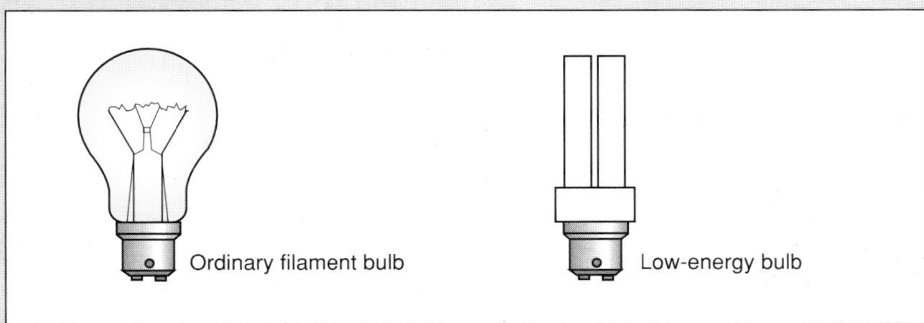

Picture 2

Energy saving in transport

The private car is the most energy-inefficient method of moving people. Most car journeys move only one person – the driver.

Public transport, such as trains and buses, uses much less energy per passenger. This also means less pollution and overcrowding of roads. To encourage people to cut down on car numbers, many countries now have special road lanes reserved only for cars which are carrying passengers.

The bicycle is one of the most efficient forms of transport ever devised. In certain cities it would be the ideal way of moving people.

- To widen a city road to carry more traffic costs £20 million per mile.
- One mile of cycle path costs £1000.

Picture 3

Questions

1 A room in a house has two lamps, one using a 100 W bulb, and the other has a 60 W bulb. A 100 W bulb costs 0.6p to run for 1 hour. A 60 W bulb costs 0.36p to run for 1 hour.

On average, the lamps are used for 4 hours every day of the year. Each light bulb costs 50p.

A 100 W bulb can be replaced by a low-energy bulb which costs 0.12p to run for 1 hour.

A 60 W bulb can be replaced by a low-energy bulb which costs 0.09p to run for 1 hour.

Each low-energy bulb costs £14, but lasts as long as ten ordinary bulbs, so the price compared to one ordinary bulb is £1.40.

a Calculate the cost of buying and using the two ordinary bulbs for one complete year.

b Calculate the cost of buying and using their low-energy replacements.

F2 Renewable energy

Some energy sources should last 'forever'.

Are there other ways of getting energy?

Most of the energy we use comes from **non-renewable** sources. Sooner or later we shall use up all the natural fossil fuels, and possibly even the radioactive elements used in nuclear reactors. Both sources of energy have environmental effects in that their waste products can cause dangerous pollution. These facts have led to a great interest in **renewable** energy sources.

Renewable energy sources

When we talk about renewable energy sources, we usually mean sources that rely on sunlight, winds, waves, flowing water or biological materials. All these rely on energy from the Sun. Our Sun is likely to keep providing this energy for the next 10 billion years or so, which is forever on a human timescale.

Tides are caused by gravitational forces exerted by the Sun and Moon. This rise and fall of sea water can be tapped as an energy source. The best known tidal power station is at the Rance Estuary in Brittany, France (picture 1). It can produce 240 megawatts (MW) of power – enough to supply a city of 300 000 people. As the tide is going out, water is trapped behind the barrage. When the difference in water level is about 3 m, water is allowed to flow out of the barrage to the sea. As it flows, it turns turbines which drive electricity generators (picture 1).

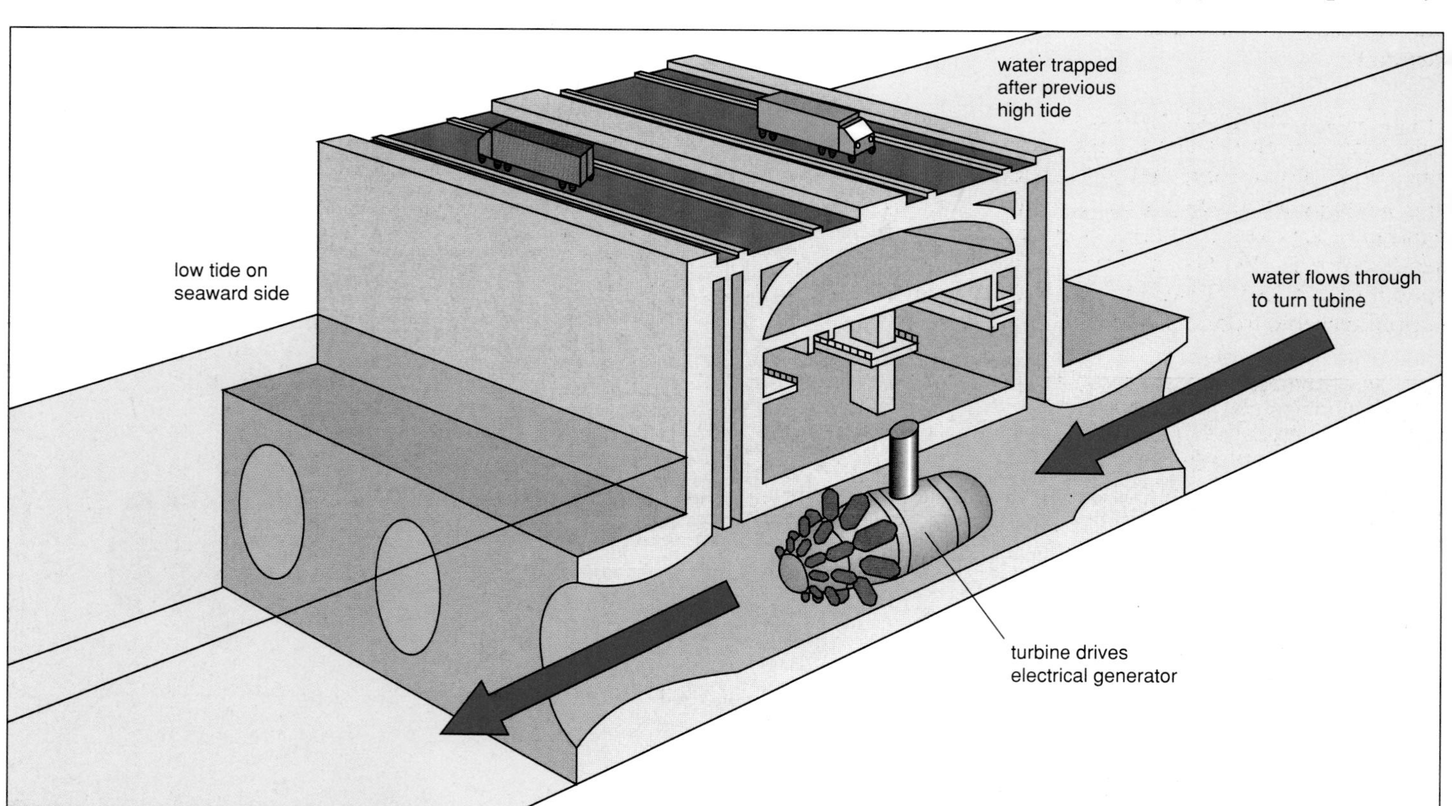

Picture 1 The workings of a tidal power station.

Hydroelectric power stations provide most of the energy transferred electrically in Norway and they are also important in Scotland. The systems rely on gravitational potential energy as an energy source. They are usually found in mountain areas with enough rainfall or snow melt to provide water that can turn turbines as it flows downhill (picture 2). The water is recycled by the natural global water cycle, powered by energy from the Sun, that returns lowland and sea water to the mountains.

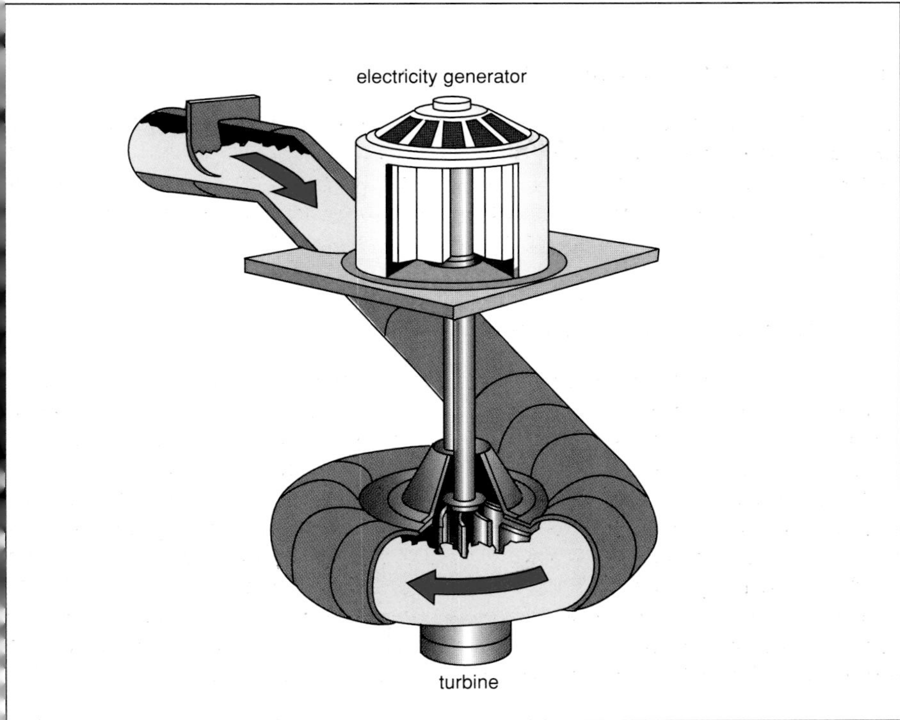

Picture 2

The kinetic energy of **wind** is one of the oldest sources of renewable energy. Sails have powered ships for thousands of years. Windmills have been in use since about 600 AD and their use as generators of electricity is becoming more and more popular. They are set up in **wind farms** containing arrays of large windmills. It is also possible to construct large wind-generating facilities out at sea (picture 3). Wind is an unreliable energy source; it doesn't blow at a steady speed at all times. However, such systems can be used to top up the steady supply available from conventional power stations.

Picture 3 Generating electricity using the wind.

Picture 4 A wave-power generator.

Sea waves also carry a great deal of kinetic energy. Consider the amount of energy involved when a massive ship is being tossed up and down by a heavy sea. The north west coast of Scotland has been suggested as a suitable area for large scale generation of electricity, using the energy of waves. Most schemes are small scale projects designed to supply island communities. As with wind, waves are unreliable because weather conditions vary.

Sunlight and the **infra-red** radiation from the Sun can be used directly to generate electricity, or heat water and buildings. Black surfaces absorb heat radiation well. In hot countries, cold water running through a black hose positioned in the Sun will provide hot water for washing. Well designed buildings, as shown in picture 5, can make best use of the available solar energy and so reduce the need for other energy sources. The house is positioned so that large windows on the south side make the most of the sunshine. Panels on the roof work on the same principle as the garden hose. They absorb energy from the Sun to heat the domestic water. In sunny countries such as Israel, 90% of houses obtain hot water in this way. The house is also insulated to a high standard.

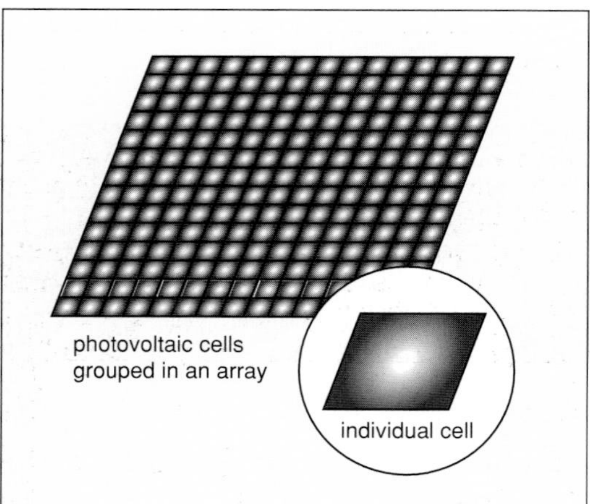

Picture 6 Photovoltaic cells.

Picture 5

Using solar energy in this way does not generate electricity directly, but does reduce the level of demand. Electricity can then be used for purposes where there is no realistic substitute. Domestic appliances such as vacuum cleaners, power tools, and electronic goods are examples of this.

Photovoltaic cells (picture 6) made from semiconductor materials *can* generate electricity from light, but at present they are expensive. They are useful in warm sunny climates where heating is not a large drain on energy sources, and particularly in isolated places which would be expensive to connect to a national grid system.

The interior of the Earth is hot and can be used as an energy source. The temperature of the rocks rises by about 1 °C for every 30 m of depth. This is greater in areas where there is volcanic activity. Iceland makes use of this **geothermal** energy to provide hot water for space heating in its main towns. Water is pumped down to the level of the hot rock and then returned to the surface, where the energy can be transferred to a heating system.

Biomass or **biological fuels** like wood may be renewable if properly managed. Wood is the main domestic fuel in many tropical countries. Agricultural wastes, like straw and sugar cane stalks, have been considered as an energy supply. Such materials may be fermented to produce an alcohol, which can be used to run internal combustion engines. By the 1980s, Brazil had succeeded in running a quarter of all new cars on alcohol, while the rest ran on an alcohol/petrol mixture. China makes widespread use of methane gas produced by fermenting animal dung and crop wastes. This can be used to heat stoves, light lamps, run machinery or generate electricity.

Picture 7 Using heat from the Earth generates electricity.

Pumped storage schemes

Coal-fired power stations can't be switched off easily. The furnaces have to be kept going all the time, because if they cool down they get badly damaged. Thus many power stations are running all the time, both day and night.

At night most people are asleep. Factories are closed down, few trains are running. The demand for electricity is much less than in the daytime.

But the power stations are still burning fuel, even if the turbines are not working at full capacity. The surplus electricity being generated can be used to pump water uphill and store it in a high reservoir. By doing this, the electrical energy is transferred and 'stored' as gravitational potential energy. When demand peaks during the day, valves are opened to allow the water to flow downhill and generate electricity. Cruachan power station in Argyll operates on this principle.

Although these schemes are still using electricity generated from a *non-renewable* source, they allow us to conserve energy by increasing the overall efficiency of the system.

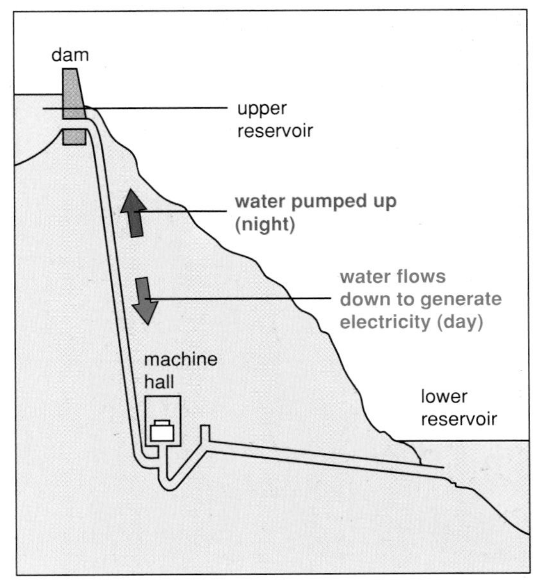

Picture 8 A pumped storage scheme.

Questions

1a Gas can be used as a fuel for heating a house. Gas is an example of a fossil fuel.

Explain briefly why it is important to cut down on the amount of fossil fuel which is being being used to produce heat.

b Some sources of energy are listed below.

coal	*waves*
wind	*oil*
biomass	*geothermal*
gas	*sunlight*

Copy and complete the table below to show which of these sources are renewable and which are non-renewable.

Renewable	Non-renewable

2 Figure 2 shows lines joining places in Britain which receive the same solar energy during one year. The number of kilowatt hours of energy received on each square metre is marked beside the lines.

a What is the solar energy which is received by each square metre in one year in Stirling?

b Calculate the area of a rooftop solar panel in Stirling which would receive 3000 kWh of energy in one year.

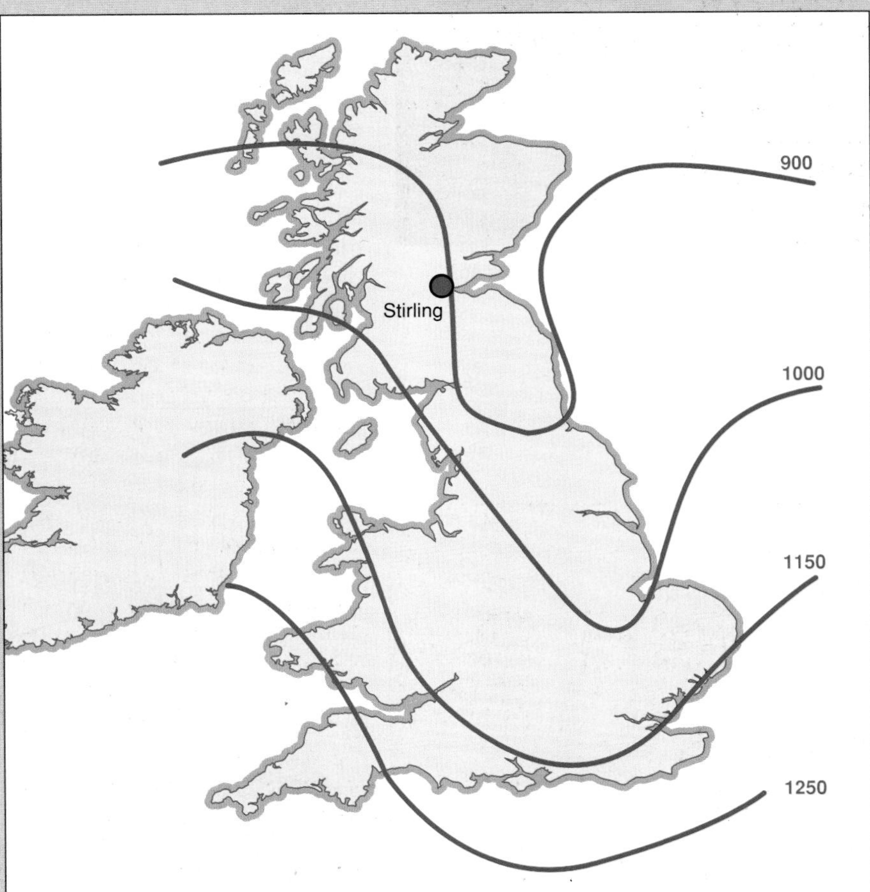

F3 The electricity industry

This topic deals with how electrical energy is generated and then transported to where it is needed.

Picture 1 Drax Power Station near Selby, North Yorkshire.

The power station

Picture 1 shows a large power station. You can see the huge stock of coal that will be taken in at one end. At the other end are the pylons holding the wires through which the electricity will be carried away. The diagram (picture 2) shows the main parts of the power station where the energy conversions take place.

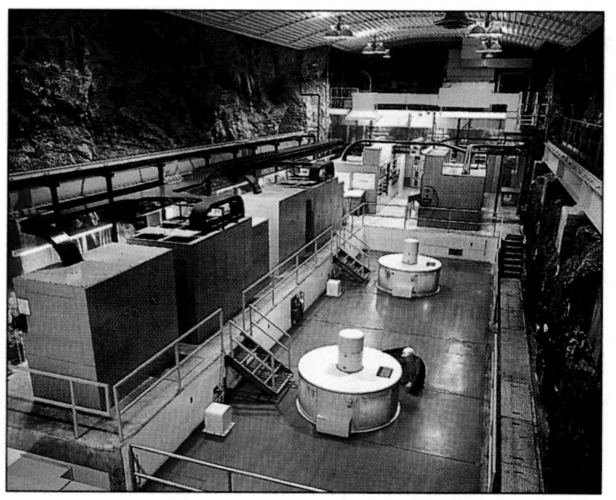

Picture 3 The turbine generator room of a power station.

The energy changes in a power station

Energy is released when coal burns with the oxygen of the air. This energy is used to boil water and then heat the steam to a high temperature. Burning coal also produces large amounts of carbon dioxide which goes into the atmosphere, together with other waste gases such as sulphur dioxide.

The steam is made very hot so that it is at a very high pressure. This means that it can provide very large forces to turn the huge steam turbines. This takes energy from the steam, which cools down, but doesn't become so cool that it condenses back into water.

The spinning turbines (picture 3) are connected to the coils of large generators. These coils carry current and act as large electromagnets. As they spin they induce a high voltage in the fixed coils surrounding them (see page 166 and picture 4). This causes a current which is fed into the **National Grid** system that carries the electricity to wherever it is needed.

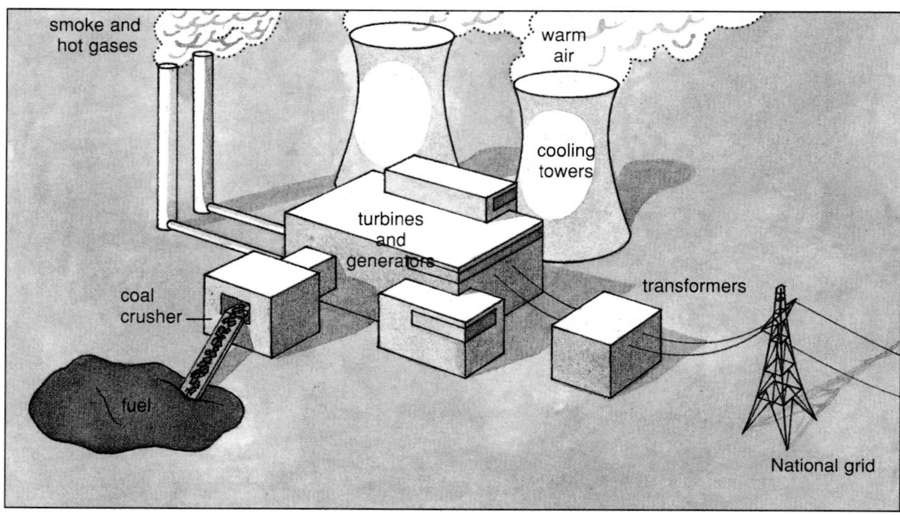

Picture 2 The main parts of a power station.

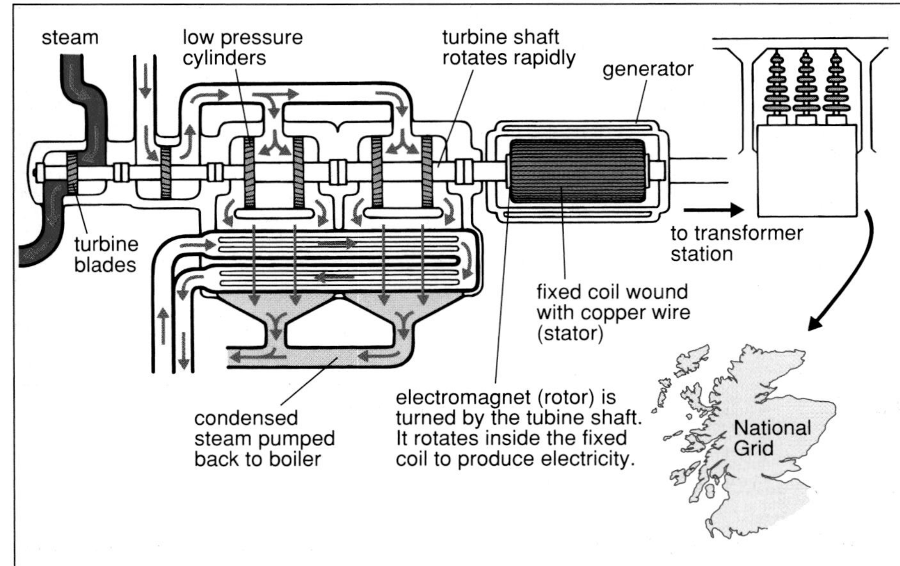

Picture 4 The structure of a large generator.

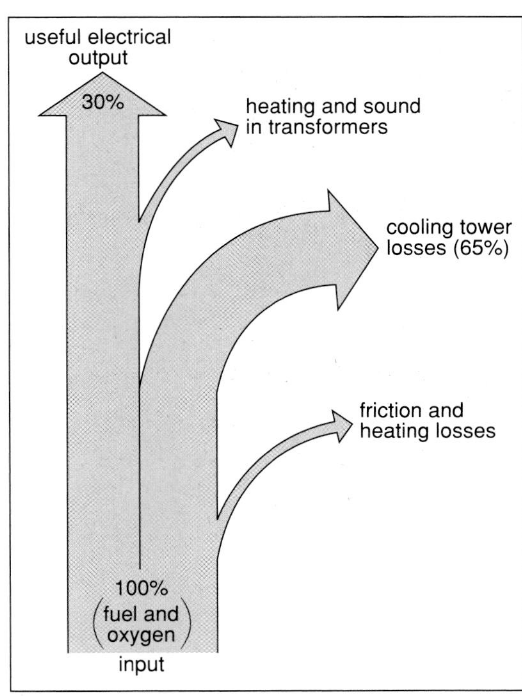

Picture 5 Energy flow in a power station that is 30% efficient.

Energy flow in a power station

Picture 5 shows the energy flow through a typical power station. A large power station might be rated at 1000 megawatts. This means that every second it delivers 1000 million joules of energy. This is about the same as the total power output that could be produced by every human being in the United Kingdom working flat out. No modern industrial country could survive on slave labour!

But to produce this energy, fuel equivalent to an energy of 3000 million joules per second has to be supplied. *Two-thirds of the energy input is wasted.*

This means that most power stations powered by fossil fuels can only be 30 to 40% **efficient**.

How is the energy wasted?

Some of the waste is 'accidental', because energy leaks out to warm up the air. For example, it moves as hot air from the boiler chimneys, and wiring gets hot.

But most of the waste is *necessary* waste. This is because the turbines can't take all of the energy out of the steam. This leaves lots of steam which is still warm, but cooler than it was when it went in, and too cool to make any turbines work.

This is the reason for the cooling towers. They are used to take energy from the 'used' steam, so condensing it back to water. This energy usually ends up warming a river or the sea.

This waste seems a great pity, but it is a consequence of one of the most ruthless laws of physics. This is the Second Law of Thermodynamics, which says that whenever you try to do something useful with thermal energy some of it always ends up in the wrong place.

In this example, the wasted energy goes into the cooling system and eventually into the surroundings.

Can we make better use of this waste energy?

The waste energy can be put to good use. It is stored in warm water. The water is not hot enough to be useful to make electricity – it could not make the steam turbines work. But is quite warm enough to heat homes and other buildings.

In Germany most towns have their own small power stations, and they often pipe the 'waste' hot water to people's homes to keep them centrally heated. These are called **combined heat and power schemes**. They reduce waste and make electricity cheaper.

Efficiency

Being *efficient* means being effective at doing a job. The **efficiency** of a machine or engine measures how good it is, in terms of how much of the energy put into it is used where you want it. Efficiency is measured by how much useful energy you get out compared with what is put in. It usually converted to a percentage:

$$\text{efficiency} = \frac{\text{useful energy output}}{\text{energy input}} \times 100\%$$

Table 1 shows the typical efficiency of some energy devices. Some of them, like engines and some machines, use energy from a fuel system to do work. Cars, bicycles, electric drills and trains do this. Other devices are used to make energy more 'usable'. They might do this by taking energy from a fuel–oxygen system and putting it into an electrical system. This is what power stations do. Electricity is very useful because it makes it so easy to move energy from one place to another.

Table 1 Typical efficiency of energy devices.

	Engines and machines producing movement or doing work %	**Energy 'movers'** %
train: diesel engine	36	
car: petrol engine	15	
train: steam engine	15	
train: electric motor	90	
car gears		93
bicycle		90
car jack		15
electric power station	35	
transformer (electrical)		97
human muscle	40	

Gears and *transmission systems* in cars, trains and bicycles are the mechanical versions of electric transmission. They carry energy from one part of a **mechanical** system to another. They also allow the force that eventually does the work to be made small or large, according to what is needed.

Calculating efficiency

The energy **output** from a device is usually in a different form from the energy **input**. For example, suppose we wish to find the efficiency of a small electrically operated pulley system.

The pulley lifts a mass of 50 kg onto a storage rack 3 m above the floor of a warehouse. The output of this system is in the form of **potential** energy.

The **input** to the motor is in the form of **electrical** energy. The motor operates from the 230 V mains, and draws a current of 2 A. The lifting operation takes 5 seconds.

Energy output $E_p = mgh = 50 \times 10 \times 3 = 1500\text{ J}$

Energy input $E = P \times t = I \times V \times t = 230 \times 2 \times 5 = 2300\text{ J}$

$$\text{Efficiency} = \frac{\text{energy output}}{\text{energy input}} \times \frac{100}{1} = \frac{1500 \times 100}{2300} = 65\%$$

Questions

1 A remote farm has its own small hydroelectric scheme. Water flows down a pipe at a rate of 17.5 kg/s from a dam to a turbine. The top of the pipe is at a height of 100 m above the turbine as shown in the diagram in figure 1.

a Calculate the change in the potential energy of the water every second as it flows from the top of the pipe to the turbine.

b The turbine drives a generator which has an output power of 7.0 kW.

What is the efficiency of the system?

c State **one** disadvantage of such a hydroelectric scheme.

d The farm has a back-up diesel fuelled generator for use in an emergency. State **one** advantage of the hydroelectric scheme over the diesel generator.

2 Tests are being carried out on a fork lift truck. The truck is designed to lift a load from the floor to the storage shelf (figure 2).

The following measurements are recorded during a test.

Time taken to raise load	=	20.0 s
Current in motor	=	6.25 A
Voltage applied to motor	=	60.0 V
Mass of load	=	150 kg
Height of shelf from floor	=	4.15 m

a Calculate the electrical energy supplied to the motor to raise the load to the shelf.

b Calculate the gain in potential energy of the load after it has been raised.

c Calculate the efficiency of the fork lift truck motor during this test.

d Explain why the efficiency of the fork lift truck is not 100%.

3 The diagrams in figure 3 compare the overall efficiency of a conventional power station and a combined heat and power station for a power input of 100 megawatts.

Summarise the information given in the diagrams by copying and completing table 1.

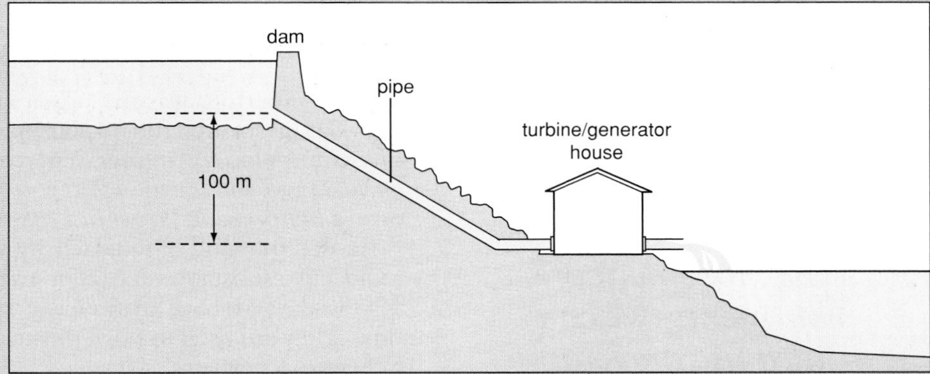

Figure 1

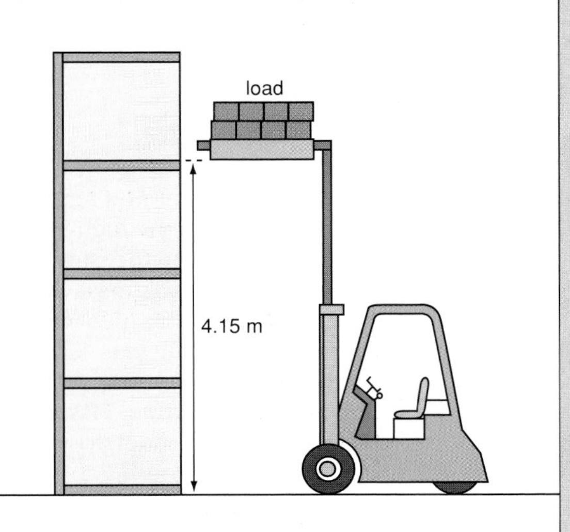

Figure 2

100 MW
fuel in
conventional power station
35 MW electricity out
waste heat
65 MW
(1 megawatt (1 MW) = 1 000 000 watts)

100 MW
fuel in
combined heat and power station
useful heat out
28 MW electricity out
waste heat
22 MW

Figure 3

Table 1

	Conventional power station	**Combined heat and power station**
power input (MW)		
electrical output power (MW)		
waste heat power (MW)		
useful heat power (MW)		

F4
Nuclear energy

Nuclear energy powers the movement of continents. We can also use nuclear energy directly – but can we do this safely?

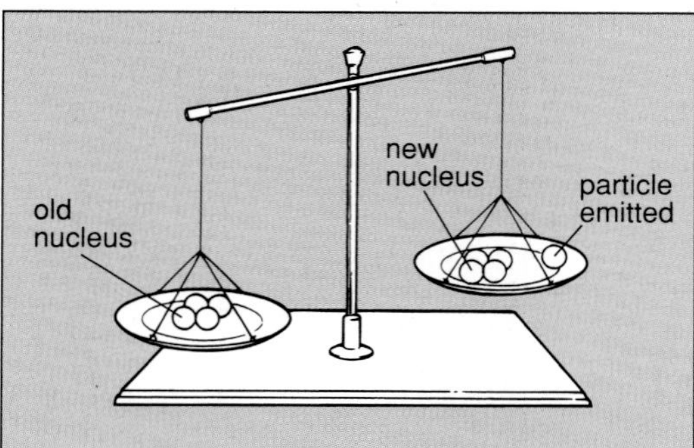

Picture 1 In a radioactive change, the new products weigh less than the original nucleus.

'Moonshine!' says top nuclear scientist

Ernest Rutherford was the physicist who found out what alpha particles were, and who discovered the nucleus of the atom. *There is enough energy in a gram of uranium to send a liner across the Atlantic!* he said in a newpaper interview, 60 years ago. *But the idea that you can actually use it is moonshine. It will take over 4 billion years to get just a half of it out!*

He was thinking of radioactivity, not nuclear power stations. When a natural radioactive substance decays, it gives out energy – but only slowly.

Nowadays we have artificial isotopes that do give out their energy in a shorter time. They are used to power instruments in Earth satellites. They are also used in heart pacemakers.

Even so, the power they can generate is very small and it is very expensive. Nuclear power stations do not rely on 'ordinary radioactivity' to produce energy. But where does the energy come from?

$E = mc^2$

When atoms decay, the energy they release appears as movement energy (kinetic energy) of the high-speed particles they send out. It was Albert Einstein who came up with the surprising theory that this energy was produced by changing some of the mass of the nucleus into energy. This theory was proved when careful measurements were made. The mass of the emitted particle plus the mass of the nucleus left behind *was less than the mass of the original nucleus* (picture 1).

Energy had appeared. Mass had disappeared. These two facts contradicted the laws of physics as understood in 1905. These laws said that:

- energy could not be lost or created (Law of Conservation of Energy),
- mass could not be made or destroyed (Law of Conservation of Matter).

Einstein would say: *If we say that matter is really a kind of stored energy, then both laws can be correct. In fact, my Theory of Relativity predicts that this should happen. The 'energy value' of any piece of matter is given by my formula* $E = mc^2$. *No problem.*

The missing mass, m, was converted to kinetic energy, E. The quantity c is the speed of light. This is a very large number – 300 000 000 m/s. It is the *square* of this number which multiplies with the mass to give the value of the energy. This means that it doesn't take much mass to produce a lot of energy.

But the main problem still remained. There was no way to speed up the rate at which ordinary, naturally radioactive materials decayed and produced their energy. The energy was there, but dammed up so well that it could only trickle out at a uselessly small rate.

Nuclear fission

The breakthrough into 'atomic energy' came in 1938. Physicists working in Berlin proved that some of the unstable uranium nuclei don't just decay by giving out a small particle or some gamma radiation. Instead, they split up into two nearly equal parts.

But just as with radioactive changes, mass was lost and converted to energy. What was more important, *the splitting could be controlled*. Then, in 1939, the Second World War began. It was clear to some physicists that the immense store of energy in a lump of uranium could be released very quickly. The result would be a huge explosion – **a nuclear bomb**.

The bomb was built (it took five years to do this) and two 'atomic bombs' were dropped on Japan by the USA in August 1945. The nuclear age had begun.

The process of splitting nuclei to give energy is called **nuclear fission**. The same process is used in a **nuclear reactor**, but of course it is controlled so that it happens much more slowly than in a bomb. To explain how it works we need to remember what the nucleus of an atom is like.

Atomic nuclei

Atoms contain negative electrons moving around a positive core – the nucleus. But a nucleus is not just a blob of positively charged matter. The main parts of a nucleus are the protons and the neutrons (see picture 2). Protons are positively charged and neutrons do not carry an electric charge.

Some nuclei have too many protons and neutrons and tend to be unstable. This causes radioactivity. But some very large nuclei may split into two parts, instead of undergoing ordinary radioactive decay.

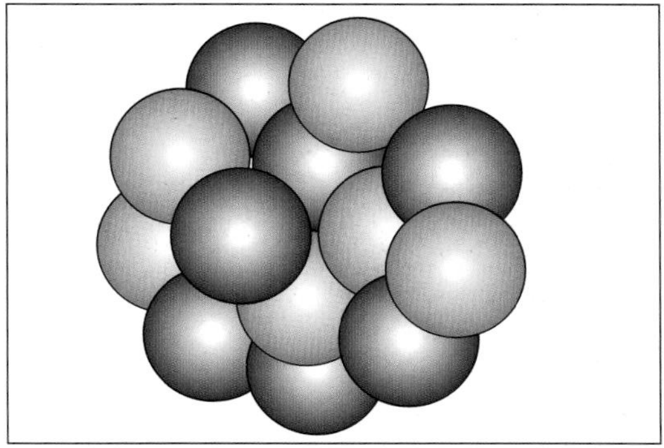

Picture 2 An oxygen nucleus. It has 8 protons and 8 neutrons.

The chain reaction

This splitting is what goes on in a nuclear bomb or reactor. When the nucleus splits in two main parts it also shoots out one or more spare neutrons. These can fly into another nearby nucleus quite easily – and make that nucleus split. In turn, the new neutrons may shoot off into other nuclei and cause them to split.

This builds up into a **chain reaction**, with nucleus after nucleus splitting and triggering off others. Each time a nucleus splits it gives out energy. This process is shown in picture 3. You can compare it to an avalanche on a mountain slope. When someone throws just one stone it can cause them all to cascade down the slope.

The result of an uncontrolled chain reaction is an explosion. This is what happens in a nuclear bomb. In a nuclear reactor the reaction is controlled. The uranium is spread out, as thin rods (**fuel rods**). In between the rods are other rods, made of a material that absorbs neutrons. If all the neutrons are absorbed no further reactions are possible and the reactor stops giving out energy.

In a typical reactor, the absorbing rods (**control rods**) are moved in and out of the fuel rods. This controls the rate of the fission reactions and the amount of energy released. Picture 4 shows the main parts of a nuclear reactor. Other rods (**moderators**) slow down the neutrons so that they are better at causing fission.

Picture 3 A chain reaction.

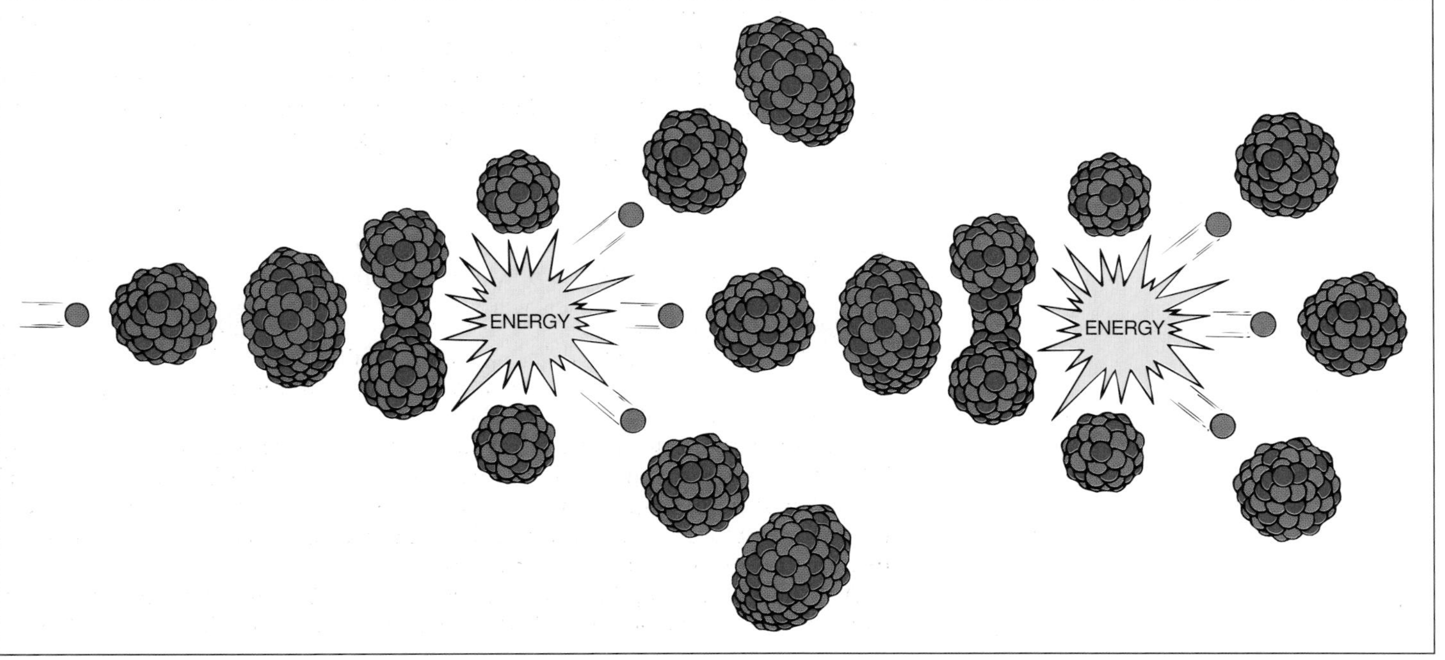

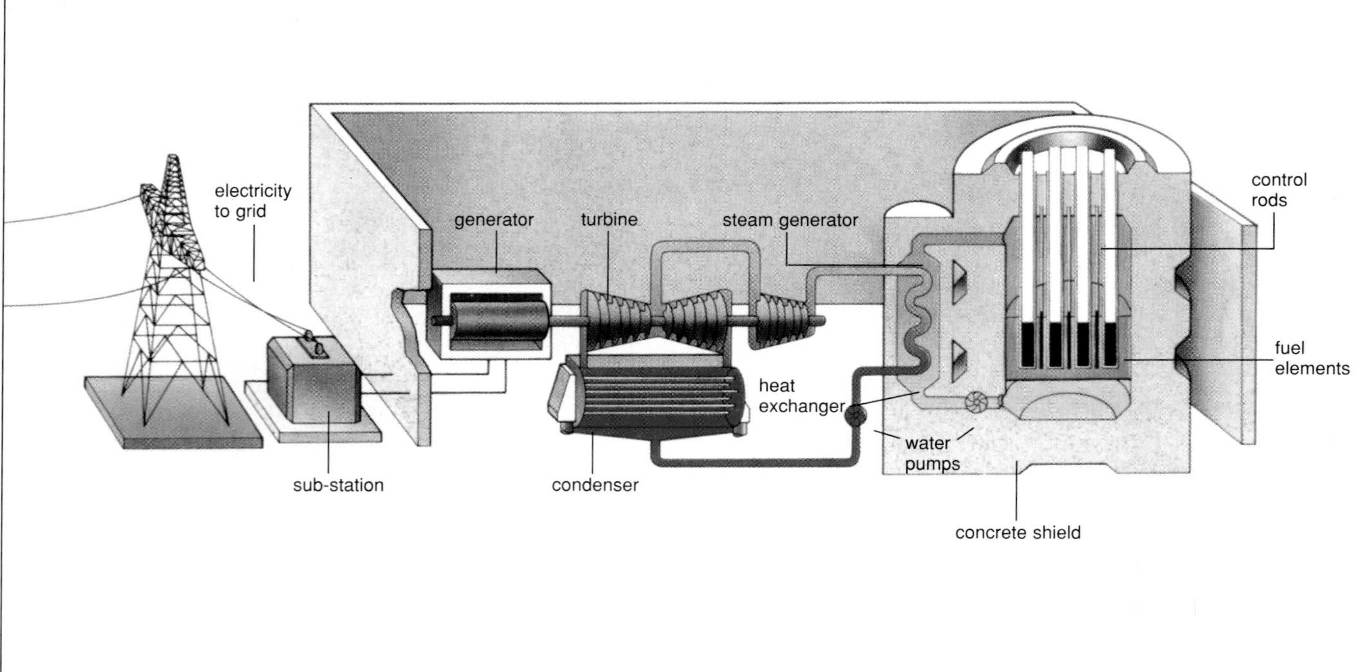

Picture 4 The workings of a nuclear reactor.

The energy released when the nuclei split up heats the fuel rods. The hot 'core' of the reactor then heats water or some other fluid. This hot fluid may become radioactive and has to be kept inside the reactor. The fluid moves to carry its energy to the heat exchanger where it is transferred to boil water. The steam produced drives an ordinary steam turbine.

The turbines turn generators, as in an ordinary coal-fired or gas-fired power station.

Nuclear waste

When the uranium nuclei in the fuel rods split they form two smaller nuclei. These nuclei are radioactive. Eventually the fuel rods are used up and have to be replaced. The old rods are now very radioactive.

Also, the neutrons that are not used in the fission process are absorbed by control rods and other parts of the reactor. This makes them become radioactive as well.

After anything from 20 to 50 years, the working parts of the reactor are worn out, and have also become highly radioactive. When the reactor is dismantled these materials have somehow to be disposed of. This process is called **decommissioning**. It now seems that this could be very expensive. This means that the total costs of nuclear power are much higher than was thought when the first nuclear power stations were built.

Storing radioactive waste

Because it is dangerous to humans, radioactive waste has to be stored safely, so that the radiations don't get out. It is stored inside containers made of metal, glass, or concrete which absorb the radiation. If waste is to be stored underground, great care will have to be taken to make sure that the containers stay unbroken, perhaps for thousands of years. Picture 5 shows how radioactive waste might be stored.

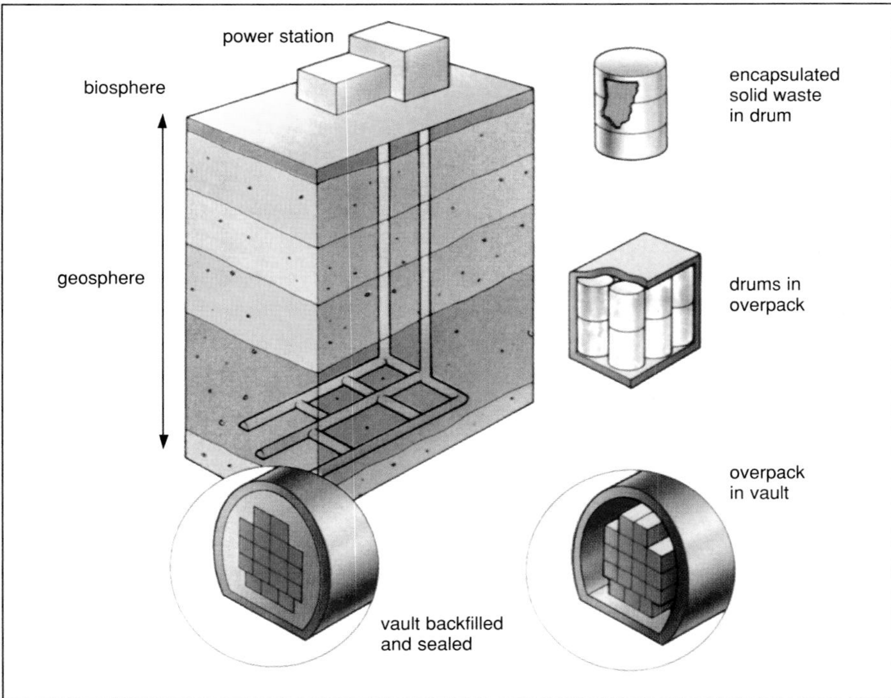

Picture 5 How radioactive waste might be stored.

Questions

1 Explain briefly why a nuclear chain reaction is like an avalanche of snow or rocks on a steep mountainside.

2 Nuclear 'fuel' – uranium – is quite cheap. Give two reasons why it is still expensive to produce electricity from nuclear power stations.

3 Explain what the control rods do in a nuclear reactor.

4 People argue a great deal about whether nuclear power stations should be built. Give three reasons in each case:

a in favour of nuclear power

b against nuclear power.

5a Use the formula $E=mc^2$ to calculate how much energy in joules could be obtained from 1 kg of matter if all of it could be turned into energy. The speed of light, c, is 300 000 00 m/s.

b The total energy we can actually get from 1 kg of uranium is very much less than the answer you should have got for part a. Why is this?

F5 Generating electricity

The modern electricity industry grew from Michael Faraday's works.

In topic B7, page 60, we saw how **Michael Faraday** discovered the basis of the electric motor. He found that a force acts on a current – carrying conductor such as a wire, when it is placed in a magnetic field.

Faraday didn't stop at making electricity and magnetism work together to produce movement. He thought that there ought to be a way of using movement and magnetism to produce electricity. It took him seven years to think of a way of doing it, but what he discovered is the scientific basis of the electricity industry – **electromagnetic induction**.

Picture 1 shows a modern version of Faraday's experiment. He wrapped two coils round an iron core, and connected one coil to a supply. The second coil was connected to a meter.

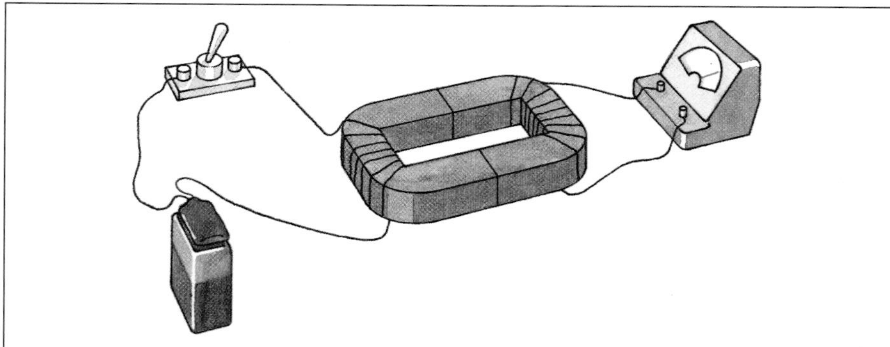

Picture 1 A modern version of Faraday's discovery of induced electricity (the transformer effect).

- When the current in the *first* coil is switched on, the meter shows a brief pulse of current in the *second* coil. **Nothing happens when the current in coil 1 is flowing steadily**.
- When the current in coil 1 is switched off, *another* pulse occurs in coil 2.
- If a variable resistor is used to steadily *change* the current in coil 1, a current flows in coil 2.

Faraday tried to imagine what must be happening. He had already thought up the idea that magnetic fields could be explained in terms of lines of force.

When a current flowed in coil 1, the coil would act as an **electromagnet**, with a magnetic field surrounding it.

When a steady current flowed, the magnetic field would also be steady – but when switching *on* or *off*, or *changing* the current, the magnetic field of coil 1 would *also* change (picture 2).

Whenever a current changed in coil 1, as the lines of force grew or died away, they 'cut across' the wires of coil 2 and produced a voltage. This voltage caused a current to flow in coil 2.

The modern application of this is the **transformer**. We will see later that transformers are vital parts of the electricity supply system.

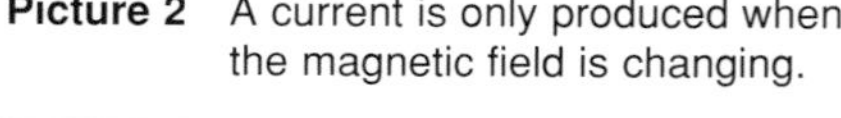

Picture 2 A current is only produced when the magnetic field is changing.

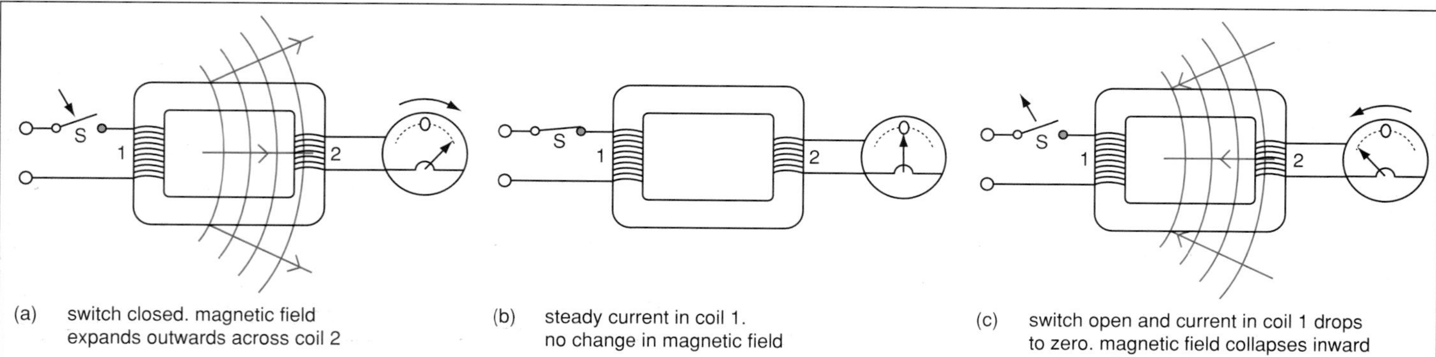

(a) switch closed. magnetic field expands outwards across coil 2

(b) steady current in coil 1. no change in magnetic field

(c) switch open and current in coil 1 drops to zero. magnetic field collapses inward across coil 2

A generator

As we said earlier, a force acts on a current-carrying conductor, such as a wire, when it is placed in a magnetic field. To be more precise, it is the moving charge in the conductor, the **electrons**, which experience the force. As they are moved by the force, the atoms in the wire move with them (picture 3(a)). This is why the beam of electrons in a television tube can be controlled by the fields produced by electromagnets (see page 27).

What would happen if, instead of sending a current through the wire, we simply moved a piece of copper wire in a magnetic field? The copper atoms of the wire possess electrons. As the wire carries the electrons through the field, a force will act on the electrons, pushing them through the wire (picture 3(b)).

We can imagine the electrons piling up at the end of the conductor. This produces a **voltage** across the ends of the wire. If the wire is coiled up, so that several lengths pass through the magnetic field at the same time, the voltage is larger. When we connect the ends of the wire together to make a complete circuit, a current will flow in the wire.

Whenever a conductor moves through the lines of force of a magnetic field, a voltage is **induced**. Alternatively we can hold the wire still and move the magnet. As long as the magnetic field is *changing*, the same effect occurs.

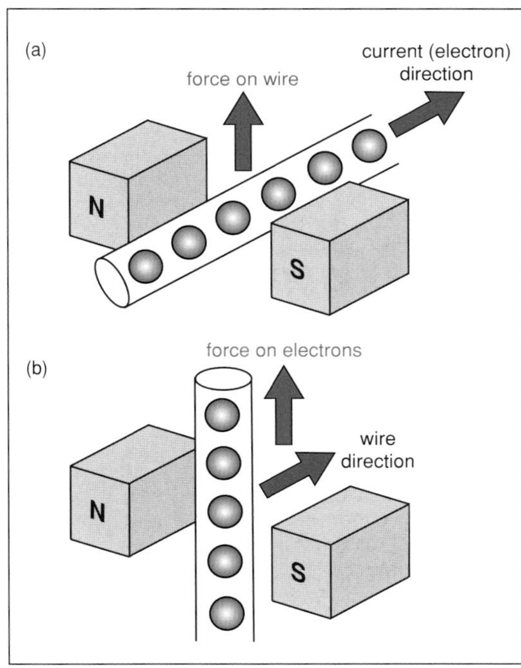

Picture 3 Moving electrons experience a force in a magnetic field.

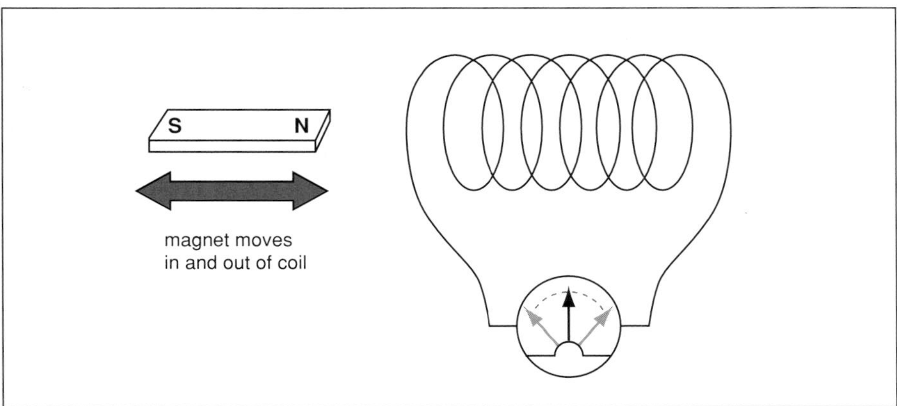

Picture 4 Moving a magnet next to a coil.

What would happen, thought Faraday, if he made the lines of force come and go by a different method, by moving a magnet in and out of a coil? As predicted above, he tried this, (picture 4) and it worked.

Once more a current was produced. The same thing happened when he kept the magnet still and moved the coil instead. He had invented the first **electric generator**, or **dynamo**.

A simple dynamo (picture 5) has the same parts as an electric motor. Both have spinning coils surrounded by magnets.

In the motor, putting a current through the coil makes it spin. **Electrical energy** is transferred as **kinetic energy**.

In a dynamo, spinning a coil induces a voltage which makes an electric current flow in the coil. **Kinetic energy** is transferred as **electrical energy**. The size of the induced voltage will depend on the the speed of rotation of the coil. It will also increase if we have *more turns* in the coil, and a *stronger* magnetic field.

Larger types of dynamo called generators are used in power stations to produce the mains supply that we use to run things in home and industry. In a generator, the magnetic field is produced by **electromagnets**.

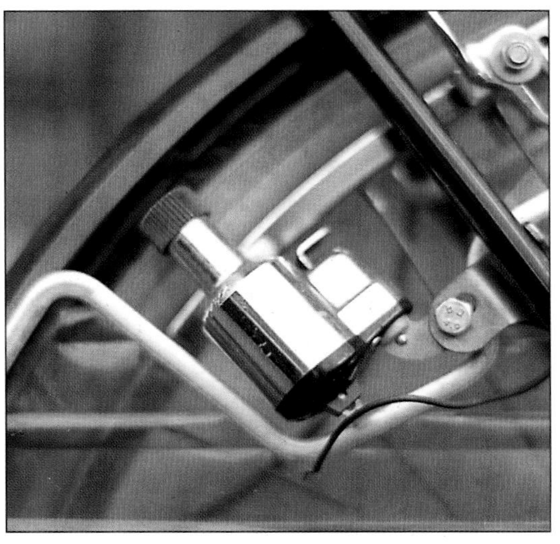

Picture 5 A bicycle dynamo.

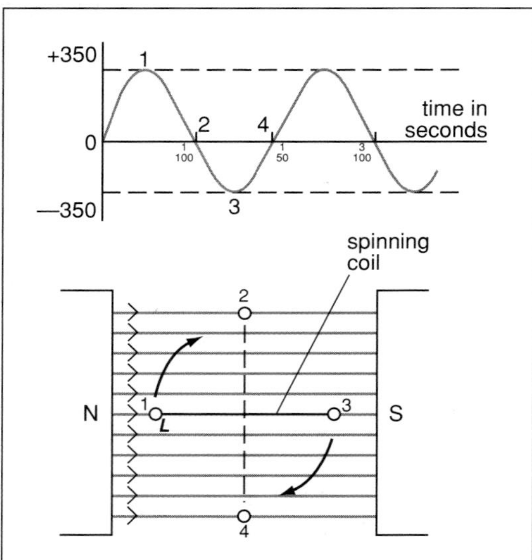

Picture 6 Numbers 1, 2, 3, 4 show where one side (L) of the spinning coil is when it produces the outputs marked 1, 2, 3, and 4 on the graph.

In a power station, the generators are turned by **turbines**. In a fossil fuel or nuclear power station, the turbines are driven by steam. In a hydroelectric station, falling water spins the turbines.

Alternating current

The turbines spin the field coils of the generators at high speeds. The wiring is arranged to give **alternating current**. This is done by making the voltage produced by each coil change direction every half-turn. This means that the current changes direction as well. It flows one way for half the time, then in the opposite direction for the next half. This change-over occurs every 1/100 of a second. How this could be done with a model in the science lab is shown in picture 6. Only one coil is drawn, to make the idea clearer. In the power station, a coil called a **rotor** acts as an electromagnet, and spins inside a larger coil called the **stator**. The generated voltage is drawn from the stator.

The rate of spinning and the number of coils is designed to make each coil change (**alternate**) its voltage and current completely 50 times a second.

The speed of movement, the large magnetic field and the large number of turns used mean that the voltage produced is quite high: 25 000 V.

There is a good reason for producing alternating current (a.c.) rather than direct current (d.c.), like a battery produces. It is because it makes it easy to change the voltage of the supply, using transformers. This is explained next.

How do we get our electricity?

The generator produces a large current at an output voltage of 25 000 V, which is extremely dangerous. It could be arranged for this to be 230 V, as used in the home, but this would be very uneconomic. In fact the voltage is made even higher as it leaves the power station. It is raised to 275 000 V or even 400 000 V. The reason for this is the resistance in the cables which take the electricity from the power station to a home or factory.

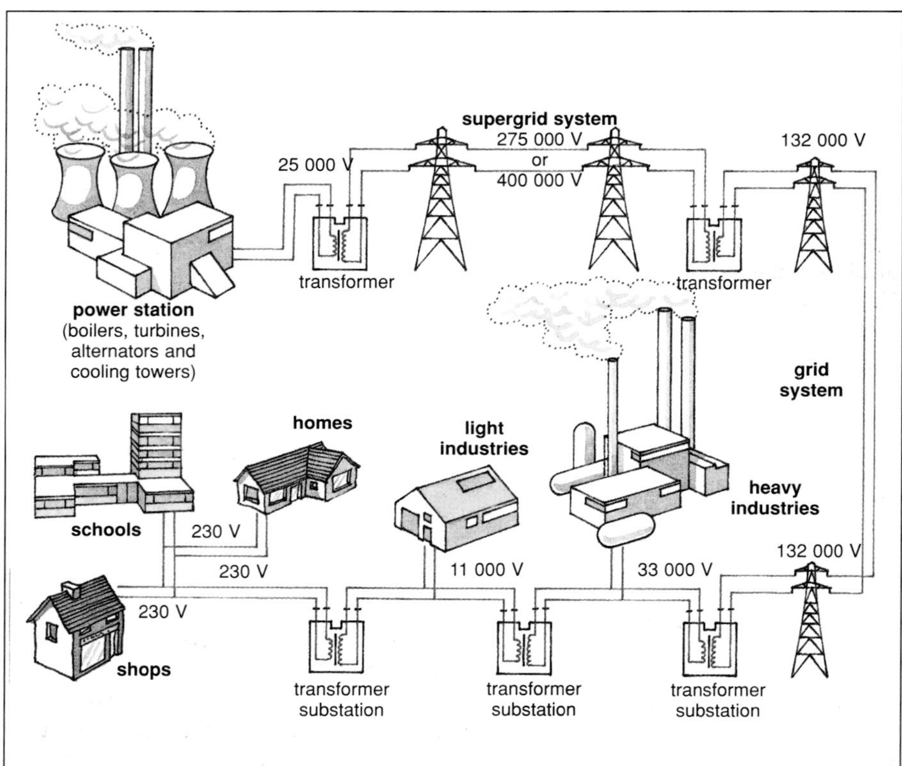

Picture 7 Voltages in the National Grid system.

Why is electricity transmitted at very high voltages?

Most people live and work many hundreds of miles from the power stations that produce their electricity. This is because the stations are built near good supplies of coal and cooling water.

Whenever a current flows in a conductor some power is lost in heating the conductor. Engineers can cut down this energy loss by supplying the current at very high voltages.

The power loss in a conductor is given by $P = IV$ where V is the voltage drop across the conductor. We can change this to give power loss in terms of the current I and the resistance R of the cable.

We know from Ohm's Law that	$V = IR$
If we substitute this into	$P = IV$
we get	$P = I\ (IR)$
This gives:	$P = I^2R$

The engineers want the loss in the cable to be as little as possible. They do this by making the resistance (R) of the cable as small as possible. The resistance can be cut down by using very thick cables (see picture 8).

Even so, there will always be some cable resistance, and there comes a point when the cost of making the cable is greater than the value of the energy we are trying to save. The only other thing they can change is the *current* in the cable.

This is done by using very high voltages.

Picture 8 A power cable.

High voltage, low current

The delivered power is given by $P = IV$. Suppose the customer wants 100 000 W of power to be delivered. This could be done, for example, either by sending:

- 200 A at 500 V. Thus $P = IV = 200 \times 500 = 100\ 000$ W

or

- 1 A at 100 000 V. Thus $P = IV = 1 \times 100\ 000 = 100\ 000$ W

Now suppose the cable resistance is 2 Ω. The cable loss in the first case (voltage 500 V, current 200 A) is:

$$\text{power loss } P = I^2R = 200 \times 200 \times 2 = 80\ 000 \text{ W}$$

Losing this amount in the cables would leave only 20 000 W for the customer!

In the second case (voltage 100 000 V, current 1 A) we get:

$$\text{power loss } P = I^2R = 1 \times 1 \times 2 = 2 \text{ W!}$$

It makes very sound economic sense to send the electric power down the cable at high voltages. But you would not be happy with a mains supply at 100 000 V. This is a very dangerous voltage. This is where transformers come in.

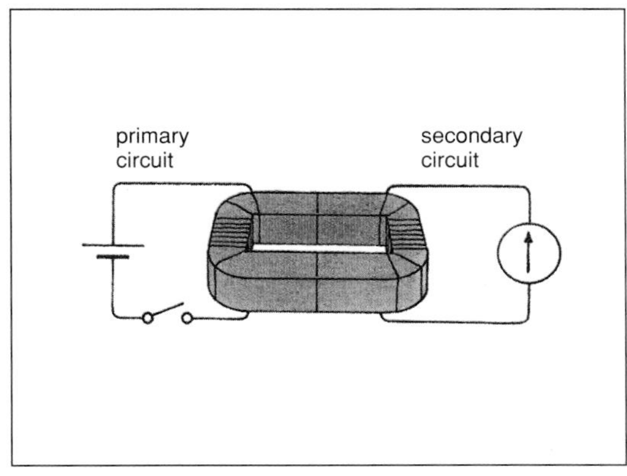

Picture 9 Electromagnetic induction happens when a magnetic field is changing or a conductor cuts through the field.

What transformers do

Faraday's experiment with two coils (page 164) gives the basic idea of how transformers work. We change a current in the primary coil. This produces a changing magnetic field (picture 9). The changing field induces a voltage in the secondary coil.

Now, when an alternating current is supplied to the primary coil it produces a changing field 50 times a second. This changing field also induces a changing voltage in the secondary.

The voltage in the secondary coil depends on *how many turns* there are in the coils. If there are *more* turns in the secondary than in the primary coil, the output voltage is *bigger* than the input voltage. If there are *fewer* turns in the secondary than in the primary, the voltage is *reduced*. Thus we can have **step-up transformers**, which increase the voltage, and **step-down transformers**, which do the opposite (picture 10).

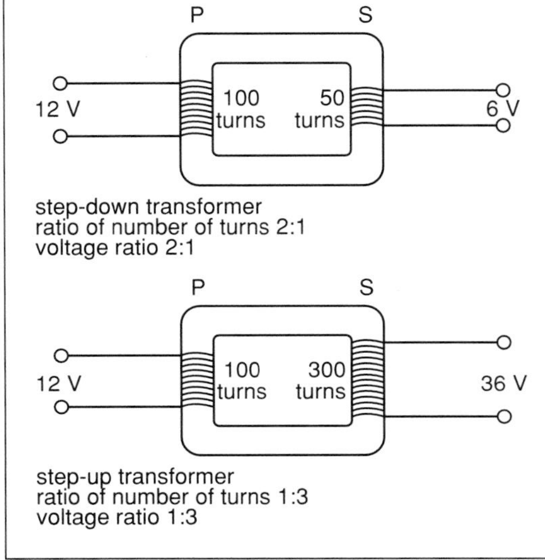

Picture 10 Step-down and step-up transformer.

This leads to the transformer rule:

$$\frac{\text{output voltage}}{\text{input voltage}} = \frac{\text{number of secondary turns}}{\text{number of primary turns}}$$

or
$$\frac{V_{out}}{V_{in}} = \frac{N_s}{N_p}$$

Which gives
$$\frac{\boldsymbol{V_s}}{\boldsymbol{V_p}} = \frac{\boldsymbol{N_s}}{\boldsymbol{N_p}}$$

Picture 11 shows a model power line. The power loss in the cables reduces the energy available at the second bulb.

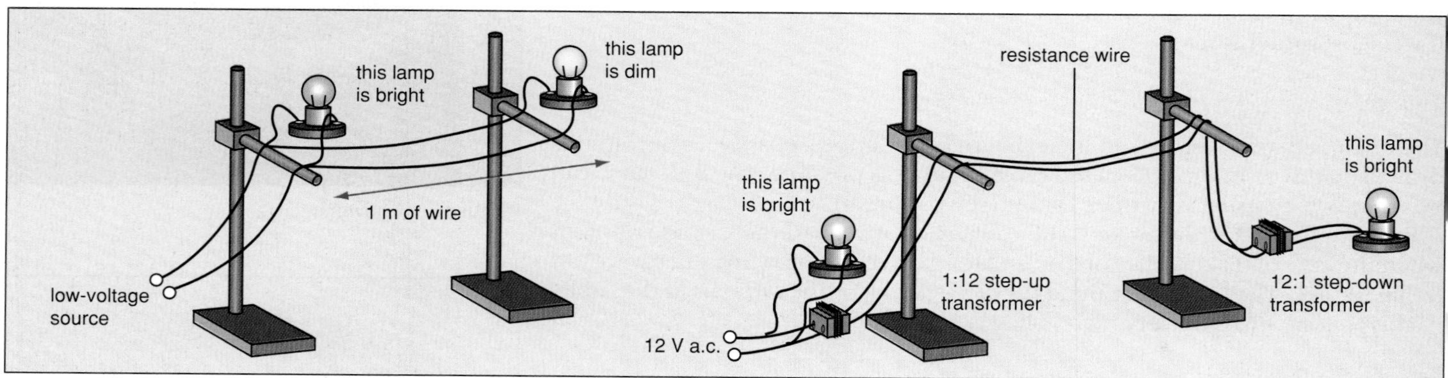

Picture 11 Using transformers reduces energy loss.

If a transformer is used to step up the voltage at the 'power station' (the power pack in the laboratory), and step down the voltage before connecting to the second bulb, we can see that the bulbs are both bright.

If we had an ideal transformer, we could say that the power in the primary coil must be equal to the power in the secondary coil (as we cannot create or destroy energy).

We can say that:
$$P_{in} = P_{out}$$

which means that
$$I_pV_p = I_sV_s$$

Which gives
$$\frac{V_s}{V_p} = \frac{I_p}{I_s}$$

Imagine this is a step-up transformer. This shows us that, if the voltage in the secondary *increases*, the current in the secondary *decreases* proportionally. The reverse is true for a step-down transformer. We know that the ratio of the voltages is equal to the ratio of turns in the coils, so we can write:

$$\frac{\boldsymbol{N_s}}{\boldsymbol{N_p}} = \frac{\boldsymbol{V_s}}{\boldsymbol{V_p}} = \frac{\boldsymbol{I_p}}{\boldsymbol{I_s}}$$

Efficiency of transformers

A transformer transfers energy from one coil to another. In a way, it is like a machine with no moving parts. Because of this, it is highly efficient, but *not* 100% efficient. The coils and the iron core heat up, and some energy is used to magnetise and demagnetise the core. We can calculate the efficiency of a transformer by comparing the power output with the input, and expressing this as a percentage.

$$\frac{P_{out}}{P_{in}} = \frac{I_sV_s}{I_pV_p}$$

$$\text{Efficiency} = \frac{\boldsymbol{I_sV_s}}{\boldsymbol{I_pV_p}} \times \frac{\mathbf{100}}{\mathbf{1}}$$

Questions

1 Explain what jobs the following do in a coal-fired power station:

a generators,

b cooling towers,

c step-up transformers.

2 a What is the National Grid?

b Why are the cables that carry electricity held so far above the ground?

c Electricity is sent along the National Grid at very high voltages. Why must they be so high?

3 The graph (right) shows the cost per metre of cable of different thickness. It also shows the cost per metre of the power loss in the cable due to resistance heating. Both of these quantities are plotted against cables of different thickness.

a Why does the cost of lost power go down when the cable gets thicker?

b Why does the cost per metre of cable rise when the cable gets thicker?

c What is the combined cost of cable-plus-power-loss for cables of thickness: (i) 10 cm, (ii) 15 cm?

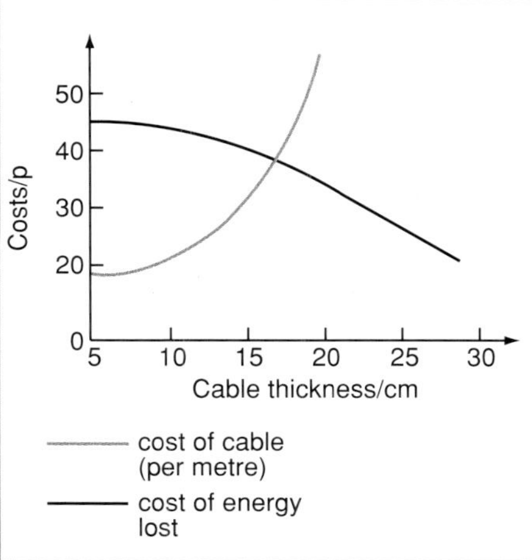

d From the graph, what is the most economical cable thickness to choose?

e The graph for the cost of the cable rises much more quickly than the power saving cost falls. Suggest a reason for this.

4 a Calculate the current that needs to be taken from a 25 MW power station at a generating voltage of 2500 V.

b What would this current be reduced to if the voltage was stepped up to 400 000 V for the National Supergrid?

c What would be the effect of this reduction in current on power loss in the cables?

5 A shop hires out transformers for use with appliances which operate at 110 V. The transformers give a 110 V output when connected to a 230 V mains supply.

a A person hires a transformer to operate a 110 V electric drill. The primary coil of the transformer is connected to a 230 V supply, and the drill to the 110 V secondary coil. The current in the drill is 18 A. Calculate the power of the drill.

b The primary coil of the transformer has 1200 turns. How many turns has each secondary coil?

c When the drill is used, the primary coil of the transformer draws a current of 11 A from the 230 V supply. Calculate the efficiency of the transformer.

d State one reason why transformers are not 100% efficient.

6 A power line has a resistance of 2 ohms for each kilometre length of cable. If it is 100 km long, and carries a current of 220 A, calculate the power loss in the line.

F6
Using energy

We use energy – and misuse it. Studying this section and the next could save you a lot of money . . . .

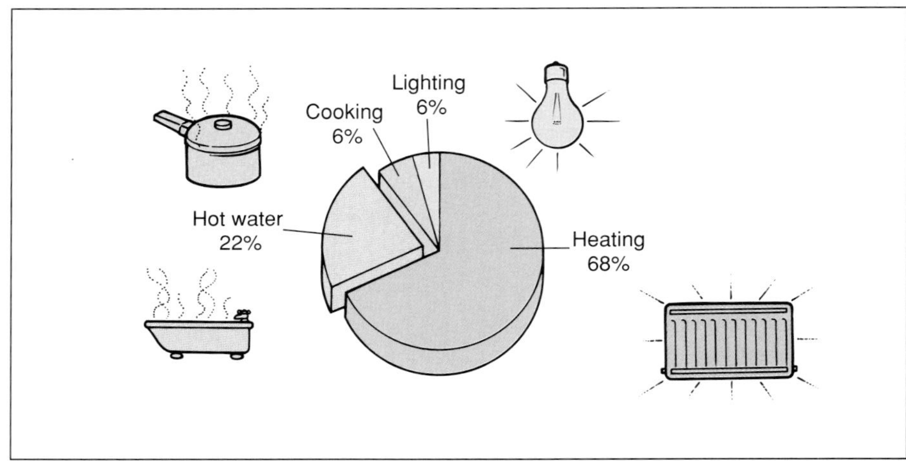

Picture 1 How we use energy in the home.

The costs of energy

Energy is expensive. You have to pay for producing it. You have to pay for moving it to where you want to use it. Getting fossil fuels out of the ground is expensive. 'Human fuel' – food – is even more expensive to produce.

But there are other costs when we use energy. We get most of our energy from fossil fuels. The unwanted by-products are carbon dioxide and some other gases, which cause pollution in one way or another. We are only now waking up to the fact that the bills for the greenhouse effect, acid rain, and other kinds of pollution have still to come in.

This section deals with the way we use energy in the home, and how we might save money by using less, and wasting less. Look at the pie chart in picture 1; it shows what we use energy for at home.

Table 1 Direct and indirect use of fuels.

Directly
coal, oil or **gas** in fires, stoves, room heaters, central heating systems
Indirectly
electricity in fires, convector heaters, storage heaters

Home heating

Most of the energy we use at home is used to keep ourselves and our surroundings warm. Nearly all of this heating energy comes from the burning of fossil fuels, such as coal, oil or gas. We can use the fuels directly or indirectly (see table 1).

Electricity is *not* a fuel: it is just a very good way of moving energy from one place to another. But the energy it carries is produced in power stations, and most of these use fossil fuels.

Table 2 Costs of producing energy.

Energy source	**Cost of producing**	
	Yearly cost for typical house (£)	1 megajoule (p)
solid fuel/coal	360	0.02
oil	250	0.015
gas	270	0.016
bottled gas (propane)	455	0.027
electricity		
– daytime	1200	2
– night-time	350	0.75

Heating costs

Table 2 shows how much it costs to provide heating using different sources of energy. The most expensive is 'daytime' electricity. Prices will change, of course. This may be due to inflation and changes in world production of oil, for example. But the prices tend to stay much the same in comparison with each other.

Energy is measured in **joules**. One joule is a very small quantity of energy. It is about how much you would use to lift this book from a chair to a table. It usually takes a lot of energy to heat things up. For example, to boil a kettle holding 1 kg of water needs about a third of a million joules (0.33 MJ). If this energy were used in lifting instead of heating, it could raise the kilogram of water higher than the top of Mount Everest!

Heating things uses up a lot of energy, and it's by far the biggest part of your household energy use. A one-bar electric fire is rated at 1 kilowatt. This fire delivers a thousand joules *every second*. In an hour it would deliver 3 600 000 J (3.6 MJ). This amount of energy is also called a **kilowatt-hour** (kWh).

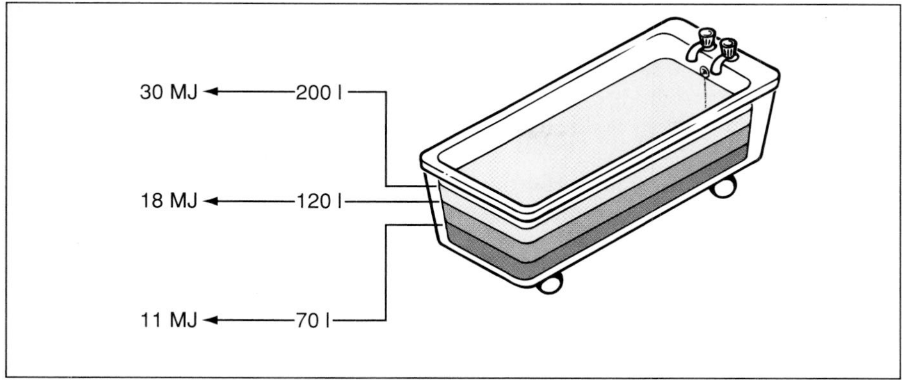

Picture 2 The energy needed to have a bath.

Table 3

Substance	Specific heat capacity (J/kg/°C)
copper	380
aluminium	886
iron	500
lead	127
glass	600
water	4200

Cleaning, washing and bathing

How much does it cost to have a bath? This depends on how hot you like it, and how much water you use. A standard bath, just about as full as you can have without it spilling, will take 200 litres of water (picture 2). A litre of water has a mass of 1 kg, so you would use 200 kg of water.

Tap water is at an average temperature of 10 °C in winter, a hot bath is about 45 °C. This means we have to *raise* the temperature of the water by 35 °C.

Raising temperature

The energy required to make a kilogram of any material hotter by 1 °C is called its **specific heat capacity (*c*)**. Different materials have different values of specific heat capacity: it takes less energy to heat a kilogram of copper by 1 °C than it does to heat a kilogram of water by 1 °C (see table 3). Water has a *very* large specific heat capacity, which is why domestic water heating accounts for a large part of fuel bills.

Table 4 Energy needed for cleaning tasks.

Washing up (using typical quantities of water)		
in a sink (8 litres)	2 MJ (very hot)	1.3 MJ (hot)
in a plastic bowl (5 litres)	1.3 MJ (very hot)	0.8 MJ (hot)
Washing machine (for clothes)		
using 17 litres of water	heating	5 MJ
	pump, motor	1 MJ

Table 4 shows how much energy is needed for different cleaning tasks.

So how much energy is needed to heat our bath?

To raise 1 kg of water through 1 °C takes 4200 J.
To raise 200 kg of water by the same amount we need: 4200×200
To raise this mass by 35 °C then we will need: $4200 \times 200 \times 35$
We have multiplied: specific heat capacity × mass × temperature rise
We can write this as: $E_h = cm\Delta T = 4200 \times 200 \times 35 = 29.4$ MJ

This formula can be used to find the amount of energy supplied to any substance if we know: the specific heat capacity, c
the mass, m
the temperature rise, ΔT

You can use the data in table 2 to work out how much this bath would cost using different energy sources. Using the most expensive, electricity, it would cost about 50p. It should be cheaper to take a shower (picture 3).

Picture 3 Taking a shower.

Changing state

Cooks in a hurry sometimes think that they can cook potatoes faster by turning up the gas or electricity under the boiling water. But all that happens is that the water boils away *faster*. It doesn't get any hotter and the potatoes take just as long to cook.

When the water is heated, the energy we put in makes its molecules move faster. Its molecules are gaining **kinetic energy**. Some molecules will move faster than others and are able to escape from the surface – they **evaporate**. We say that the water is **boiling**. At 100 °C, molecules of water are moving from being part of a liquid to being part of a gas: the water is gradually **changing state**.

The same thing happens when we warm a beaker of ice. The temperature rises until it reaches 0 °C, and then stops rising. We are adding energy, but we have no temperature rise to show for it.

The temperature does not start to rise again until *all* the ice has melted. When the ice reaches 0 °C, the energy is being used to change its state, not raise its temperature. It is as if the energy is being taken in and 'hidden'. Anything concealed or hidden can be described as 'latent', so the energy needed to change state is called **latent heat**.

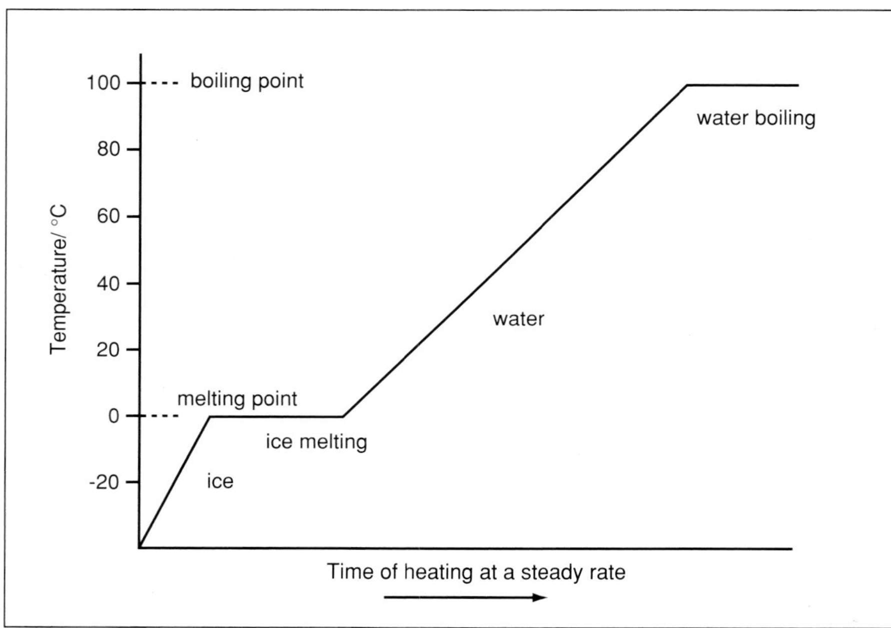

Picture 4 Temperature changes when heating water from ice to steam.

Specific latent heat is the energy transferred when a kilogram of a substance *changes state*. For example, it takes 334 kJ to **melt** a kilogram of ice and 2.26 MJ to **vaporise** a kilogram of water. The temperature changes of ice as it is steadily heated are shown in picture 4.

The energy required to change the state of a mass m of a substance already at the melting or boiling temperature is given by $\boldsymbol{E_h = mL}$ where $\boldsymbol{L}$ is the specific latent heat. L is measured in **joules per kilogram** (J/kg).

Changing from a solid to a liquid (melting) is also known as **fusion**. As mentioned above, for water:

$$\text{specific latent heat of fusion, } L_f = 334 \text{ kJ/kg}$$

When water evaporates:

$$\text{specific latent heat of vaporisation, } L_v = 2.26 \text{ MJ/kg}$$

Our own body's cooling method, sweating, relies on latent heat being used to vaporise a liquid. Moisture on our skin evaporates, and the latent heat is taken from our body.

When this process happens in reverse, that is when we **condense** a gas, the latent heat is *given out*. Office and apartment buildings in the United States once used a form of central heating based on this principle. Picture 5 shows steam at 100 °C entering a radiator, and condensing to water at 100 °C. Notice that there is *no temperature change* – the latent heat of vaporisation is given off into the room to warm it.

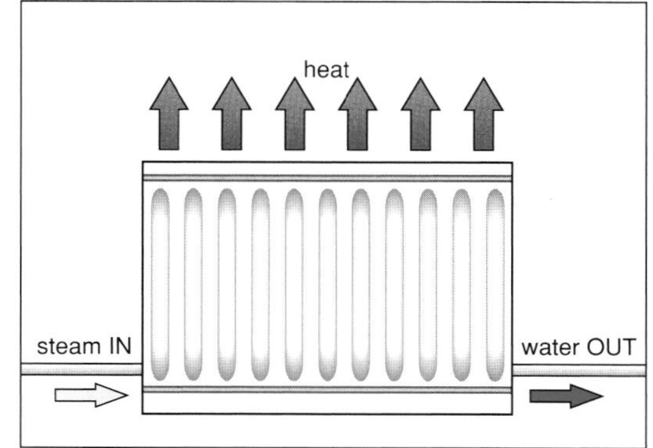

Picture 5 Steam heating.

Pumping heat

Refrigerators rely on the high specific latent heat of the refrigerant liquid. Liquids evaporate more easily under a low pressure. In a refrigerator the liquid is made to flow into a chamber at a low pressure. The liquid evaporates and takes energy from its surroundings (the inside of the fridge) to do so. The temperature inside the fridge drops.

The vapour is then pumped into long tubes *outside* the refrigerator where it is compressed by a pump and liquefies. The condensing vapour releases its latent heat to the surroundings. You can see the tubes at the back of the refrigerator in picture 6 – they get quite hot when the refrigerator is working hard.

What if we used the same idea, say, to take energy *out of the surroundings* and feed it into our homes? This is simply using a 'refrigerator' in reverse! Such heaters do exist, and they are called **heat pumps**. They take energy out of the air or the ground instead of out of food, and 'pump' it *into* the house to warm it.

Picture 7 shows a commercial heat pump. It is used in large buildings. These need ventilating, which means that warmed, smelly air has to be taken out of the building. This has to be replaced by fresh air, which is cold in winter. One end of the heat pump is placed in the warm 'exhaust air' and takes the heat energy out of it. This energy is pumped to the cold air coming into the building, so that it is 'prewarmed'. This cuts down the heating bills.

Picture 6 In a fridge the energy taken out of the cooling food warms the air.

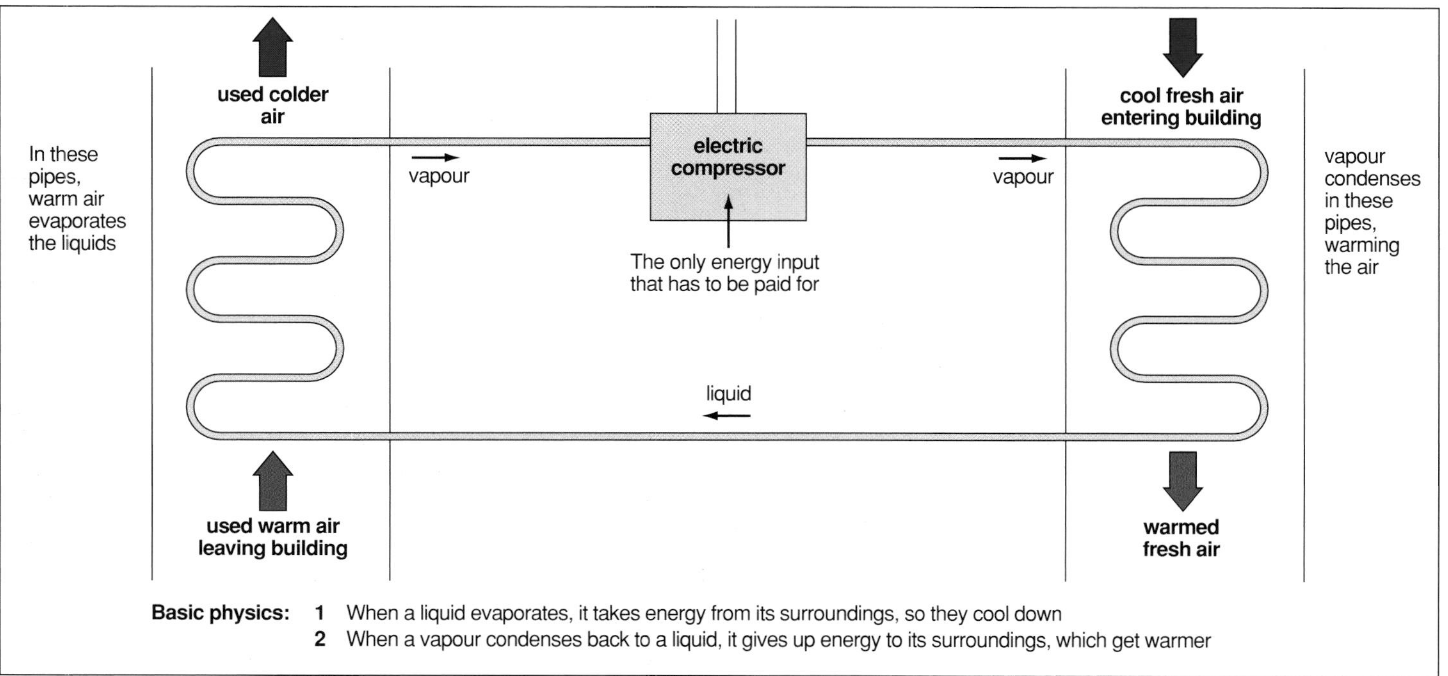

Picture 7 How a heat pump works.

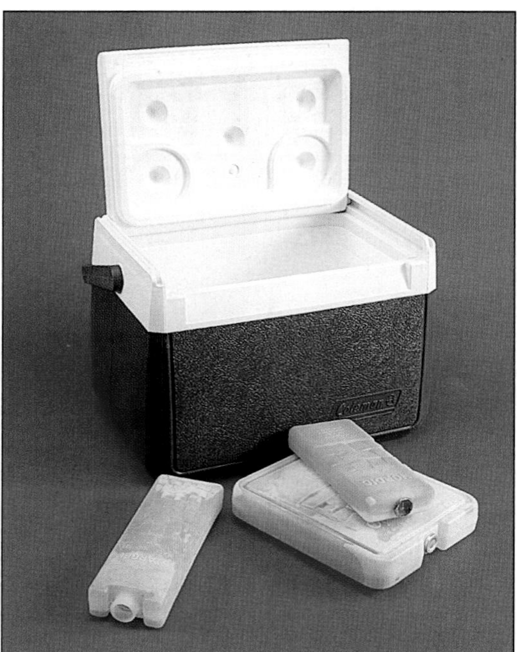

Picture 8 Using latent heat to keep things cool.

Keeping it cool

Many people take a picnic 'cool box' with them when going for a trip during the summer. On a warm day, you can enjoy a cold drink from a can that has been kept in the box. The box is heavily insulated, so that very little heat can get in but additional cooling can be provided by adding a 'freezer block'. This is a plastic container filled with a liquid which has a melting point below 0 °C. As the temperature inside the cool box rises, the liquid in the block starts to melt.

When it does, it takes its latent heat of **fusion** from the contents of the box. The block, and the inside of the cool box, stay at the melting point temperature for a long time.

Heating calculations

If we think back to our calculations of the cost of a hot bath (page 171), we can see that in real life things are a bit more complicated. When you have a bath, the bathroom is usually full of steam – although the bath water isn't boiling, some of it *has* vaporised, requiring latent heat in addition to the energy used to raise the water temperature. In most situations, for the sake of simplicity, we assume that no latent heat is used until the boiling point is reached. This gives us workable calculations.

For example, many people use steam wallpaper strippers (picture 9) to remove old and stubborn wallpaper. The boiler section is filled with water and switched on. The water is heated to 100 °C, and the steam then flows up a hose to a flat section which is pressed against the wall. This moistens and loosens the wallpaper, making it easy to remove.

Picture 9 A steam wallpaper stripper.

The model shown has a capacity of 15 litres of water, which is a mass of 15 kg. It is filled with water at a temperature of 20 °C. The decorator switches it on, and starts to remove the wallpaper when the steam begins to flow. After a while he takes a break, and finds he has to add 5 litres to refill it to its starting level. How much energy has he used during the first session?

The specific heat capacity, c, of water is 4200 J/kg/°C.
To heat the water to 100 °C involves a temperature rise, ΔT, of 80 °C.
The energy used is:

$$E_h = cm\Delta T = 4200 \times 15 \times 80 = 5040 \text{ kJ}$$

But the machine has also evaporated 5 litres (5 kg) of water. The energy required for this is given by:

$$E_h = mL_v = 5 \times 2\,260\,000 = 11\,300 \text{ kJ}$$

This gives us a *total* energy of 16 340 kJ or 16.34 MJ.

We are assuming that *all* the energy used by the heater has been transferred to the water. In real life, would the figure be higher or lower than the one above?

We know that **power** is the rate of transfer of energy, and so we can write:

$$E = P \times t = I \times V \times t$$

If the machine takes a constant electrical current of 10 A, for how long was it switched on? Mains voltage is 230 V, so $E = I \times V \times t$ gives us:

$$16\,340\,000 = 10 \times 230 \times t$$

which gives t = 7104 seconds = 118 minutes.

In other words, our decorator did nearly two hours of extremely hot and steamy work! He would also have to be careful – a scald from steam at 100 °C is much worse than a scald from water at the same temperature. Can you think why?

Questions

1 A jug containing 0.5 kilograms of milk at 20 degrees celsius is cooled in a refrigerator to 4 degrees celsius.

How much energy is removed from the milk?

(Specific heat capacity of milk = 4000 joules per kilogram per degree celsius)

2 A hotel swimming pool contains 300 tonnes of water which should be at a temperature of 24 °C.

A customer complains to the hotel manager that the water is too cold. The manager measures the temperature and finds that it is 20 °C.

a How much heat energy is required to bring the water in the pool up to the required temperature?

b The pool's electrical heating system has a power of 50 kilowatts.

How many hours will it take to heat the water to the required temperature?

c The actual time to heat the water was 32 hours.

Explain why this time is different from your answer to part (b).

d i) How many kilowatt hours of electrical energy are used by the heating system in the 32 hours?

ii) Electricity costs 6p per kilowatt hour.

What is the cost of heating the pool from 20 °C to 24 °C?

e Many outdoor pools are covered with a thick plastic sheet at night.

Apart from the fact that it helps to keep the pool clean, suggest a reason for doing this.

3 A pupil, working in a laboratory, sets up an experiment to measure the specific latent heat of fusion of ice.

He places ice around an immersion heater in a beaker and switches the heater on for 5 minutes. He then pours off the melted ice and measures its mass. The immersion heater is rated at 50 W and the mass of melted ice is 0.05 kg.

a Calculate the value of the specific latent heat of fusion of ice given by the above measurements.

b Why will the above method not give an accurate value for the specific latent heat of fusion of ice?

c Suggest a way in which the experiment could be improved to give a more accurate result.

4 A pupil sets up the apparatus shown below in an experiment to calculate a value for the specific latent heat of vaporisation of water.

The reading on the balance remains steady as the water is brought to the boil.

The pupil then observes that the reading on the balance gradually decreases.

The energy supplied during the time taken for the reading on the balance to drop by 0.15 kg is measured by the pupil to be 3.15 x 105 J.

Calculate a value for the specific latent heat of vaporisation of water from the pupil's experiment.

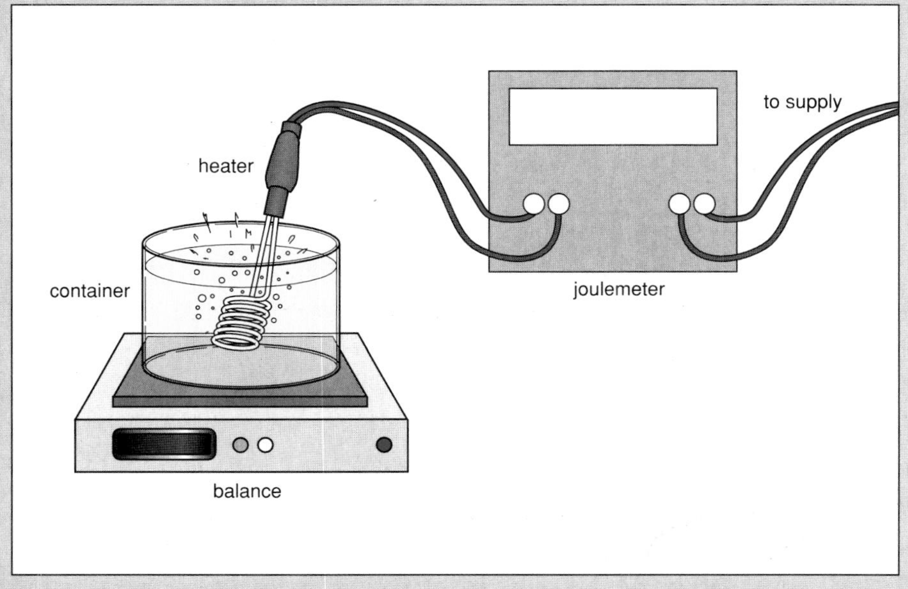

5a The diagram below shows the percentage of heat lost through various parts of a house.

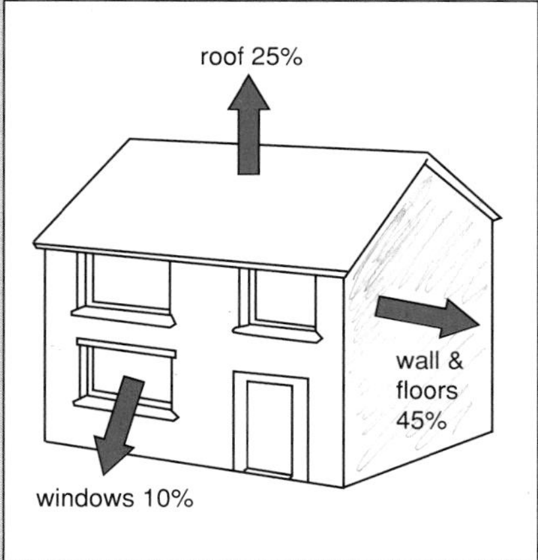

All the remaining heat lost from the house is due to draughts.

What percentage of heat is lost due to draughts?

b The rate at which heat is lost by conduction from a house can be reduced by installing double glazing.

A typical double glazed window allows 60 joules of heat to pass through each square metre every second.

For one particular window, 300 joules of heat pass through every second.

Calculate the area of the window.

Saving energy in the home

No matter how much energy you put into heating a house, it will escape to the outside. The rate at which it escapes will increase if there is a large temperature difference between the inside and the outside. Heat loss is far greater on a cold winter day than on a mild day in spring. Making a house more energy efficient will not only save money, but helps to reduce the damage done to the environment by producing energy.

Energy can be transferred in three different ways. **Conduction** occurs in solids, but only metals are good conductors. Non-metals do not allow energy to flow through them easily, and gases and liquids are very poor conductors. A poor conductor is an **insulator**.

Energy is transferred in liquids and gases by **convection**. If part of a liquid or gas is at a higher temperature than the rest, it expands and becomes less dense. This causes it to rise. As it moves, the energy is carried to cooler regions. This type of flow is called a **convection current**.

Particular frequencies of electromagnetic **radiation** (the *infra-red* range) are easily absorbed by atoms and molecules of substances. This raises their temperature. They also re-radiate this energy, and the greater the temperature difference between a substance and its surroundings, the greater the amount of energy radiated.

If we consider how heat escapes from a house, we find that energy losses through radiation are a very small portion of the total. Conduction and convection losses can be reduced by insulation techniques.

1 Warm air rises to the top of a house, and heat escapes through the roof. **Loft insulation** uses fibreglass or similar materials, which trap tiny pockets of air. The air cannot move suficiently to form convection currents, and heat cannot escape by conduction as air is a very poor conductor. Loft insulation is one of the most cost-effective ways of saving energy.

2 Metals are good conductors of heat, and copper is one of the best. Unfortunately, most domestic hot water travels through copper pipes! This means that energy can easily travel from the inside to the outside surface of the pipe. **Lagging** is the term used to describe covering the pipes and hot water tank with layers of insulating material. This can save a great deal of money.

3 Modern brick houses have a double wall, and the space between is called a cavity. The air in the cavity is a good insulator, but it can move and form convection currents. These can transfer energy from the inner wall to the outer wall. **Cavity wall insulation** involves filling the gap with an insulating foam plastic or mineral wool. This stops the movement of air, and can cut heat losses by half.

4 Gaps around badly fitting doors, windows, and floorboards let warm air escape and cold air enter. **Draught excluders** and carpets with underlay can reduce draughts and increase comfort.

5 A single glazed window has one surface at the temperature of the outside, and heat can travel from the warm inner surface by conduction through the glass. A **double-glazed** window has an air gap between the two panes. This prevents conduction, but the air gap must also be narrow to restrict air flow due to convection currents.

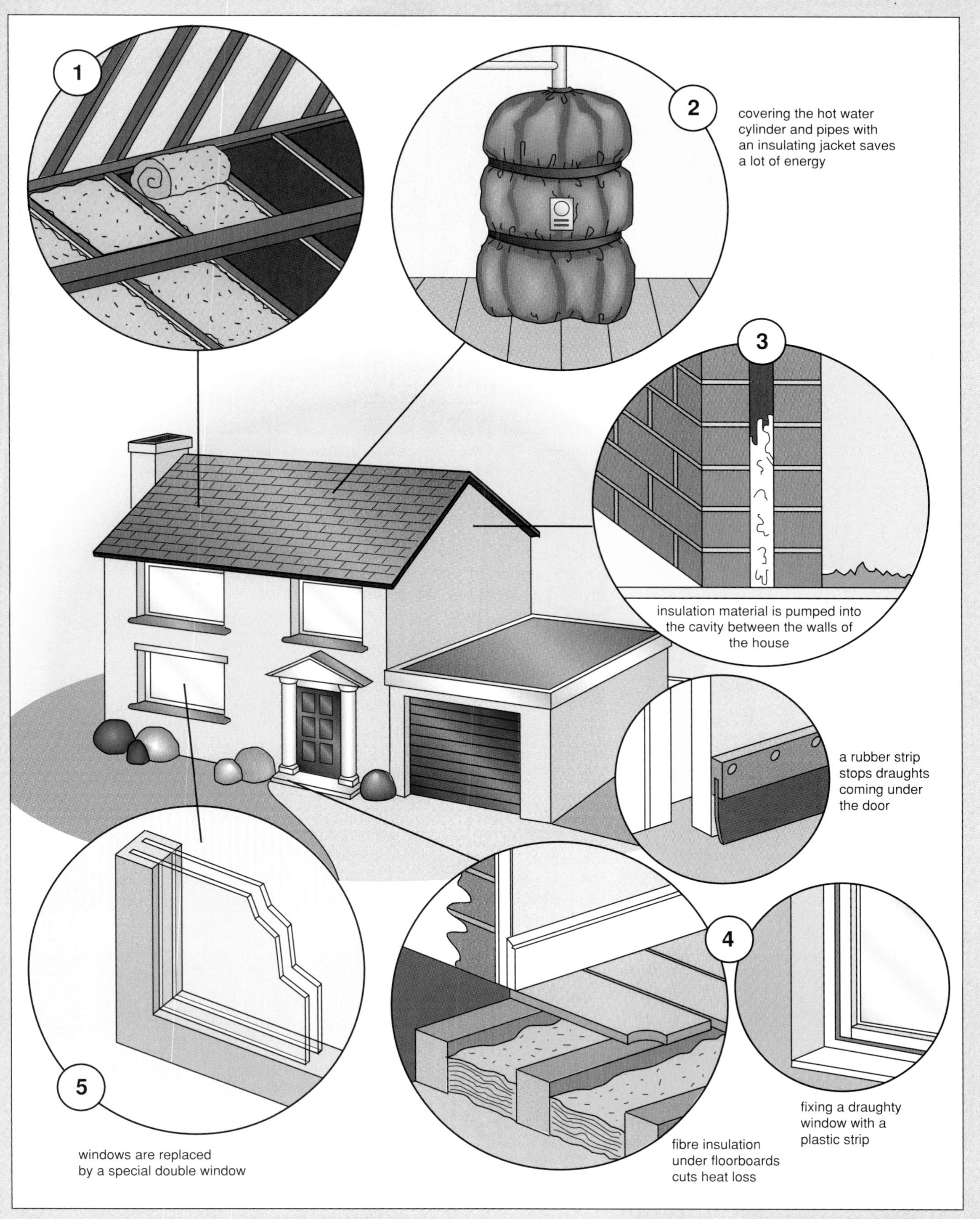
1
2
covering the hot water cylinder and pipes with an insulating jacket saves a lot of energy
3
insulation material is pumped into the cavity between the walls of the house
a rubber strip stops draughts coming under the door
4
fixing a draughty window with a plastic strip
fibre insulation under floorboards cuts heat loss
5
windows are replaced by a special double window

G1
Patterns in space

The Sun, Earth and planets are part of a pattern in space called the Solar System.

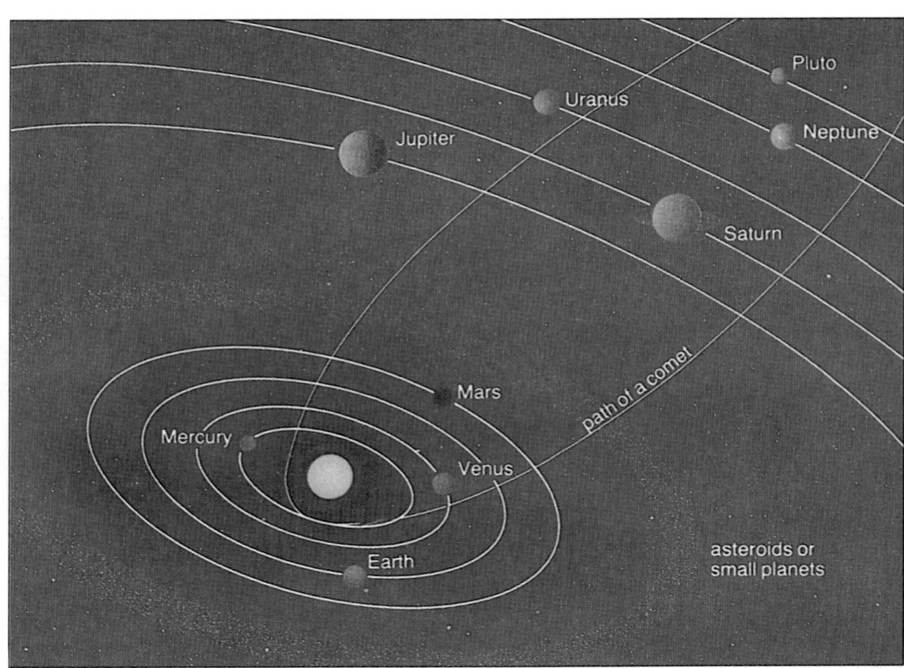

Picture 1 The Solar System. It is not drawn to scale because the outer planets are so far away from the Sun compared with the inner ones.

The Solar System

The Sun is the centre of the Solar System. It contains 99.8% of all the mass in the System, and so produces a huge gravity field that holds the planets in their orbits around it. Picture 1 shows the Sun and the planets, viewed from outside the Solar System. The actual masses and distances of the planets from the Sun are given in table 1.

The Sun

The Sun is a star. It is quite a small one, as stars go, and it isn't very bright. It is the brightest object in the sky because it is so close to us, compared with other stars. The energy it provides supports all life on Earth. This energy comes from the Sun's own mass, which it uses up at a rate of 4 million tonnes per second.

The Sun emits energy at the rate of 400 000 000 000 000 000 000 000 000 watts (4×10^{26} W). Only a tiny fraction of this energy reaches Earth. Most is radiated into empty space.

The energy is produced by a process called **nuclear fusion**. The Sun is mostly hydrogen. Hydrogen nuclei in the centre of the Sun are under a huge

Table 1 Planetary data.

	Mass (Earth = 1)	Diameter (km)	Density (tonnes per m^3)	Surface gravity field (N/kg)	Distance from Sun (10^9 km)	Period 'year'	'Day'
Mercury	0.05	4 880	5.4	3.7	58	88 d	59 d
Venus	0.81	12 112	5.25	8.9	107.5	224 d	243 d
Earth	1	12 742	5.51	9.8	149.6	365	23 h 56 min
Mars	0.11	6 790	3.95	3.8	228	687 d	24 h 37 min
Jupiter	318	142 600	1.34	24.9	778	11.9 y	9 h 50 min
Saturn	95	120 200	0.70	10.5	1427	29.5 y	10 h 14 min
Uranus	14.6	49 000	1.27	8.8	2870	84.0 y	17 h 14 min
Neptune	17.2	50 000	1.64	11.2	4497	165 y	16 h 07 min
Pluto system	0.003	2 284	2.0	0.6	5900 (variable)	248 y	6.4 d

pressure and at a very high temperature. Some of the hydrogen nuclei collide to form helium nuclei. In doing this they lose a tiny fraction of their mass which is converted to the kinetic energy of the particles that are left.

Picture 2 shows the surface of the Sun. The surface is a gas at a temperature of about 5500 °C, and the picture shows a typical 'Sun storm' in which hot gas is hurled far out into space. These storms reach a peak every 11 years. At times of peak activity the Sun sends out far more ionised particles than usual, which affect our atmosphere and so the weather on Earth.

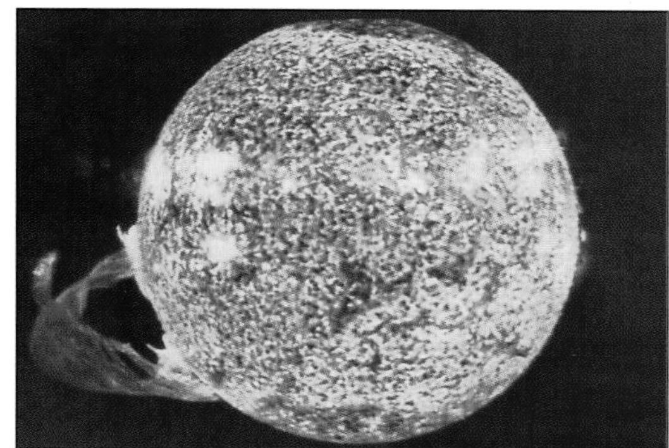

Picture 2 A Sun storm. On the scale of the picture the Earth would be about the size of one of the dark blobs or about half a millimetre across.

The planets

The planets move in orbit around the Sun. They all move in the same direction, which is anticlockwise when viewed from above. The nearer the planet is to the Sun the faster it moves. Thus the orbital speed of Mercury is 55 m/s while Neptune travels at a tenth of that speed, about 5.4 m/s.

Neptune has a larger orbit than Mercury and travels much more slowly. This means that Neptune takes much longer than Mercury to complete its path around the Sun. This orbit time is called the planet's 'year'. A 'year' for Mercury is just over 12 Earth weeks, while Neptune takes 247.8 Earth years to make one orbit around the Sun.

Mercury is so close to the Sun that its surface is heated up to over 400 °C, which is hot enough to melt tin. It spins on its axis rather slowly, managing to get three spins ('days') for every two orbits ('years') around the Sun. It is too small to have an atmosphere.

The next planet out from the Sun is **Venus** (picture 3). It is almost exactly the same size as the Earth and is only a little less massive. You might think it would be a good place to go for a sunshine holiday, but you would be wrong. Its atmosphere is mostly carbon dioxide, so the greenhouse effect is so great that it is even hotter than Mercury, with a surface temperature of 460 °C.

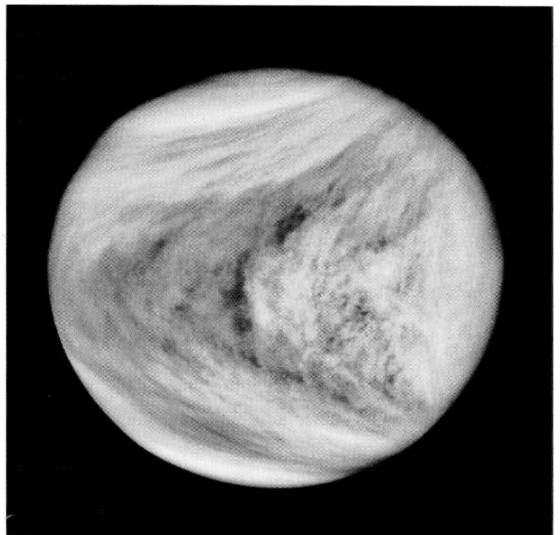

Picture 3 Venus.

The atmosphere of Venus is very corrosive, containing hydrogen chloride and hydrogen fluoride. No one has seen the surface of Venus, as it is hidden by clouds of concentrated sulphuric acid and particles of pure sulphur. Also, the atmospheric pressure is 95 times what it is on Earth, so that a very well-designed space suit would be needed. When the Russian Venus Probe landed by parachute on the surface of Venus in 1972 it managed to survive for only about 30 minutes in these very nasty conditions.

Bypassing planet **Earth**, we next reach the planet **Mars**. At one time it was thought that Mars could support life. Indeed, a nineteenth century astronomer was convinced that the markings he could see on its surface were canals. He was wrong; he might have seen lines of craters or dust blown by the wind and used his very vivid imagination!

But spacecraft sent to Mars have taken photographs which seem to show old river beds. It may be that at one time there was enough surface water on Mars to support life. It also looks as if Mars once had volcanoes (picture 4). This suggests an internal source of energy which might have been able to support

	Surface temperature/ (°C)	Number of moons	Atmosphere
Mercury	350	0	none
Venus	460	0	thick: carbon dioxide, sulphuric acid
Earth	20	1	nitrogen, oxygen
Mars	-23	2	thin: carbon dioxide
Jupiter	-120	16, 1 ring	hydrogen, helium, ammonia, methane
Saturn	-180	17, plus rings	hydrogen, helium, ammonia, methane
Uranus	-210	15, plus rings	hydrogen, helium, ammonia, methane
Neptune	-220	8	hydrogen, helium, methane
Pluto system	-230	1	none – frozen

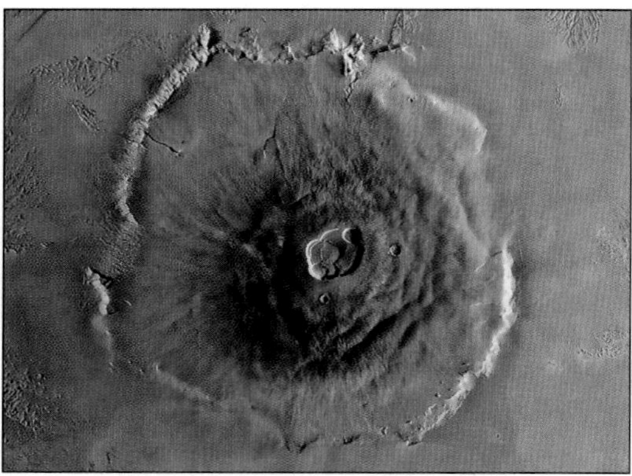

Picture 4 A Martian volcano.

some kind of life. Mars even has an atmosphere, but it is much thinner than the Earth's.

In 1976 the American Viking Spacecraft managed to 'soft-land' probes which were able to take pictures of the Martian surface.

These probes also looked for signs of life. They scooped up some Martian soil and tested it to see if carbon dioxide or any other chemical signs of life were present. The first experiment seemed to give a positive result. But when the experiment was repeated many times no more of the chemicals were detected.

Asteroids

Between Mars and the giant planet Jupiter astronomers have discovered hundreds of stony objects. These range in size from the largest (Ceres) which is just over 700 km in diameter to rocks which are less than a few kilometres across. There are probably thousands of others too small to see. These objects should be called **planetoids** (little planets) rather than **asteroids** (little stars).

The asteroids are mostly clustered in their orbits between Mars and Jupiter. But some of them wander away from this region. They climb high above the plane in which the planets move, or have strange orbits which bring them closer to the Sun even than Earth. It is calculated that one of them, Hermes, might one day pass between Earth and the Moon.

Picture 5 Jupiter's Great Red Spot.

The Giant Planets – Jupiter, Saturn, Uranus and Neptune

Beyond the asteroids lies the largest planet, **Jupiter** (picture 8). It is big enough to hold 1300 Earths. If it was just a little more massive it would turn into a star. As it is, the energy generated as it slowly collapses on itself creates huge storms in its atmosphere. One of these storms, a huge hurricane 48 000 kilometres long by 11 000 wide, has probably existed for thousands of years. This is the famous Great Red Spot, which you can see in picture 5.

At the visible 'surface', Jupiter's gravity field is 2.6 times stronger than Earth's. But what we see is not the planet's real surface, but the top of its atmosphere. This is made of swirling clouds of hydrogen, methane and ammonia. The bands on its surface are huge **jet streams**. Below the atmosphere is a very deep 'sea' of liquid, metallic hydrogen. This covers a comparatively small solid core. The planet's core is very hot. It might be rocky, or even white hot, solid hydrogen.

Like Jupiter, the next three planets are large and have a low density (see table 1). They are also likely to be made mostly of hydrogen and helium.

Saturn is famous for its 'rings', shown in picture 6. These are made of small rocks, pebbles and grains which orbit the planet, all together in the same plane. The Voyager spacecraft discovered that both **Uranus** and **Neptune** have rings as well. They are not so large or as clearly visible as Saturn's.

All these outer planets have several moons. Some orbit so close to their planet that they are in danger of being pulled apart by its gravity forces. One of the moons of Jupiter, **Io**, is being shaken up so much that it is hot enough inside for volcanoes to exist.

Picture 6 Saturn and its orbiting rings.

The odd one out

Pluto is the furthest known planet of the Solar System. But it isn't always the furthest – it moves in an orbit that cuts inside the orbit of Neptune.

Pluto is small and very hard to see. It was not discovered until 1930, 14 years after its existence had been predicted, because of its effect on the movement of the other outer planets.

It seemed to be a very small planet, probably smaller than Earth. We now know that it is a very strange object indeed. It is a 'double planet', with a moon, Charon, almost as big as itself.

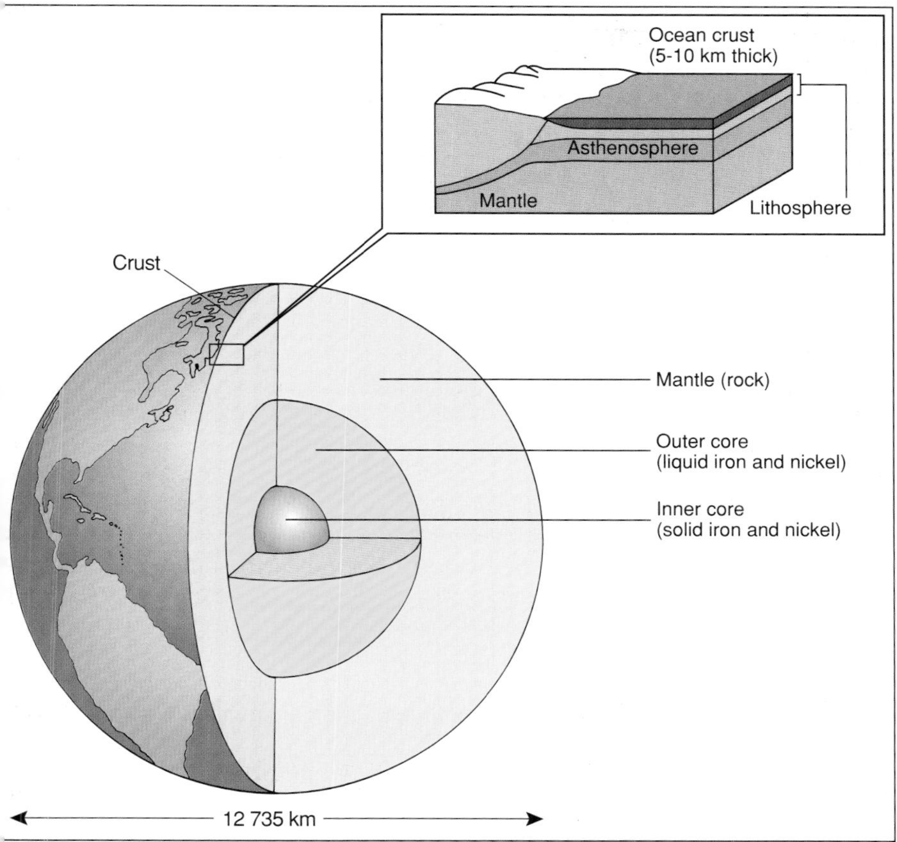

Picture 8

Picture 7 The layered structure of the Earth.

The Earth

The Earth is the largest of the inner, dense planets. Even so, its mass is only 0.3% the mass of Jupiter. It finished being formed about 4.5 billion years ago, according to measurements of the age of the oldest rocks.

The Earth can be called an iron planet. Its core is mostly iron, with some nickel mixed in. It has a very thin layer of lighter materials on top, forming the Earth's crust (picture 7). It is just the right distance from the Sun for life as we know it to exist. It is not too cold, so water doesn't freeze all the time. It is not too hot, so water doesn't boil.

The Earth's crust is amazingly thin, compared with the size of the Earth, and so is the atmosphere. When you trace the outline of a coin with a pencil to represent the Earth, the thickness of the line would cover both crust and atmosphere. It is this crust, and the thin layer of gases surrounding it, which provide the materials that all life on Earth needs.

The surface of the Earth's crust is changed by the action of wind, water, earthquakes and the mysterious upwellings of new rocks from deeper inside the Earth. The energy that produces volcanoes and earthquakes comes from deep inside the Earth.

The oldest unmelted rock found on Earth is about 4 billion years old. The oldest rocks brought back by the American astronauts from the Moon were 4.5 billion years old. The Earth and Moon were probably formed at the same time, but the Earth is so active geologically that we are unlikely to find the oldest rocks still unchanged.

The best evidence for the age of the Earth comes from measurements of the radioactivity of minerals in rocks. Radioactive elements decay into lighter elements. They decay at a known rate. So, using a machine called a mass spectrometer, scientists can measure how much of the original radioactive element is left, and how much of the newer lighter elements are present. The ratio of the two gives a fairly accurate estimate of the age of the rock.

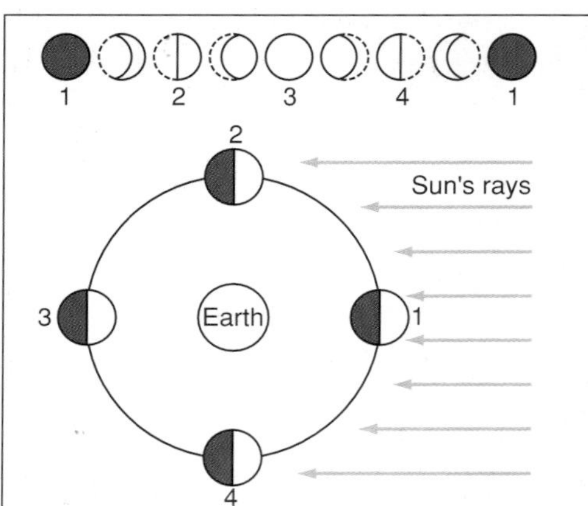

Picture 9 Why the Moon seems to change its shape: The phases of the Moon.

The Moon

The Moon, like the Sun, rises and sets. But its appearance also changes to give the **phases** of the Moon. These changes are caused by the fact that the Moon actually does move on its own. It is a **satellite** of the Earth. It moves around the Earth in an orbit, taking 28 days to complete it. This is shown in picture 9, which also explains how the changes occur. What we see is only the part of the Moon that is in sunlight.

Because it moves on its own, the Moon doesn't keep pace with the stars. If you look at the Moon at the same time every night you will see it in a slightly different part of the sky each night.

But the Moon also moves in front of the Sun. When this happens the sunlight is cut off. We then have an **eclipse** of the Sun, or **solar eclipse** (picture 10). It can only happen when the Moon is 'new', lying directly between us and the Sun.

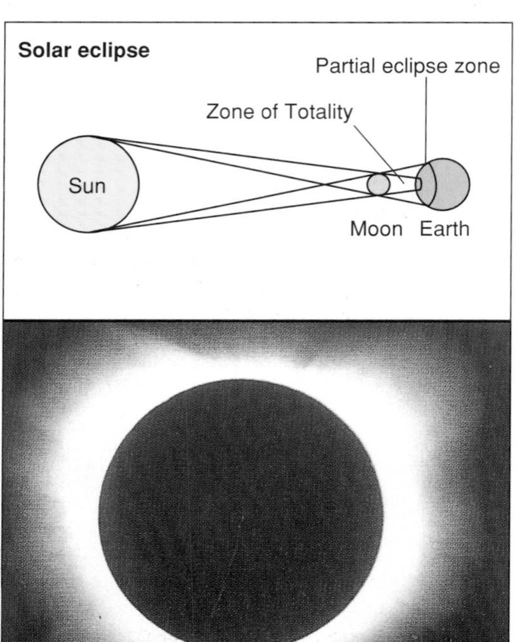

Picture 10 Eclipse of the sun.

Meteorites

Meteorites are what we call 'shooting stars'. They are bits of dust and rock that enter the Earth's atmosphere from time to time. They travel at high speed and most of them are burnt up by friction before they reach the surface. They are the remains of the original cloud of dust and gas from which the Solar System was formed.

The surface of the Moon, and many of the moons of other planets, show the effects of large meteorite collisions, which made huge craters. The oldest parts of the Earth also show large craters, probably formed by huge meteorites. Picture 11 shows Meteor Crater in Arizona. This was made 2000 years ago by a meteorite made of iron.

Picture 12 shows a meteorite burning up in the Earth's atmosphere on 10 August, 1972. It was estimated to have a mass of 1000 tonnes, and its trail was

Picture 11 The Barringer Meteor Crater in Arizona. It is over a kilometre wide and 200 metres deep. The largest we know on Earth is 26 km across.

Picture 12 The daytime meteorite of 10 August 1972. It weighed 1000 tonnes and could have destroyed a small village.

large enough to he seen in daylight. Luckily it burnt out before reaching the ground.

A window on the heavens

In 1608, so the story goes, an apprentice to a Dutch spectacle maker amused himself by looking at objects with two lenses held one behind the other. To his amazement, far-off objects appeared close at hand. His master, Hans Lippershey, built the first **telescope** by fitting the lenses into a tube. When Galileo heard of this, he built his own and turned it to the sky. This began the age of optical astronomy. He discovered that the Sun had spots and that the Moon had mountains. More astonishingly, he showed that the planets appeared as tiny discs, and that Jupiter had four moons. As more and more powerful telescopes were constructed, our understanding of the Solar System grew. It also became obvious that the stars must be much further away than the planets – even in the most powerful telescope they still remained as tiny points of light.

Picture 13 A small optical telescope.

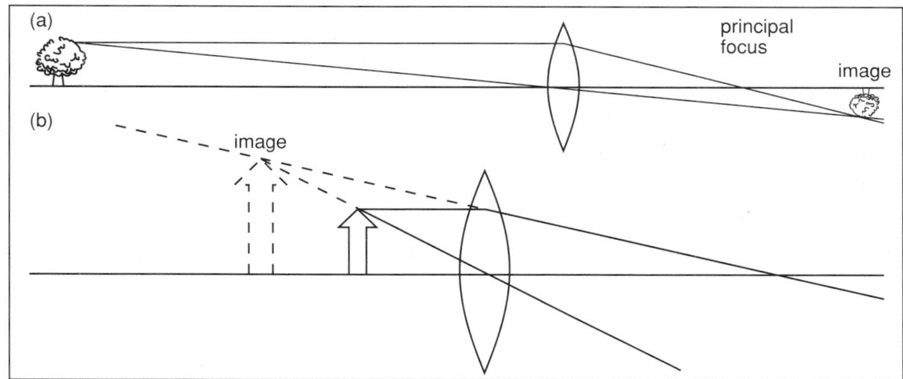

Picture 14 (a) A convex lens makes a small, upside down image of a distant object.
(b) The same lens can make a magnified, upright image of a close object. It acts as a magnifying glass.

When you look through a convex lens at an object some distance away it looks smaller, and the image is upside down. If you bring the lens closer and closer to the object you will reach a position where it makes an enlarged image of the object. This image is the right way up. The lens is now acting as a **magnifying glass**. Pictures 14(a) and 14(b) show what the light is doing to produce these two different kinds of image.

Two convex lenses can be used to make a simple telescope. The first, weaker **objective** lens again makes an upside down image. The second **eyepiece** lens is more powerful. You use it as a magnifying glass to look at the image made by the first lens. Picture 15 shows how this is done.

Notice that the image stays upside down. This kind of telescope is used by astronomers to look at stars and planets. They don't seem to mind that they see the universe upside down. In most astronomy books the pictures of the Moon are actually printed upside down, so that astronomers don't get confused!

Picture 15 What a simple telescope does to light. The lenses have been drawn much thicker than they really are on this scale, so the light is drawn changing direction at their centre lines.

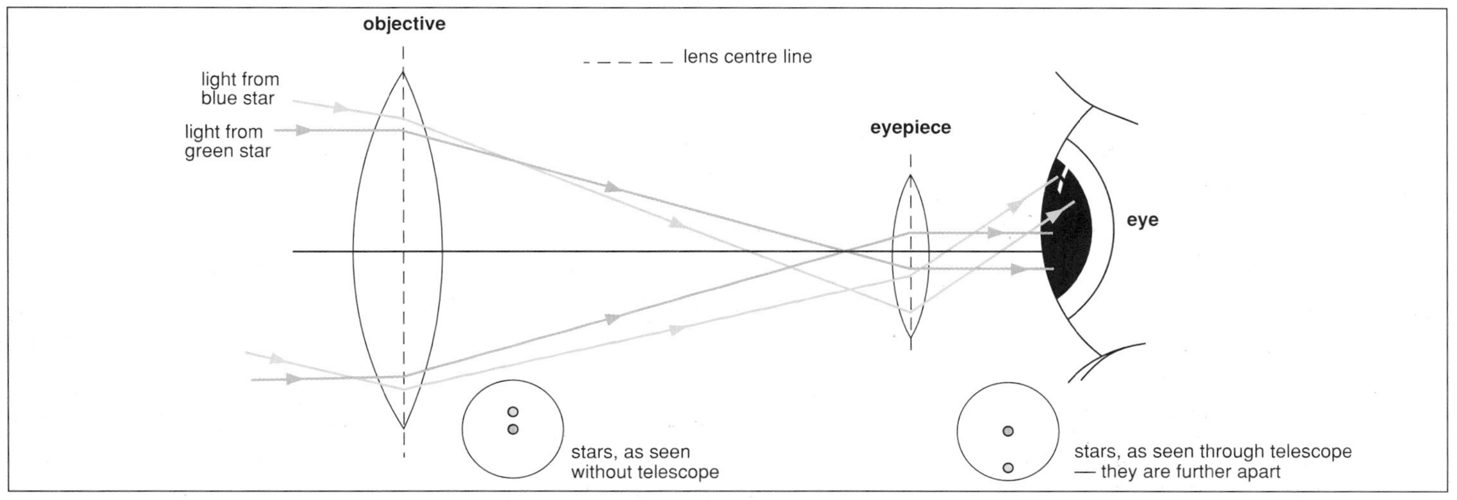

G2
Light, colour and spectra

The world is full of colour. What makes colours? How can we use them?

Picture 1 The spectrum of white light.

Splitting up light

White light is a mixture of colours. When we pass white light through a prism the colours become separated out into a **spectrum**. Picture 1 shows a prism splitting up white light. The same effect can be produced by tiny drops of water, and causes the **rainbow**.

Keen-eyed people say they can detect seven colours in this spectrum. In order, they are red, orange, yellow, green, blue, indigo and violet. You can remember this by the sentence 'Richard Of York Gave Battle In Vain'. Light from the Sun, or any white hot object, also includes invisible radiations, like ultra-violet and infra-red.

How prisms separate colours

When light goes from air into glass it slows down. This is why it changes direction – it is **refracted**. All light waves travel at the same speed in a vacuum. They slow down when they enter a transparent medium, like glass. This change of speed causes refraction.

But the different colours of the spectrum travel at **different** speeds in glass. For example, violet light travels more slowly than red light. This means that it is refracted more, so that its direction is changed more than red light. The other colours fit in between, depending on their speeds in glass. Light of different colours is thus spread out into the spectrum. This spreading out is called **dispersion** (picture 2).

Wavelengths of light are so small that they are measured in **nanometres** (nm). A nanometre is **one thousand millionth** of a metre (10^{-9} m). Red light has the lowest frequency and therefore the longest wavelength, at about **700 nm**.

As we move towards the violet end of the visible spectrum, the frequency increases, and the wavelength gets shorter. Violet light has a wavelength of approximately **400 nm**. Picture 3 illustrates this.

Picture 2 Light of different colours travels in different paths.

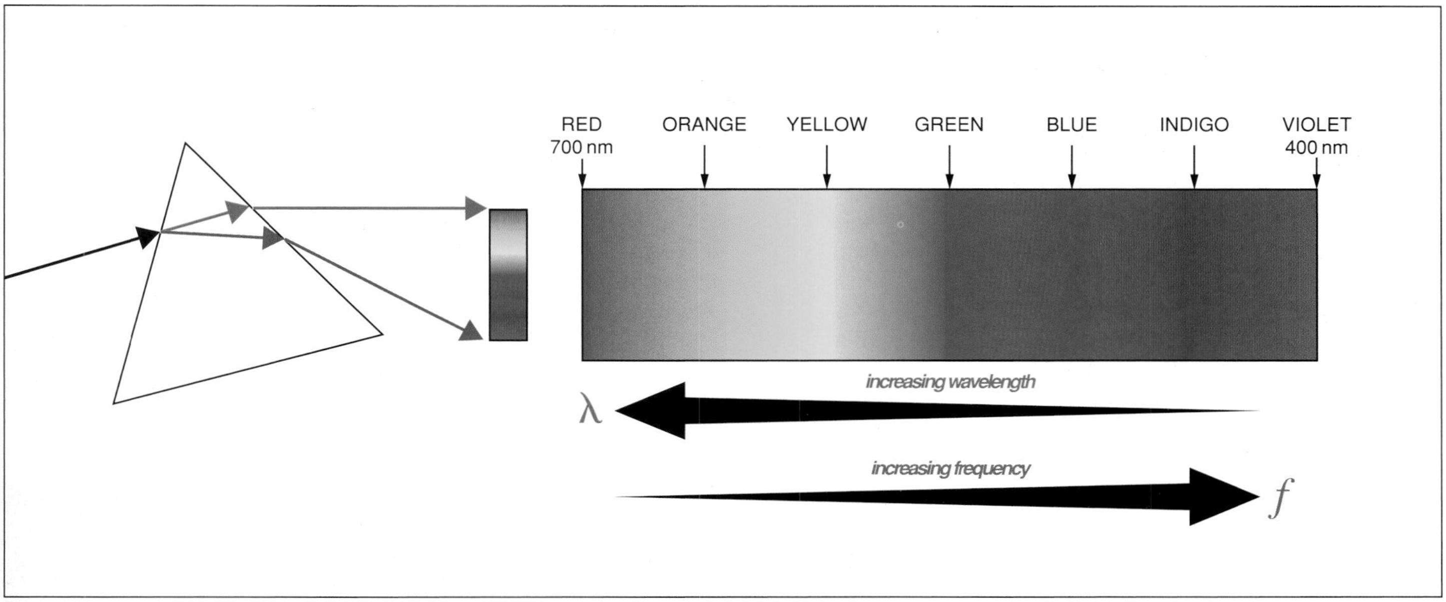

Picture 3

Making light

Light usually comes from very hot objects – flames, the Sun, hot filaments in lamps, but it can also come from insects (fireflies and glow worms), phosphor dots in TV tubes, and the glowing gases in advertising lights ('neon lights'). Whether hot or 'cold', all these sources produce light in the same basic way – by giving energy to atoms.

Picture 4 reminds you what an atom is like – a positive nucleus with some electrons round it. If an atom is given the right amount of energy, an electron can jump up to a slightly higher energy level. After a short time, it falls back to its normal energy level, and as it does this it gives back the energy as *light*. A small jump involves a small amount of energy, which gives us low frequency light, such as red. A large amount of energy produces higher frequencies such as blue.

Imagine heating a piece of steel. When it is too hot to touch, it may not look any different but it emits invisible infra-red radiation, which you can feel with your skin. As it gets hotter it begins to glow a dull red. Hotter still, and yellow appears. If an object has a very high temperature it will send out a mixture of all the colours in the spectrum, giving white light – we say it is **white hot**.

Solids, liquids, and high pressure gases give out a **continuous spectrum**, similar to the spectrum of our star, the Sun. Light from a hotter star will have more blue in the spectrum. This enables astronomers to work out the temperature of a star.

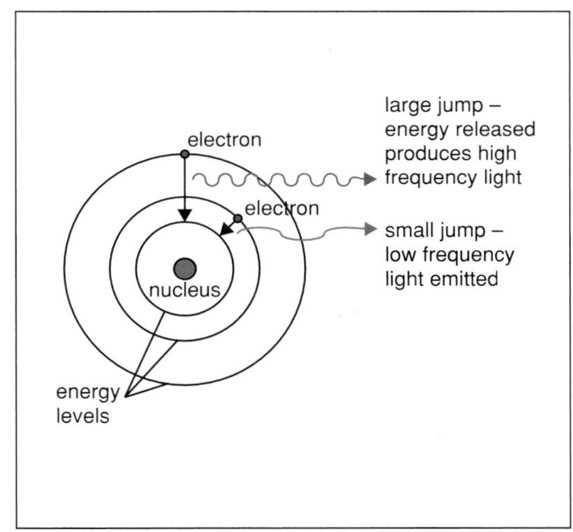

Picture 4

Why some stars are brighter than others

The brightness of a star is called its **magnitude**. One star can look brighter than another for several reasons. It could be that it is hotter than normal stars. If a study of its spectrum shows that it has the temperature of an average star, it may be that it appears brighter because it is bigger than average, or is nearer to the Earth than others. The brightest star in the sky is Sirius, the 'Dog Star'. Sirius is close to the Solar System, at a distance of about nine **light years** (see page 189). It is also hotter than average. If Sirius were twice as far away, it would look just a quarter as bright. To compare the brightness of stars, astronomers work out how bright they would look at a *standard* distance from Earth. This gives a standard brightness value called the **absolute magnitude** of the star.

Picture 5 Stars vary in colour and brightness.

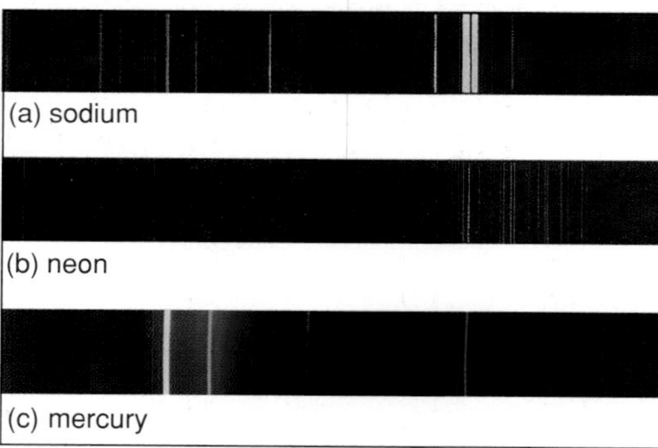

Picture 6 Sodium, neon and mercury line spectra.

Fingerprints of light

If light from a neon lamp is passed through a narrow slit and then a prism, we do not see a continuous spectrum. Instead, we see a pattern of coloured lines. This is called a **line spectrum**. Sodium or mercury vapour lamps will also produce line spectra, but each element has its own distinctive pattern.

As we saw on the previous page, when electrons in an atom move between energy levels, they give off light. Different elements have a different number of electrons in their atoms, and so the size and number of electron 'jumps' will also be different. This means that each element gives out different frequencies of light. Picture 6(a) shows the line spectrum of sodium.

If a scientist detects this pattern of lines in light from a substance, this proves that the material contains sodium – no other element has this pattern. A line spectrum can be regarded as the 'fingerprint' of an element. Pictures 6(b) and (c) show neon and mercury line spectra.

Picture 7

Picture 7 shows the spectrum of white light after it is passed through sodium vapour. The dark 'gaps' correspond to the lines in the sodium spectrum. These are called **absorption lines**, because the sodium vapour has absorbed these frequencies of light. Similar dark lines in the Sun's spectrum were first observed by a German optician, Joseph von Fraunhofer, in 1814 (picture 8). Later, in the 1850s, it was realised that light produced inside the Sun was being absorbed by elements in its outer layers. The pattern of absorption lines could be matched to others, enabling scientists to work out which elements were present in the Sun.

In 1868, spectral lines were identified that could not be matched to any known element. This new element was called **helium**, after *helios*, the Greek word for 'sun'. It was not until 30 years later that helium was found on Earth.

The faint light from distant stars can produce a usable spectrum if allowed to strike photographic film over a long period of time. By studying the photographic records of spectra, astronomers can analyse the composition of stars that are extremely distant.

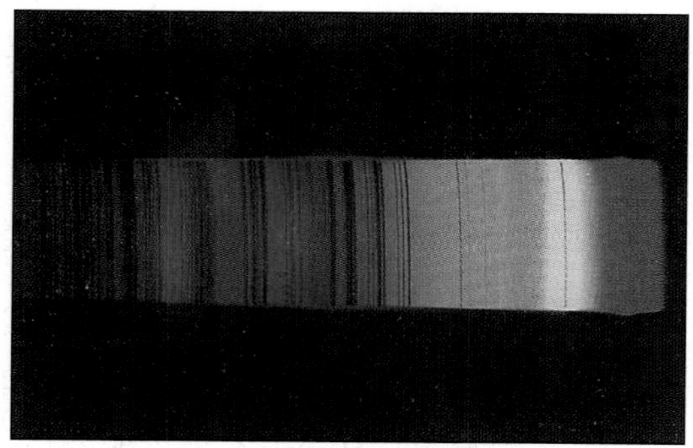

Picture 8 The dark lines in the spectrum of light from the Sun. These lines show what elements are present in the Sun's atmosphere.

Other ways of seeing

Optical astronomy relies on visible light. It can produce an image of objects, take measurements of position or brightness, or use spectra to discover the make up of stars, galaxies and the huge gas clouds that cover vast regions of space. These same gas clouds, however, also *block* light. To see through them, we must use radiations at wavelengths other than light – we must use the other sections of the **electromagnetic spectrum**, such as infra-red and radio.

Questions

1 Table 1 on the right gives some information about our Solar System.

a Which **planet** in the table has the greatest mass?

b Which object in the table is a star?

c Name two planets which would have almost the same weight.

d Which planet is nearest to Earth?

Table 1

	Mass (Earth masses)	Distance from Sun (million kilometres)	Weight of 1 kilogram at surface (newtons)
Sun	333.000	–	270
Mercury	0.06	58	4
Venus	0.82	110	9
Earth	1	150	10
Moon	0.013	150	1.6
Mars	0.11	228	4
Jupiter	318	780	26
Saturn	95	1430	11

2 Kirsty investigates the properties of light by setting up an experiment as shown below.

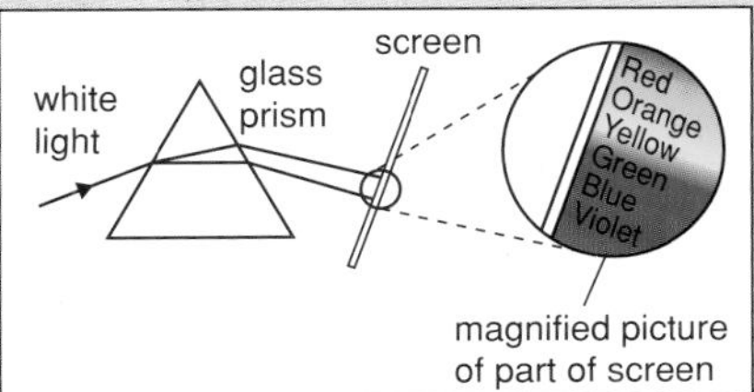

The colours appear on the screen in order of wavelength.

a What name is given to the effect on the light as it enters the glass?

b List the colours green, blue and red in order of wavelength, starting with the shortest wavelength.

c State **one** colour, listed on the diagram, which has a higher **frequency** than blue.

3a A telescope may be used to look at distant objects such as stars. A simple refracting telescope is shown below.

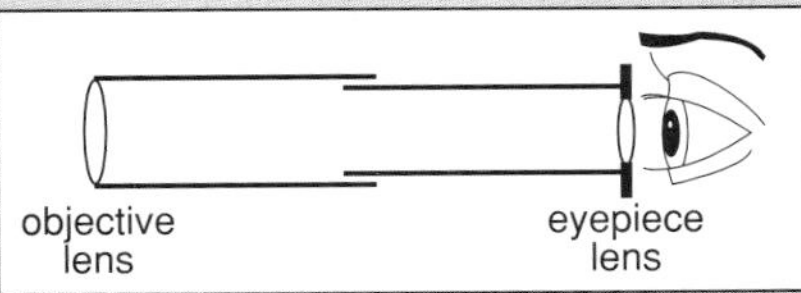

b The pupil removes the objective lens from the telescope and uses it to produce an image of an object on a screen.

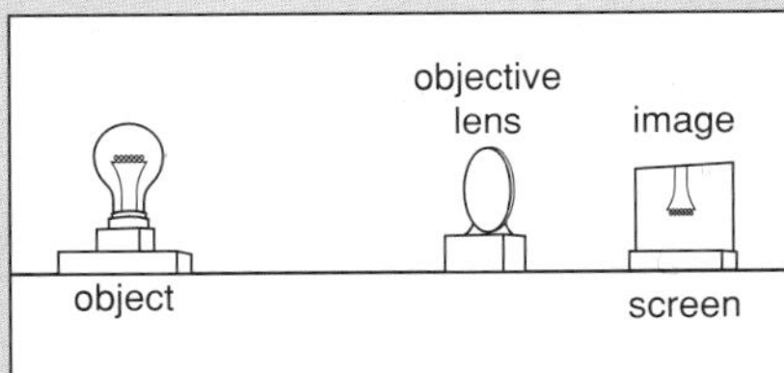

Copy and complete the diagram in figure 1 to show how the lens forms an image of the object. Clearly show the position of this image on your diagram.

The points marked F are one focal length from the centre of the lens.

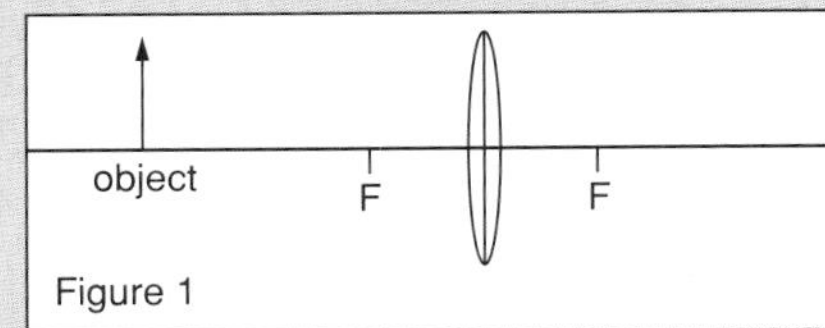

Figure 1

4a The diagram shows a refracting telescope.

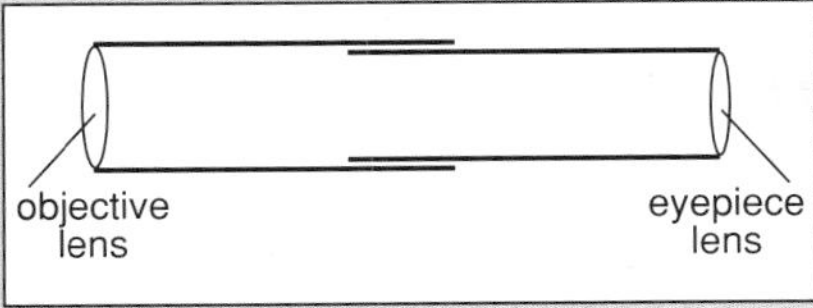

i) The eyepiece lens can be used as a magnifying glass.

Copy and complete the diagram below to show how a magnified image of an object is formed. The points marked F are one focal length from the centre of the lens.

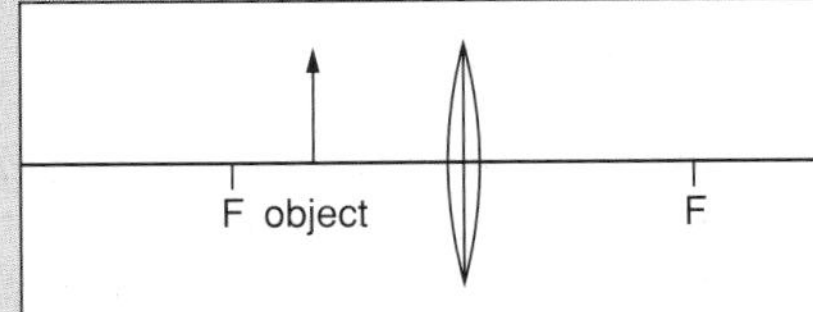

ii) How could the design of the telescope be altered to increase the brightness of the image when viewing a star?

b The Hubble telescope was put in orbit around the Earth in 1990.

i) The telescope uses a curved mirror to collect light rays from a star as shown below.

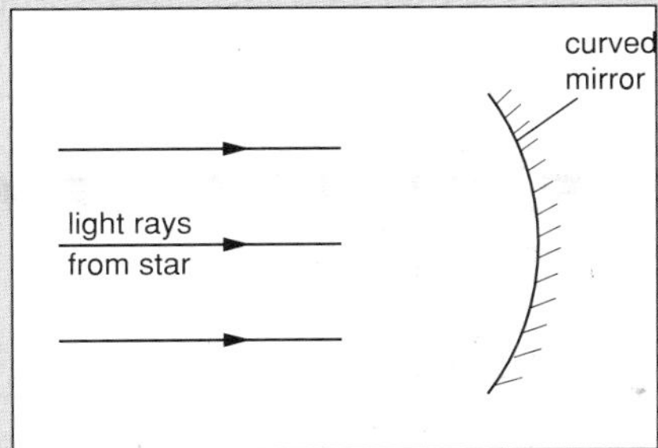

Copy and complete the diagram to show what happens to the rays of light after they reach the mirror.

ii) The spectral lines of radiation from a distant star are shown in figure 2. Figure 3 shows the spectral lines of a number of elements.

Use the spectral lines of the elements in figure 3 to identify which elements are present in the star.

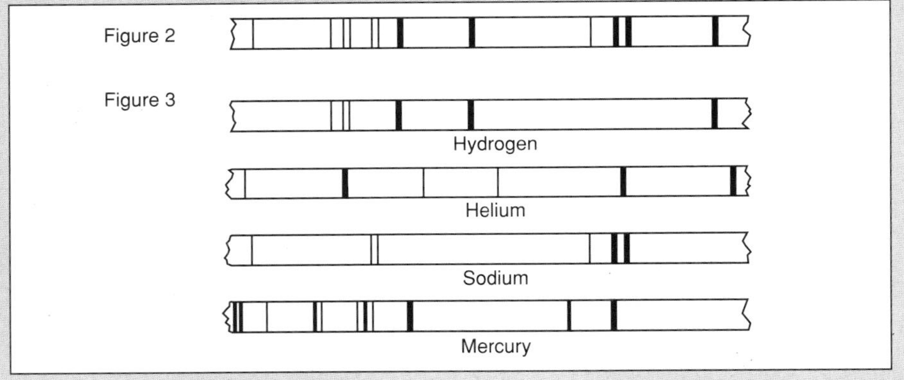

G3 Electromagnetic spectrum

We take light, and the fact that we can see it, for granted. But light has strange properties . . .

Light is just the *visible* part of a whole family of 'radiations' that we call the **electromagnetic spectrum**. These radiations all travel through space at the same speed, 300 million metres per second (3×10^8 m/s).

The speed of light

This was first measured by a tidy-minded Danish astronomer, Olaf Römer, as long ago as 1676. He noticed that the moons of Jupiter were sometimes a few minutes late in disappearing behind the planet. The moons of Jupiter orbit at a constant rate, and it was easy to calculate when this disappearance should take place. Römer explained why the moons were late by saying that light took time to travel.

This might be obvious to us, but at that time many scientists believed that light took no time at all to go from one place to another. But Römer said that this was not so: light had a definite speed. He said that light took longer to get to the Earth from Jupiter when the two planets were further apart.

As picture 1 shows, at its furthest point from Earth the light from Jupiter has to cross an extra distance equal to the diameter of the Earth's orbit. He measured the time difference this extra distance caused. The size of the Earth's orbit around the Sun was known fairly accurately in 1676, and so Römer was able to calculate a value for the speed of light.

His measurements of the times were not very accurate, however. His measurements gave the speed of light as only two-thirds of the modern value. But it was a start. The speed of light is now very accurately measured, and is so reliable that we use it to measure distance. Accurate surveying is done by measuring the time it takes for laser beams to travel a particular distance. The times are then converted to distances:

distance = light speed × time of travel.

All electromagnetic waves travel at the same speed in a vacuum. Short radio waves are used in **radar** systems to measure the distances of aircraft in air traffic control.

Radar has been used to measure the distances of planets from Earth. This has given us an accurate measurement of the scale of the Solar System.

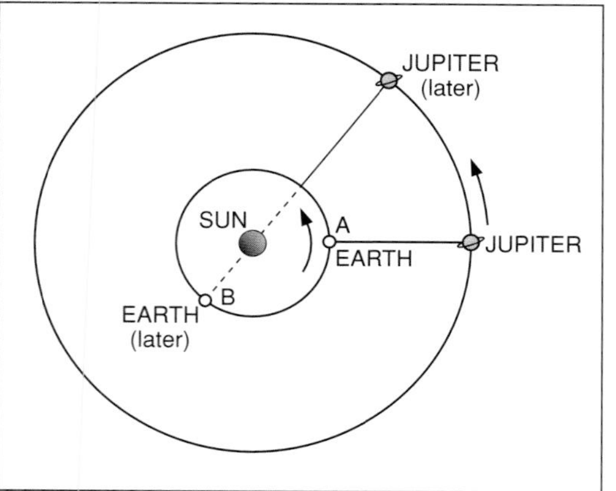

Picture 1 How Römer measured the speed of light.

Picture 2 Modern laser surveying instrument in use.

So what happens next? For a very long time – nothing much. In the very, very distant future, long after the Earth has been swallowed up by an exploding Sun, one of three things might happen:

1 the Universe will reach a steady state and stop expanding,
2 the Universe will keep on expanding for ever and ever,
3 the Universe will stop expanding and start to fall back in on itself.

These options are illustrated in picture 7.

Gravity will decide which of the above actually happens. The Universe is held together by gravitational forces. These are produced by the combined mass of all the stars, dust and gas in all the galaxies and all the spaces in between them.

If there is not enough of this mass, the Universe will keep on expanding. If there is enough mass, its gravity force will stop the expansion and make the Universe collapse again, perhaps producing another Big Bang.

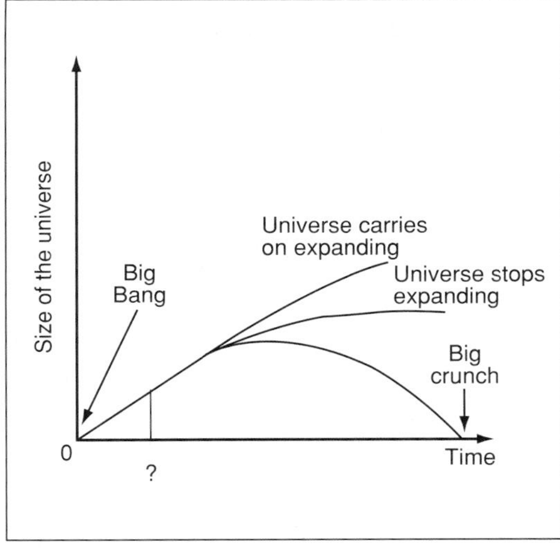

Picture 7 Three possible fates of the Universe.

Table 1 Distances of stars and galaxies.

Object	Name	Distance from Earth (light-years)	
star	Alpha Centauri	4.3	nearest star to Earth
star	Sirius	8.7	the brightest star we can see, the 'dog star' in Canis Major
star	Canopus	650	in Carina, used by air navigators
star	Polaris	142	the Pole Star, in Ursa Major
star	Betelgeuse	520	a red supergiant, the brightest star in Orion
galaxy	M31	2 200 000	the Andromeda galaxy, our nearest galaxy
	M81	10 000 000	in Ursa Major (The Plough)
	M87	42 000 000	the Sombrero Galaxy, in Virgo
clusters of galaxies	Virgo	78 000 000	in the constellation Virgo
	Hydra 3	3 960 000 000	in the constellation Hydra

Questions

1a The speed of light is 300 000 km/s. How long, in kilometres, are the following distances: i) a light-second, ii) a light-minute, iii) a light-day?

b Why is the 'light-year' a more useful unit for measuring astronomical distances than the metre?

2 Look at table 1, showing the distances of stars from the Earth. Canopus is the second brightest star in the sky, and is just about half as bright as Sirius. Which of these stars has the greater real brightness? Give a reason for your answer.

3 Put the following in order of size, with the smallest first:

star asteroid galaxy planet meteorite

4 The energy for the expansion of the Universe probably came from the 'Big Bang'. The rate at which the Universe is expanding is getting less. What could be making it slow down?

5 Russia and America are planning to send astronauts to the planet Mars and back. It is the second nearest planet to Earth.

a What are the problems that they might have to solve so that people could make this journey safely?

b This expedition will be very expensive, costing perhaps billions of dollars. Is it worth it?

6 Outline the problems of setting up a permanent human settlement on the Moon. Suggest some solutions to these problems.

Summary: Signals from space

The only way we can learn about the Universe is from the signals it sends us. For millions of years the only signals from space that humans could detect were carried by light. The ancient astronomers of Egypt, Babylon and Greece observed the Sun, the Moon and the stars. They saw how they changed and plotted their movements through the heavens. They produced the first theories about what the Universe was like, as shown in picture 1.

The ancient Romans weren't very interested in astronomy, and when Italy and Western Europe were overrun by 'barbarians' from the steppes of Asia in around 400 AD the old knowledge of astronomy was almost completely lost. But the study of astronomy was carried on by the Arab Muslims who conquered the Middle East and parts of Europe in the years 700 to 1500 AD. If you look at a good sky map you will find that many of the star names are in Arabic.

The telescope was invented in 1610 and over the next two centuries telescopes got bigger and better. Fainter and more distant stars could be seen. Knowledge about the Universe increased, but these instruments still used ordinary, visible light.

A breakthrough was to come with the marriage of two old ideas – the **spectrum** of light and the **telescope** – with a new technique: **photography**. But like many scientific discoveries, it was a long time before what had been discovered made any sense.

Newton had explained the 'colours of the rainbow' back in 1666, and had investigated the spectrum of white light. Then in 1802 an English scientist, William Wollaston, noticed that the coloured spectrum of sunlight was crossed with a number of dark lines. He did not know what caused them, and it was 40 years before the mystery was solved.

High technology 1857: the Bunsen burner

Robert Bunsen invented the Bunsen burner to investigate spectra. He looked at the coloured light given out by elements heated in his clear, colourless gas flame. He discovered that each element had its own spectrum, different from all the others. When heated, it gave out light energy in definite wavelengths and in its own pattern. It could be used as a 'fingerprint', to detect the very tiniest traces of any element (see picture 2).

Picture 1 The Egyptian Universe.

His fellow worker Gustav Kirchhoff made the key connection. The dark lines in the spectrum of sunlight were caused by elements in the Sun that **absorbed** light energy at their own special wavelengths. Immediately, astronomers were able to work out what the Sun was made of! In fact, one *new* element was discovered, up until that time unknown on Earth. It was named helium, after the Greek sun-god Helios.

Photography was discovered in about 1800, and the solar spectrum was first photographed in 1842. Since then, millions of photographs of the spectra of stars, planets, galaxies and comets have been taken. Photographs are needed because some of these objects are very faint. A photograph can collect light for many hours, and so build up its image until it is clear enough to be developed and measured. The details of the spectrum can tell us what elements there are in the star, its temperature, and even whether it is moving or not.

Then, in 1931, a new radiation was observed coming from outer space: **radio waves**. This led to the development of **radio astronomy**, and the discovery of radio stars and galaxies, pulsars and quasars.

Since then, astronomers have been able to use nearly every part of the whole electromagnetic spectrum, from gamma rays at one end to long radio waves at the other. They have found that the *pattern* of the spectrum of a given element is the same all over the Universe. But they also noticed that the actual wavelengths were sometimes different. This effect was caused by the movement of the star.

The American Edwin Hubble noticed that this difference was greater, the further away the stars or galaxies were. This could only be explained by the theory that these objects were moving away from us. This led to the theory of the expanding Universe – and of the Big Bang that started it. The new 'space telescope' is named after this great astronomer.

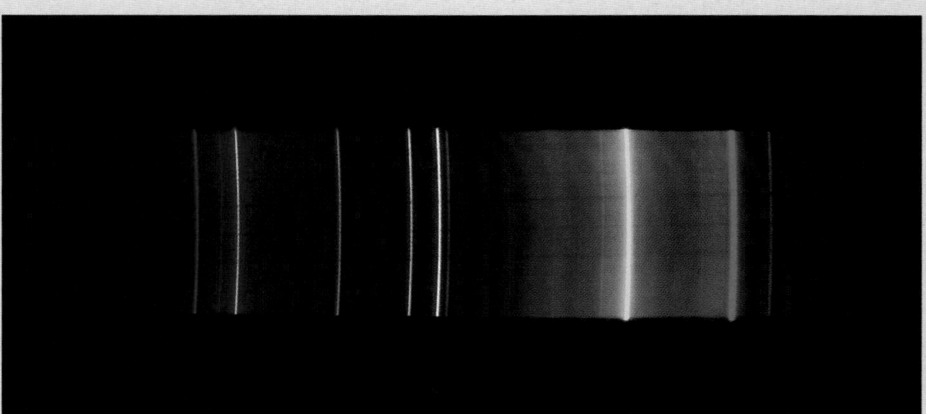

Picture 2 The helium spectrum.

Seeing further and more clearly

The Hubble Space Telescope was launched in April 1990. It had been designed over a period of 20 years, and will cost $8 billion. It will be effective in space for just 15 years. Picture 1 shows what it looks like in space. The main tube is a Newtonian telescope, with a very large main mirror.

The telescope is designed to see further and more clearly into the depths of space than ever before. The telescope can be used to send its images to one of several detecting instruments in turn. The most spectacular results will probably come from the 'wide-field' camera. This can take large, clear pictures of large objects like nearby galaxies and planets.

Picture 1 The Hubble Space Telescope.

It will get its advantages by being outside the Earth's atmosphere. Earthbound telescopes have to look through many kilometres of air. This air makes stars 'twinkle' – which means that their images dance about and aren't clear. Using bigger telescopes just means getting a bigger blur. Also, some radiations are absorbed by the atmosphere, and so never reach the Earth's surface.

Astronomers rarely look through telescopes. The images of stars and galaxies are usually recorded on film. But this method is no good for the Hubble Telescope! Instead, it uses silicon chips.

These chips are very thin layers of semiconductor material. They contain thousands of tiny photon detectors, the pixels. There are a quarter of a million of these to every square centimetre of chip. The photons of light trigger off each pixel when they hit it. They are over a hundred times more sensitive than the best film, so they can detect much fainter images. They are also small enough to make accurate pictures.

They are called **charge-coupled devices** (CCDs), and picture 2 shows a part of one of them. Four of them are used together in the wide-field camera in the Space Telescope. When photons of light hit a pixel, it releases an electron. This charged particle then moves to form a current. The currents from all the pixels are very carefully aligned to form a signal which can be sent back to Earth. The number of electrons from each pixel tells us how much light hit it. A computer is used to convert the signal current into a picture.

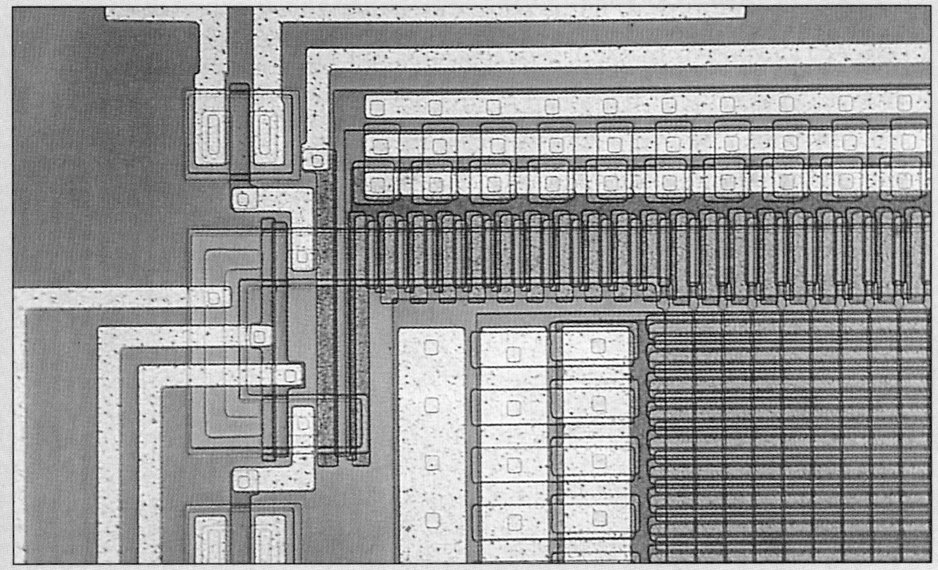

Picture 2 A CCD screen.

This is just like the way TV works. Indeed, modern TV cameras use CCDs, which means that they are sensitive enough to take pictures in the dark – you can see this in nearly every TV news bulletin.

The image is made on the array of CCDs by the main telescope. They can detect all kinds of radiation – light, UV and even X-rays. The telescope can't focus X-rays – they go straight through it! But light and UV can be focused very accurately by the mirror. The mirror is curved, and 2 metres in diameter. Its aluminium surface is smoothed to a tenth of a wavelength of light. If it was scaled up to be the size of the USA the biggest bump on it would be just 2 centimetres high. This means it can make best use of the accuracy given by the CCDs.

Now try the following questions.

1. What are the advantages of having a telescope in space, compared with one on Earth?
2. Give a reason why cameras with photographic film would not be much use in the Hubble Telescope.
3. Why does the mirror surface have to be so smooth?
4. What is the advantage of having the main mirror as large as possible?
5. Give two advantages of using CCDs in this telescope.

G5 Space travel

Newton's laws of motion explain how things move in space.

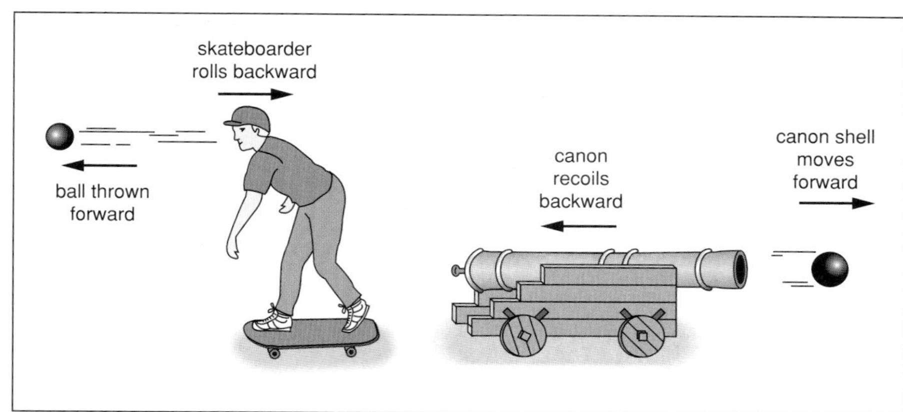

Picture 1

Twin forces

Stand on a skateboard and throw a large and heavy ball. As the ball moves forwards, you and your skateboard will move backwards. When a cannon is fired, exploding gases push the shell forward, but the cannon also **recoils** – it rolls backward. Even when you walk, your foot pushing backwards on the ground causes a reaction that drives you forward.

Sir Isaac Newton was the first person to devise a simple law which described these situations. He said that action and reaction are always equal and opposite. Another way of looking at this is to assume that forces always occur in pairs – they are *equal* in size, but *opposite* in direction.

If the forces are equal in size, why does the shell move away at high speed, while the cannon rolls slowly backwards? The answer is that there is a large difference in **mass**. From **Newton's Second Law**, (see topic E4, page 137), we know that:

$$a = \frac{F}{m}$$

If the forces on the shell and on the cannon are equal, the object with the *smaller* mass will have the *greater* acceleration. Notice something else – the cannon and shell are only accelerated *while the explosion is happening*. This means that the *time* for each acceleration is the same. The final speed of each object should depend on the size of the acceleration, which depends on their different masses.

We can investigate this in the Physics laboratory, using the equipment shown in picture 2. The two air-track vehicles have different masses. When they are released, the repulsion between the magnets produces a force which acts on both vehicles, and they 'explode' in opposite directions.

Picture 2

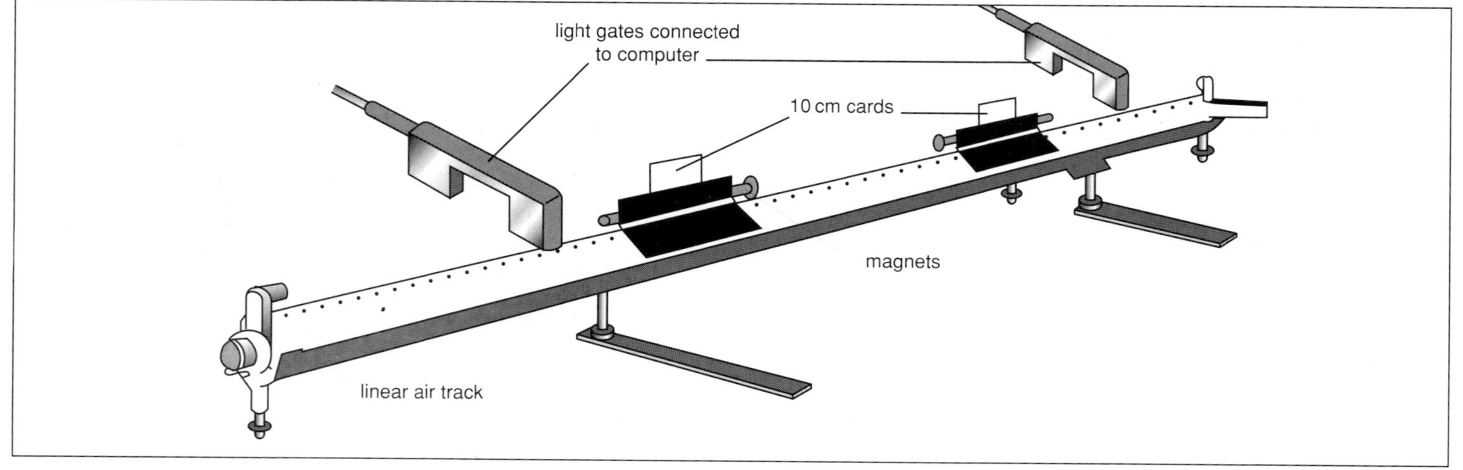

How are satellites launched?

No mountain on Earth is high enough for Newton's method to work. There is no gun powerful enough to fire a satellite at the speed needed to stay in orbit. And if there were, the force needed to accelerate the satellite inside the gun barrel would squash it flat!

Instead a rocket system is used to lift the satellite to the top of an 'invisible mountain'. This is called the **injection point**, and it is at least 200 km high (see picture 5).

Picture 4 shows the rocket system used to launch the American Space Shuttle. Most of what you see of the rocket is simply a hollow tank filled with fuel. Most of this fuel is used to lift itself through the atmosphere. There is just enough spare fuel to accelerate the Shuttle sideways when it gets high enough to be put into orbit.

A rocket system has three stages, each with its own engine and fuel supply. The first stage contains the most fuel and has the biggest engine. It lifts itself and the next two stages as high as it can. Then it falls off. Stages two and three take over, in turn, and in their turn are thrown away. The satellite is left travelling in orbit at the speed required to stop it falling closer to Earth (see picture 5).

Picture 4 The rocket system used to launch the Space Shuttle.

Why do some satellites fall down?

Newton explained why satellites stay up – but they don't stay up for ever. The main reason for this is air friction. The Earth's atmosphere gets thinner and thinner the higher you go, but it never thins away to nothing. Even at a height of 1000 km there is enough air left to cause a drag on a satellite which slows it down. Eventually it is travelling too slowly to stay in orbit. It re-enters the thicker part of the atmosphere where friction becomes so great that the satellite 'burns up'.

The energy transferred from movement energy by this air friction heats up the satellite until it melts and burns away.

Weightlessness

Astronauts orbiting the Earth in a spacecraft are often said to be 'weightless'. Although this appears to be the case in picture 6, this is actually an illusion. To be truly weightless, the astronauts would have to be in a region of space far away from the gravitational pull of any planet.

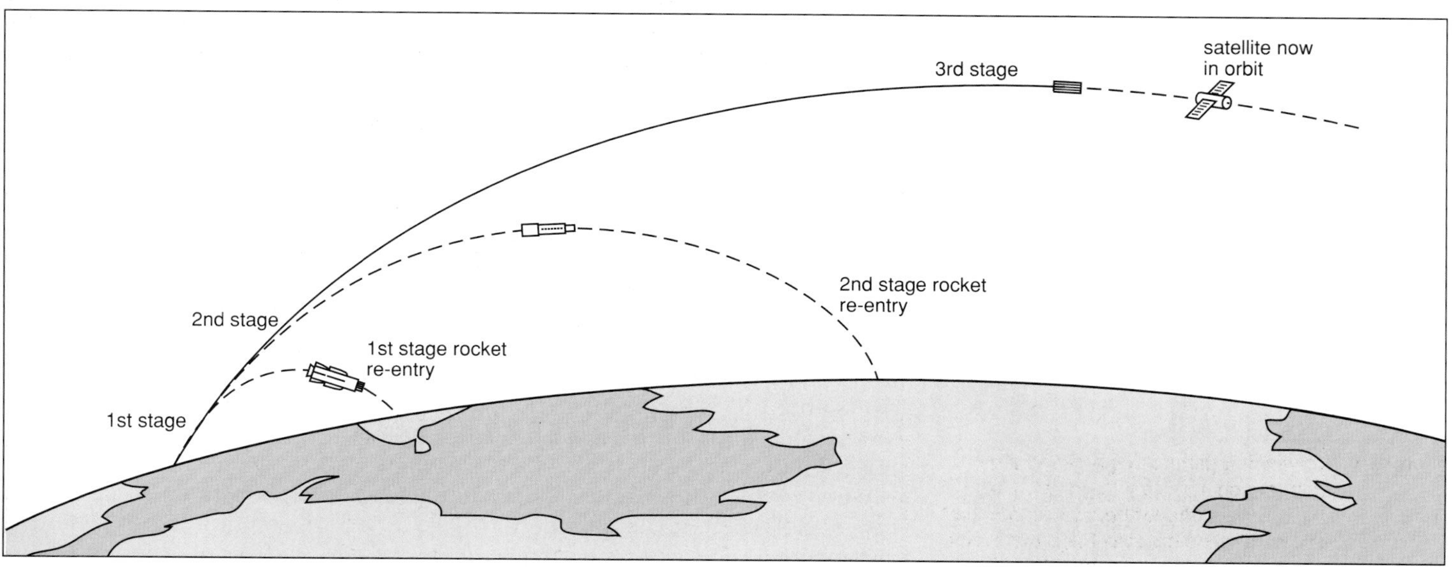

Picture 5 How a satellite is put into orbit.

Picture 6

When a spacecraft or satellite is in orbit, it is moving in a circle *because* of the the pull of gravity. Gravity provides the force that keeps a satellite in orbit (picture 7), just as the string in picture 8 keeps the conker moving in a circle. If gravity were to be 'switched off', the spacecraft would obey Newton's First Law and carry on in a straight line, just as the conker would when the string breaks. The astronauts experience the *sensation* of weightlessness because they are falling round the Earth under the same gravitational pull as their ship.

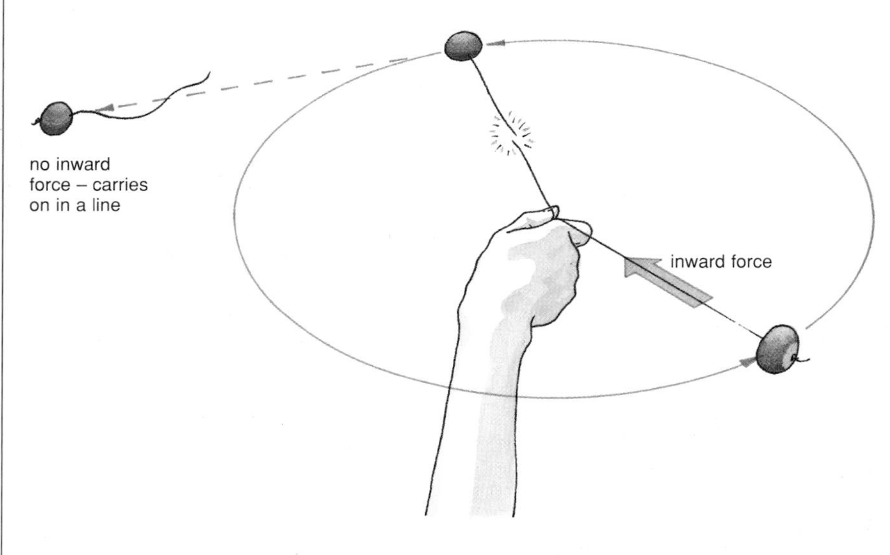

Picture 8 No inward force, so no circular motion.

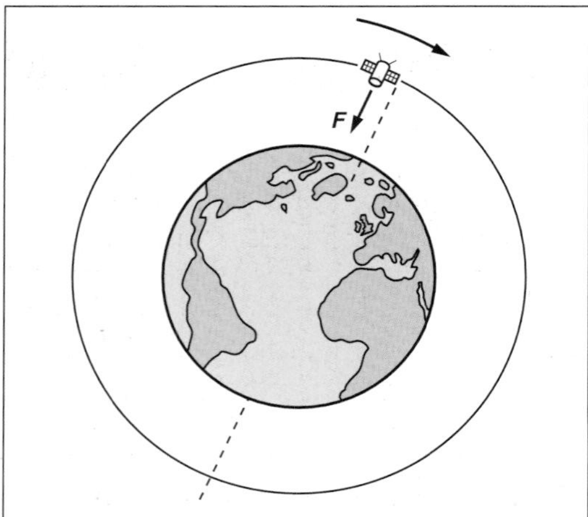

Picture 7 Gravity provides the force ***F*** that keeps a satellite in orbit.

We say that they are in 'free fall', just as if they were skydiving from an aircraft. Every other object in the cabin is experiencing the same effect, and falling at the same rate.

Imagine yourself in a lift which started to fall after the cable snapped. With no windows to the outside, it would be impossible to tell whether you were really falling, or had suddenly been transported to outer space. Yourself and the other contents of the lift would accelerate downwards at the rate of 10 m/s^2. If you took your pen from your pocket and let go, it would float in front of your eyes. For a (short!) time, you would be just like an astronaut.

Getting home

As mentioned on the previous page, satellites do not stay in orbit forever. Eventually their orbit decays, and they burn up when entering the atmosphere. A space vehicle such as the Shuttle has to make a controlled re-entry, so that the spacecraft and crew can return safely to the ground.

When it is time to descend, the Shuttle is manoeuvred so that it is travelling 'tail first' along its orbit. The engines are fired to reduce its speed, and it starts to lose height. When it reaches the outer fringes of the atmosphere, its kinetic energy is transferred as heat, due to friction.

The Shuttle may be travelling at a speed of 10 km/s when it enters the atmosphere. This large energy transfer produces extremely high temperatures, so the Shuttle has a thermal protection system to prevent it being damaged. Special tiles coat the surfaces which are exposed to the highest risk.

When most of the Shuttle's kinetic energy has been transferred, it has slowed to a speed where it can now perform like a normal aircraft and can glide to a landing on a runway. After a refit, it will be ready to perform another mission.

Picture 9 The shuttle in orbit.

Questions

1a The navigation satellite shown in the diagram below moves in a circular orbit above the Earth's atmosphere.

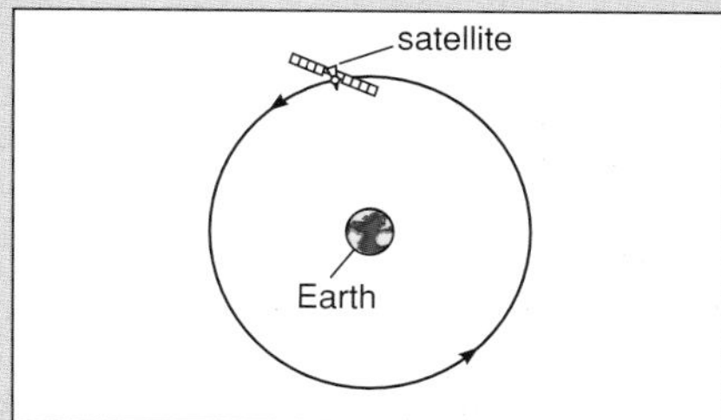

Explain why:

i) the satellite does not move in a straight line into space;

ii) the satellite does not fall straight down to Earth.

b Many Satellites do not have circular orbits but travel as shown in the diagram below.

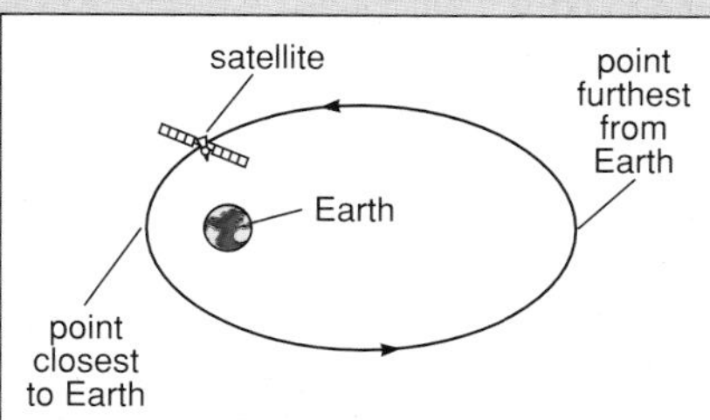

The Earth's atmosphere gradually becomes thinner until at a height of 1000 km above the surface there is almost no air.

Table 1

Satellite	Minimum height above Earth (km)	Maximum height above Earth (km)	Life-time in orbit
'Spy'	120	450	2 weeks
Sputnik I	225	945	3 months
Explorer I	360	2550	12 years
Navigation	1110	1110	1000 years

Study the information given in table 1 above.

Explain why the 'spy' satellite has such a short life-time in orbit while the navigation satellite is expected to remain in orbit much longer.

c A satellite of mass 80 kg orbits the Earth at a speed of 4000 m/s. The satellite is constructed mainly from a metal alloy of specific heat capacity 320 J/kg °C.

i) Calculate the kinetic energy of the satellite when in orbit.

ii) Calculate the change in the temperature of the satellite which might be expected if all its kinetic energy is rapidly converted to heat energy as the satellite comes back to Earth.

iii) Suggest why in practice the change in temperature you have calculated in part ii will not be obtained.

2a A space shuttle is used to launch a satellite. The period of the satellite's orbit is 12 hours.

State what would have to happen to the height of the orbit to make it geostationary.

b The satellite has solar panels, as shown below, which use solar power to produce electricity.

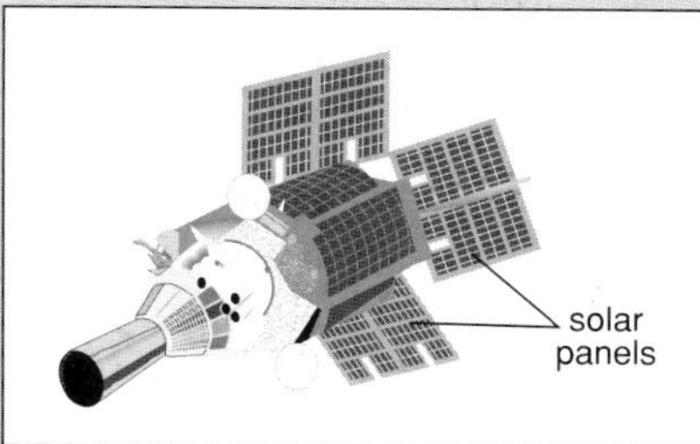

The solar power received on each square metre of panel is 1.5 kW.

The total area of the panels is 12 m^2 and their efficiency is 10%.

Calculate the electrical power from the panels.

c During re-entry to the Earth's atmosphere, the heat shield of the shuttle gains 4.7×10^9 J of heat as the Shuttle's kinetic energy is reduced.

i) Calculate the *minimum* reduction in the speed of the Shuttle. (Shuttle mass = 2×10^6 kg)

ii) Explain why the actual figure would be much higher than this.

Index